Elements of Physical Geology

adapted by Doris L. Holmes D.Sc., F.R.S.E., F.G.S.

from Principles of Physical Geology by Arthur Holmes D.Sc., LL.D., F.R.S.

Nelson

Elements of Physical Geology

THE STUDY OF LANDFORMS

THOMAS NELSON AND SONS LTD

36 Park Street London W1Y 4DE
P.O. Box 18123 Nairobi Kenya

THOMAS NELSON (AUSTRALIA) LTD
597 Little Collins Street Melbourne 3000

THOMAS NELSON AND SONS (CANADA) LTD
81 Curlew Drive Don Mills Ontario

THOMAS NELSON (NIGERIA) LTD
P.O. Box 336 Apapa Lagos

THOMAS NELSON AND SONS (SOUTH AFRICA) (PROPRIETARY) LTD
51 Commissioner Street Johannesburg

Photoset in Malta by St Paul's Press Ltd
and printed in Great Britain by Fletcher & Son Ltd, Norwich

Acknowledgements

The thanks of the author and the publishers are due to all concerned for permission to reproduce the photographs and drawings that contribute so much to this book. Individual credits appear with the relevant captions. Photographs from the Geological Survey collection (Crown copyright reserved) are reproduced by permission of the Controller of H.M. Stationery Office. Fig. 7–26 (Crown copyright reserved) is reproduced by permission of the Ministry of Defence, and Fig. 3–1 (also Crown copyright reserved) by permission of the Director of the Natural History Museum (British Museum). Photographs by the late Mr R. Welch are reproduced by permission of the Director of the Ulster Museum, Belfast.

Preface

The first edition of Arthur Holmes' *Principles of Physical Geology* was widely used in schools and by first-year university students, and when in 1964 it was replaced by a second greatly enlarged and more expensive edition, many geography teachers asked the publishers whether a smaller book suitable for A Level geography could be prepared from it. *Elements of Physical Geology* is the reply to this request. As its subsidiary title 'The Study of Landforms' may suggest, it has been prepared with the requirements of A Level geography particularly in mind. The various earth sciences, however, are intimately related: physical geography, the study of man's natural physical environment, for example, cannot be separated from physical geology, which is concerned with the earth's materials and with all the terrestrial agents and processes of change, past and present. Nor can either of these subjects be considered apart from discoveries in the field of geophysics, for it is by the application of physical techniques that the concealed structure of the earth's crust is deciphered, and oil and gas fields are located. *Elements of Physical Geology*, like the first edition of *Principles of Physical Geology*, approaches the study of landforms through physical geology, with due attention to discoveries in the geophysical field. The book therefore similarly provides an introduction to geology.

In plan the book follows the first edition of *Principles of Physical Geology*, where the processes operative on the earth were divided into those of external and those of internal origin. As Arthur Holmes there wrote, however, it must be borne in mind that: "The earth's activities may be compared to an intricate interplay of combined operations, and the results, whether they be landscapes, natural catastrophies, or materials such as building stones and fuels, are correspondingly varied. It is inherent in the character of the subject that the full significance of any one aspect can be properly appreciated only in relation to the whole." The broad Preliminary Survey, presented in Part I, has therefore been retained to serve as an introduction to the more detailed treatment that follows. Part II deals with the outer earth in greater detail, and Part III is mainly concerned with the activities of the inner earth and their surface expressions. In order to keep the price of the book as low as possible it has been necessary to reduce

its size even in comparison with the first edition of *Principles of Physical Geology*, and this reduction has mainly been made in Part III. Interested readers will therefore discover a wealth of further information about volcanoes and mountain building in Chapters XXV to XXXI of the second edition of *Principles of Physical Geology*.

In comparison with the first edition of the *Principles*, the present book has been brought up to date in accordance with the second edition. For example, it includes: a brief account of the methods of geochronology whereby minerals and rocks are dated, and of the consequent possibilities of estimating the rates of some of the earth's long-term activities including the evolution of landforms; an introduction to the concept of rheidity and its application to the flow of glaciers, the intrusion of migmatites, and to movements within the earth's mantle; reference to the industrial process of fluidization which provides a key to understanding some aspects of volcanic activity; geophysical discoveries about the floor of the oceans; discoveries concerning magnetism preserved in rocks as a compass-guide to the positions of the magnetic poles in past geological periods and hence to the drift of continents; reference to laboratory techniques applied to the study of river and wave action. Amongst discoveries more recent than the time of writing of the second edition of the *Principles*, it includes a short account of North Sea gas.

It must not be overlooked, however, that physical geography and physical geology are essentially field subjects. The countryside and the sea-coasts are the school-rooms where the fundamentals should be learnt. In discussing landforms such as escarpments, flood-plains, raised beaches, sea-stacks, etc. typical British examples are cited wherever possible and illustrated photographically, so that the observant student can recognize further examples and add a wealth of interest to holidays. In such field studies the Ordnance Survey maps on the scale of 1 inch to the mile will be found invaluable since their contours depict the scenery. Moreover, if these maps are compared with the corresponding maps of the Geological Survey, on the same scale, the extent to which the evolution of scenic features has been influenced by the ground rocks can be appreciated.

At this time, just before the proposed change over to the metric system, the expression of measurements has presented some problems. In this book large measurements which can be expressed in miles or hundreds of feet are followed, in brackets, by the corresponding measurement in kilometres or metres respectively. Usually the two measurements have not been made to correspond exactly, both being expressed in round numbers. Small measurements expressed in inches or a few feet, such as the height of waves, are not always followed by the corresponding measurement in centimetres or metres because an unwarranted impression of exact accuracy might be created if the metric measurements were made to correspond exactly, whereas the difference between the two measurements can be relatively great if both are expressed in round numbers. On the other hand where small measurements were originally made in metres or centimetres it is these measurements only that are expressed. For readers who may wish to make their own calculations some useful conversion figures are given on p. 8.

Arthur Holmes had intended to write a book for schools and first-year university students based on the second edition of *Principles of Physical Geology*, and it will be deeply regreted that he died before this project was begun. It is with sad pleasure that I, his wife and fellow geologist, have undertaken this task. I am deeply grateful to those teachers who have taken the trouble to indicate their requirements, and I would particularly like to thank Miss H. Davey, Geography Mistress, Bromley Grammar School for Girls, Kent; Mr J. A. Morris, formerly Geography Master at Latymer School, Edmonton, London; Miss Y. Paterson, Geography Mistress, Reigate County School for Girls, Surrey; and Dr G. T. Warwick, Senior Lecturer in Geography, University of Birmingham. Mr Alan C. Coase, Geography Master, Hinckley Grammar School, Leicester, caver and photographer, kindly provided the photograph of stalactites and stalagmites, Fig. 6–9.

London   Doris L. Holmes
July 1968

Contents

Part 3 Internal Processes: Major Architectural Forms

Part 1
A Preliminary Survey

1

The Shape and Surface
Relief of the Earth

THE OUTER ZONES OF THE EARTH

As it presents itself to direct experience, the earth can be physically described as a ball of rock (the lithosphere), partly covered by water (the hydrosphere) and wrapped in an envelope of air (the atmosphere). To these three physical zones it is convenient to add a biological zone (the biosphere).

The *atmosphere* is the layer of gases and vapour which envelopes the earth. It is essentially a mixture of nitrogen and oxygen with smaller quantities of water vapour, carbon dioxide, and inert gases such as argon. Geologically and geographically it is important as the medium of climate and weather, of wind, cloud, rain, and snow.

The *hydrosphere* includes all the natural waters of the outer earth. Oceans, seas, lakes, and rivers cover about three-quarters of the surface. But this is not all. Underground, for hundreds and even thousands of feet in some places, the pore spaces and fissures of the rocks are also filled with water. This ground water, as it is called, is tapped in

springs and wells, and is sometimes encountered in disastrous quantities in mines. Thus there is a somewhat irregular but nearly continuous mantle of water around the earth, saturating the rocks, and over the enormous depressions of the ocean floors completely submerging them. If it were uniformly distributed over the earth's surface it would form an ocean about 9,000 feet (2,743 m) deep.

The *biosphere*, the sphere of life, is probably a less familiar conception. But think of the great forests and prairies with their countless swarms of animals and insects. Think of the tangles of seaweed, of the widespread banks of molluscs, of reefs of coral and shoals of fishes. Add to these the inconceivable numbers of bacteria and other microscopic plants and animals; myriads of these minute organisms are present in every cubic inch of air and water and soil. Taken altogether, the diverse forms of life constitute an intricate and ever-changing network, clothing the

FIG. 1–1
Two celebrated products of the biosphere. Many millions of years ago the coin-shaped shells of innumerable generations of nummulites accumulated on the floor of a vanished sea to form the thick and widespread deposits of Nummulitic Limestone that is now the bedrock of much of the Egyptian and Libian Desert. From a conspicuous outcrop of this rock the Sphinx was carved, probably during the reign of Chephren, about 2,900 B.C., whose Pyramid is seen close by, built of gigantic blocks of the same Nummulitic Limestone quarried from the hills on the other (east) side of the Nile. Stone and builders alike were once part of the biosphere. (*Syndication International*)

surface with a tapestry that is nearly continuous. Even high snows and desert sands fail to interrupt it completely, and lava fields fresh from the craters of volcanoes are quickly invaded by the pressure of life outside. Such is the sphere of life, and both geologically and geographically it is of no less importance than the physical zones. Amongst its many products are coal and oil, most of the oxygen of the air we breathe, and limestones in great abundance (Fig. 1–1).

The *crust* or *lithosphere* is the outer solid shell of the earth. It is made of rocks in great variety, and where it forms land masses its uppermost layer is commonly a blanket of soil or other loose deposits, such as desert sands.

THE CRUST AND INNER ZONES
OF THE EARTH

The earth has a zoned structure. The deep interior, called the *core*, has metallic properties and a very high density* (mean density about 10·72). The surrounding zone of "heavy rock" (mean density 4·53) is known as the

mantle or *substratum*, and this is enveloped by the *crust*, with a mean density of about 2·8 (Fig. 1–2).

The boundary surface between the crust and the mantle is known as the Mohorovičić discontinuity, or more briefly as the M-discontinuity or *Moho*, after a Croatian seismologist who discovered in 1909 that earthquake waves increase in velocity as they pass downwards from the crustal rocks into the denser mantle. This discovery has made it possible to "X-ray" the earth as it were, with its own earthquake waves, or with similar waves specially generated for the purpose by controlled explosions, and hence to estimate with fair accuracy the depth of the boundary surface between the crust and the mantle in different parts of the earth. By this method it has been found that the earth's crust varies in thickness from about 50 or 60 km where there are mountain ranges, to about 30 km under plains near sea level. Beneath the oceans the average thickness of the crust is only about 8 km (Fig. 13–45).

The dominant rocks forming the *crust* fall into two contrasting groups:

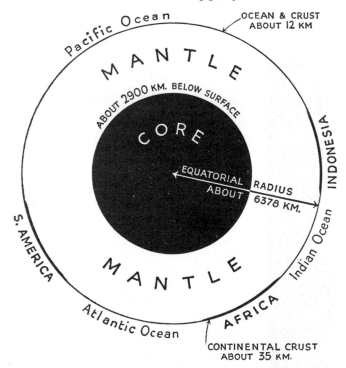

FIG. 1–2
Equatorial section through the earth, showing crust (continental and oceanic), mantle, and core.

---

*The *density* of a substance is the mass of unit volume of the substance, generally expressed as the mass in grams of one cubic centimetre. Since one cubic centimetre of water has a mass of one gram, the density of water is 1.

The *specific gravity* of a substance = $\dfrac{\text{the mass of any volume of the substance}}{\text{the mass of an equal volume of water}}$.

In c.g.s. units specific gravity and density are numerically the same.

(*a*) *The light rocks*, including granite and related types, and sediments such as sandstones and shales, which have an average specific gravity or density of about 2·7. Since the main constituent of these rocks is *si*lica, and *al*umina is the most abundant of the remaining constituents, these crustal rocks are collectively known by the mnemonic term *sial*.

(*b*) *The dark and heavy rocks*, consisting mainly of basalt and related types (density about 2·8–3·0) and still heavier ultrabasic rocks (density up to 3·4). In all these rocks *si*lica is still the most abundant constituent, but iron oxides and *magnesia*, either singly or together, take second place, and the whole group is known as *sima*.

The crust flooring the oceans differs from that forming the continents. Apart from a surprisingly thin surface layer of loose sediment and organic oozes, the *sub-oceanic crust* seems to be made almost entirely of basic rocks, most of them probably submarine flows of basalt. The *continental crust*, on the other hand, is dominantly sial, although it includes basaltic lavas and minor intrusions and in some places, such as Co. Antrim (Northern Ireland) and Iceland, the sial is covered by thick accumulations of basaltic lava flows (Figs. 1–3 and 14–14). Apart from these local volcanic rocks, however, in most of the regions so far tested, basaltic and other rocks of the sima group become increasingly abundant in the lower part of the continental crust.

FIG. 1–3
Basaltic lava flows of the Antrim Plateau. Above the cliff path three tiers of columns (columnar jointing) can be seen, corresponding to three successive lava flows, the lowest of which is that of the Causeway itself. (*Aerofilms Ltd*)

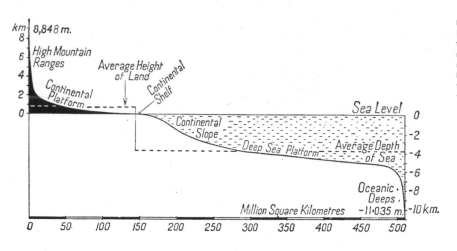

FIG. 1—4
Hypsographic curve, showing the areas of the earth's solid surface between successive levels from the highest mountain peak to the greatest known depth of the oceanic trenches.

CONTINENTS AND OCEAN FLOORS

The surface of the crust reaches very different levels in different places. The areas of land and sea floor between successive levels have been estimated, and the results can be graphically represented as shown in Fig. 1–4. From this diagram it is clear that there are two dominant levels: the continental platform and the oceanic or deep-sea platform. The slope connecting them, which is actually quite gentle, is called the continental slope.

The continental platform includes a submerged outer border, known as the *continental shelf*, which extends beyond the shore zone to an average depth of about 200 metres. Structurally, the real ocean basins must be regarded as commencing, not at the visible shoreline, but at the edge of the shelf. The basins, however, are more than full, and the overflow of sea water inundates about 11 million square miles (28,490,000 km²) of the continental platform. The North Sea, the Baltic, and Hudson Bay are examples of shallow seas (epicontinental or shelf seas) which lie on the continental shelf. It is of interest to notice that during the Ice Age, when enormous quantities of water were abstracted from the oceans to form the great ice sheets that then lay over Europe and North America, much of the continental shelf must have been land. Conversely, if the ice now covering Antarctica and Greenland were to melt away, the sea level would rise and the continents would be still further submerged.

The continents themselves have a varied relief of plains, plateaux, and mountain ranges, the last rising to a maximum height of 29,028 feet (8,848 m) in Mt Everest. The ocean floors were once thought to have a relatively monotonous surface. However, they are now being actively investigated both by geophysical methods and by direct observations made by descending to the ocean depths in bathyscapes. Submarine ridges and mountains, have- been charted, in addition to great numbers of seamounts some of which represent the deeply submerged ruins of ancient volcanic islands. Submarine canyons have been charted and new ones are continually being found. Particular attention is being given to great trenches and deeps that carry the surface down to more than twice the average depth. The greatest depth so far determined is 36,204 feet (11,035 m), nearly seven miles, in the Marianas Trench (Nero Trench in Fig. 1–5).

The hypsographic curve, Fig. 1–4, might suggest that the greatest deeps are farthest away from the lands, but such is not the case. The deeps lie close against the continental edge, and along the Asiatic side of the Pacific they are particularly strongly developed (Fig. 1–5).

From the figures given above it is clear that the total vertical range of the surface of the lithosphere is well over 12 miles (about 20 km). To grasp the true relation between the surface relief and the earth itself, draw a circle with a radius of 2 inches. A moderately thin pencil line has a thickness of about 1/100 inch. If 2 inches represents 4,000 miles, then the thickness of the outline of the circle represents 20 miles. On this scale the relief is all contained well within the thickness of a pencil line (compare Fig. 1–2).

Nevertheless, the relief is very great by human standards, and the question arises how it is that there are such differences of level.

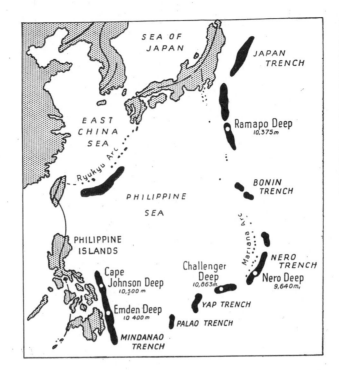

FIG. 1—5
The oceanic deeps of the western Pacific. Prior to 1959 the greatest depth located by echo-sounding was 35,640 feet (10,863 m) in the Challenger Deep. In 1959 the Russian survey ship *Vitiaz* reported a depth of 36,204 feet (11,035 m) in the Marianas Trench. In 1960 Jacques Piccard and Don Walsh descended in the United States bathyscape *Trieste* to a depth of 35,802 feet (10,912 m) in the same vicinity.

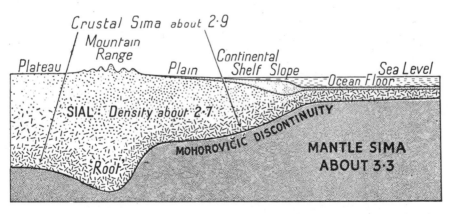

FIG. 1—6
Diagrammatic section through the earth's crust and the upper part of the mantle to illustrate the relationship between surface features and crustal structure. Based on gravity determinations and exploration of the distribution of sial, crustal sima, and mantle sima by earthquake waves.

The earth might very well have been a smooth globe with a uniform oceanic cover. Just how it comes about that continental land areas exist at all is still an unsolved problem. But there is no mystery in the fact that the continents stand up like platforms above the ocean floor. Like ships riding light, the continents protrude just because their rocks (sial) are light compared with the heavier rocks (sima) which underlie the oceans. In the same way, mountain ranges stand high above the continental platforms because the sialic rocks beneath them go down to correspondingly greater depths. High mountains have deep "roots" (see Figs. 1–6 and 1–8). To understand how these curious facts came to be ascertained, it is convenient to begin by considering the effects of gravitation and rotation on the shape of the earth.

SOME NUMERICAL FACTS ABOUT THE EARTH

LAND	RELIEF		OCEANS AND SEAS		
	feet	metres		feet	metres
Greatest known height:			Greatest known depth:		
Mt Everest	29,028	8,848	Marianas Trench	36,204	11,035
Average height	2,757	840	Average depth	12,460	3,808

SIZE AND SHAPE

	miles	km
Equatorial semi-axis, a	3,963·4	6,378·4
Polar semi-axis, b	3,950·0	6,356·9
Mean radius	3,956·4	6,371·0
Equatorial circumference	24,902	40,077
Polar (meridian) circumference	24,857	40,009
Ellipticity, $(a - b)/a$	1/297	

AREA

	millions of sq. miles	km^2
Land (29·22 per cent)	57·5	149
Ice sheets and glaciers	6	15·6
Oceans and seas (70·78 per cent)	139·4	361
Land plus continental shelf	68·5	177·4
Oceans and seas minus continental shelf	128·4	332·6
Total area of the earth	196·9	510·0

VOLUME, DENSITY, AND MASS

	average thickness or radius (km)	volume ($\times 10^6 km^3$)	mean density (g/cm^3)	mass ($\times 10^{24}g$)
Atmosphere	—	—		0·005
Oceans and seas	3·8	1,370	1·03	1·41
Ice sheets and glaciers	1·6	25	0·90	0·023
Continental crust*	35	6,210	2·8	17·39
Oceanic crust †	8	2,660	2·9	7·71
Mantle	2,881	898,000	4·53	4,068
Core	3,473	175,500	10·72	1,881
Whole Earth	6,371	1,083,230	5·517	5,976

*Including continental shelves   †Excluding continental shelves

Conversion factors:

1 mile	= 1·609 km	1 km	= 0·621 mile
1 foot	= 0.3048 metre (m)	1 m	= 3·281 feet
1 sq. mile	= 2·59 km²	1 km²	= 0·386 sq. mile
1 cubic mile	= 4·17 km³	1 km³	= 0·24 cubic mile

THE SHAPE OF THE EARTH

The first voyage around the world, begun at Seville by Magellan in 1519 and completed at Seville by del Cano in 1522, established beyond dispute that the earth is a globe. Today it is possible to girdle the earth, like Puck, "in forty minutes" and to photograph its surface at heights from which the curvature of the globe is plainly seen (Fig. 1–7).

The reason for the spherical shape of the earth became clear when Newton discovered the law of gravitation. All the particles of the earth are pulled towards the centre of gravity and the spherical shape is the natural response to the maximum possible concentration. Even if a body the size of the earth were stronger than steel, it could not maintain

FIG. 1—7
Mosaic of photographs taken
from a rocket 100 miles
(161 km) above the earth
on 5 October 1954. The
photographs cover an area,
indicated within the
semi-circle of the index map,
of 1,250,000 square miles
(3,037,500 km²). The
length of the horizon is
about 2,500 miles (4,023 km).
Apart from its spectacular
demonstration of the curvature
of the earth, the photograph
depicts a tropical storm. The
cloud spirals (upper left)
represent a hurricane which
invaded Texas and adjoining
States from the Gulf of
Mexico. (*Photograph obtained
by the United States Naval
Research Laboratory*)

a shape such as, let us say, that of a cube. The pressure exerted by the weight of the edges and corners would squeeze out material in depth. Equilibrium would be reached only when the faces had bulged out, and the edges and corners had sunk in, until every part of the surface was equidistant from the centre.

The earth is not exactly spherical, however. Again it was Newton who first showed that, because of the earth's daily rotation, its matter is affected not only by inward gravitation, but also by an outward centrifugal force, which reaches its maximum at the equator. He deduced that there should be an equatorial bulge, where the apparent value of gravity was reduced, and a complementary polar flattening, where the centrifugal force becomes vanishingly small. Clearly, if this were so, the length of a degree of latitude along a meridian would be greatest across the poles, where the curvature is flattened, and least across the equator, where the curvature bulges out. Newton's inference was at variance with the few crude measurements that had then been made, according to which the earth was shaped like a lemon, with a long polar axis. To settle the matter, the French Academy in 1735 dispatched a surveying expedition to the neighbourhood of Chimborazo in the Andes of what is now Ecuador, and followed

it up in 1736 by another to Lapland. The results showed that Newton was right. It is, moreover, highly significant that before these expeditions returned, Clairaut, a celebrated French mathematician, had calculated what the shape of the earth would be, assuming the earth to be a fluid and subject only to the effects of its own rotation and gravitational attraction. The ellipsoid of rotation now internationally adopted for surveying purposes as most closely representing the real shape of the earth corresponds almost exactly to that calculated by Clairaut.

To sum up: if the surface of the earth were everywhere at sea level its shape—the *geoid* or figure of the earth—would closely approximate to that of an ellipsoid of rotation (an oblate spheroid) with a polar diameter of 7,900 miles (12,713·8 km), nearly 27 miles (43·4 km) shorter than the equatorial diameter.

How is it, then, that the earth is not exactly a spheroid? The reason is that the crustal rocks are not everywhere of the same density. Since the equatorial bulge is a consequence of the relatively low value of gravity around the equatorial zone, it follows that there should be bulges in other places where gravity is relatively low; that is to say, wherever the crust is composed of light sialic rocks. Such places are the continents. On the other hand, wherever the crust is composed of heavy rocks (sima) the surface should be correspondingly depressed. Such regions are the ocean basins.

The earth continuously tends towards a state of gravitational equilibrium. If there were no rotation and no lateral differences in the density of the rocks, the earth would be a sphere. As a result of rotation it becomes a spheroid. As a further result of density differences in the crustal rocks, continents, mountain ranges, and oceanic basins occur as irregularities superimposed upon the surface of the spheroid.

ISOSTASY

For the ideal condition of gravitational equilibrium that controls the heights of continents and ocean floors, in accordance with the densities of their underlying rocks, the term *isostasy* (Gr. *isostasios*, "in equipoise") was proposed by Dutton, an American geologist, in 1889. The idea may be grasped by thinking of a series of wooden blocks of different heights floating in water (Fig. 1–8). The blocks emerge by amounts which are proportional to their respective heights: they are said to be in a state of hydrostatic balance. Isostasy is the corresponding state of balance which exists between extensive blocks of the earth's crust, which rise to different levels and appear at the surface as mountain ranges, widespread plateaux, plains, or ocean floors. The idea implies that there is a certain minimum depth below sea level where the pressure due to the weight of the overlying material in each unit column is everywhere the same. In Fig. 1–8 this level of uniform pressure is that of the base of the highest block. The earth's major relief is said to be *compensated* by the differences of density within the crust, and the level where the compensation is estimated to be complete—that is, the level of uniform pressure—is often referred to as the *level of compensation*. Naturally, individual

peaks and valleys are not separately balanced in this way; the minor relief features of the surface are easily maintained by the strength of the crustal rocks.

If a mountain range were simply a protuberance of rock resting on the continental platform and wholly supported by the strength of the foundation, then a plumb line—such as is used for levelling surveying instruments—would be deflected from the true vertical by an amount proportional to the gravitational attraction of the mass of the mountain range. The first hint that mountains are not merely masses stuck on an unyielding crust was provided by the Andes expedition of 1735. Pierre Bouguer, the leader of the expedition, found that the deflection of the plumb line by the Andes was surprisingly small, and he expressed his suspicion that the gravitational attraction of the Andes "is much smaller than that to be expected from the mass represented by these mountains". This apparent gravitational anomaly has since been amply confirmed by the results of innumerable measurements of gravity on and near mountains and high plateaux.

Only one physical explanation of these discrepancies is available. There must be a deficiency of mass in the crustal columns underlying the visible mountain ranges—that is, the density of the rocks must be relatively low, down to considerable depths. The possible density distributions are, of course, infinite. Fortunately, we know something of the rocks within the crust and can say what the probable densities are. Moreover,

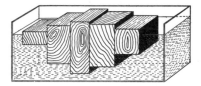

FIG. 1–8
Wooden blocks of different heights floating in water. (shown in front as a section through the tank), to illustrate the concept of isostatic balance between adjacent columns of the earth's crust.

as already mentioned, exploration of the crust by earthquake waves confirms the inference that mountain ranges have sialic roots going down to depths of as much as 50 or 60 km; that under plains near sea level the thickness of the sial is only 30 km, sometimes less; and that beneath the deeper parts of the ocean sial cannot be detected. Fig. 1–6 illustrates the relationships between surface relief and crustal structure in a general way.

CONTINENTAL DRIFT

The arrangement of the continents and oceans, and the fact that the sial appears as continents, rather than being spread thinly over the whole surface of the earth, provide problems that are as yet unsolved. When it was realized, about a hundred years ago, that the occurrence, on the land, of rocks formed from marine sediments proved no more than flooding of the lands by shallow seas, it was generally thought that the continents and ocean basins were permanent features of the earth. For biologists, however, this hypothesis raised difficulties in explaining how certain animals and plants had migrated from one continent to another, unless some parts of the oceans had formerly been land that linked present-day continents.

So began the long controversy regarding the permanency of the continents and ocean basins. Support for the permanency was found in the fact that deep-sea deposits, like those now forming on the ocean floors, have been discovered only in a few marginal islands, where their presence can be accounted for by the vertical movements of mountain building. Such deposits, appear to be consistently absent from the continents proper. The discovery that sial is absent from the oceanic crust now makes it impossible to suppose that parts of the oceans represent sunken land masses.

glacial period, which is quite inexplicable with the continents in their present position (Fig. 1–9). At the same time, great forests flourished in tropical swamps (now coalfields) that extended from North America across Europe to China, indicating an equatorial climate. Furthermore, deposits of laterite, which could only have been formed in a tropical climate, are found in the upper Carboniferous of the United States, Scotland, Germany, Russia, and China. The inference that the equatorial zone of the time is roughly indicated by this belt of coalfields and laterite is irresistible.

From evidence such as this the idea of continental drift arose. If South America, Africa, Arabia, Peninsular India, Australia and Antarctica were assembled, somewhat as in Fig. 1–10, the resultant major continent, known as Gondwanaland, would have been located at the South Pole during the Permo-Carboniferous glaciation, while the laterite belt of the time comes into line with what would then have been the equator. Further evidence that the positions of climatic zones have changed through geological time is provided by evidence of the wind directions of past geological ages (pp. 178–9), and the distribution of ancient coral reefs. The parallelism of the opposing shores of the

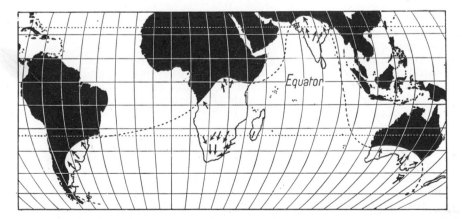

FIG. 1–9
Map showing the distribution of the late Carboniferous glaciations of Gondwanaland with the continents in their present positions; arrows indicate directions of ice flow.

Equator

It has been increasingly recognized, however, that through geological time the positions of the climatic zones and hence the positions of the continents relative to the equator have fundamentally changed. For example, roughly 300 million years ago, in Permo-Carboniferous times, considerable areas in southern Africa, South America, India, and Australia were in the middle of a

Atlantic was long ago interpreted as evidence of continental drift—for example, South America fits into Africa (Fig. 1–10). Furthermore, the truncated ends of fold-mountain belts against shore lines appear to correspond from one continent to another.

The germ of the idea of continental drift can be traced back to the seventeenth and nineteenth centuries, but it was not until

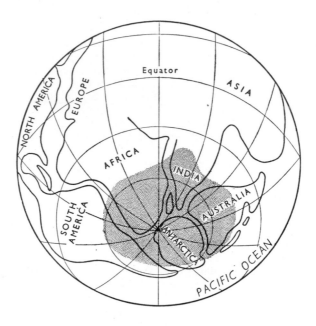

FIG. 1–10
Map showing the distribution of the late Carboniferous glaciations of Gondwanaland with the continents reassembled, though not quite so closely, as interpreted by Alfred Wegener in 1915.

Wegener published his famous book on the subject in 1915 that the possibility of continental drift began to be widely discussed, although it was far from being generally accepted. Recent work on *palaeomagnetism* has tipped the scales decisively in favour of continental drift, by providing substantial evidence that in past geological ages the continents occupied positions, relative to the poles and to each other, very different from those of today's familiar geography.

Broadly speaking, the earth's magnetic field is like that of a powerful bar magnet placed near the middle of the earth and along the axis joining the North and South Magnetic Poles. When certain rocks are formed—for example, when lava flows and minor intrusions of basalt solidify, minute crystals of certain iron ores, such as magnetite and ilmenite, acquire a stable magnetism that is orientated in accordance with the earth's magnetic field of the time. From these magnetized minerals it is therefore possible to discover the north–south direction corresponding to the magnetic poles of the time when they were formed. By collating such evidence from rocks of the same geological age but from widely scattered places the approximate positions of the magnetic poles of the time can be discovered. In this way it has been found that back through geological time the magnetic poles were situated farther and farther away from their present positions.

When Gondwanaland existed, for example, the Magnetic North Pole was situated in what is now the North Pacific Ocean (Fig. 1–11) and the British Isles were near the equator, as had already been recognized from geological evidence concerning the climatic zones (Fig. 1–10).

Until about 1956, most geophysicists favoured *polar wandering* as an explanation for changes of latitude disclosed by the palaeomagnetic data. This was generally understood to mean that an outer shell of the earth—the crust and probably part of the mantle—has slid as a whole over the main body of the earth. If this were an adequate explanation by itself, then the geographic position of the poles during any given geological period would be the same for all the continents. Sufficient work has now been done to know that this is not so; each continent gives a different result. From this it can be inferred that not only have the positions of the magnetic poles changed through geological time, but also the positions of the continents relative to one another; continental drift is obviously implied.

The ocean floors have never been continents, nor have the continents ever formed the ocean floors, but the relative positions of the continents have changed. Although there is no firm knowledge as to how this lateral movement has been accomplished, it is usual to refer to it as *continental drift*.

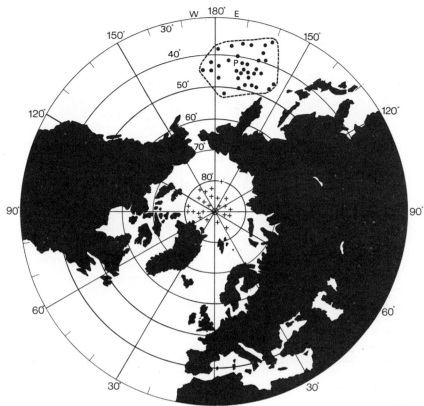

FIG. 1—11
Sketch map of
the northern hemisphere
(from the N Pole to
Latitude 30°). *Crosses*
clustered around the N Pole
indicate the positions of
Pleistocene and Pliocene
geomagnetic poles (from 2
to 12 million years ago).
Black dots clustered around
P indicate the positions of
Permian geomagnetic poles
(about 225 to 270 million
years ago) determined from
European sites undisturbed
by Alpine orogenesis. (*Data
mainly from R. R. Doell
and A. Cox, 1961; and D.
van Hilten, 1964*)

2

The Changing Face of the Earth

WEATHERING, EROSION, AND DENUDATION

The circulations of matter that are continually going on in the zones of air and water, and even of life, constitute a very complicated mechanism which is maintained, essentially, by the heat from the sun. A familiar example of such a circulation is that of the winds (Fig. 10–1). Another, more complex, is the circulation of water. Heat from the sun lifts water vapour from the surface of oceans, seas, lakes, and rivers, and wind distributes the vapour far and wide through the lower levels of the atmosphere. Clouds are formed, rain and snow are precipitated, and on the land these gather into rivers and glaciers. Finally, most of the water is returned to the oceanic and other reservoirs from which it came (Fig. 2–1). These circulations are responsible for an important group of geological processes, for the agents involved—wind, rain, rivers, and glaciers—act on the land by breaking up the rocks and so producing rock waste which is gradually carried away.

Part of every shower of rain sinks into the soil and promotes the work of decay by solution and by loosening the particles. Every frost shatters the rocks with its expanding wedges of freezing water (Fig. 2–2). Life also co-operates in the work of destruction. The roots of trees grow down into cracks, and assist in splitting up the rocks (Fig. 2–3). Worms and other burrowing animals bring up the finer particles of soil to the surface, where they fall a ready prey to wind and rain. The soil is a phase through which much of the rock waste of the lands must pass before it is ultimately removed. The production of rock waste by these various agents, partly by mechanical breaking and partly by solution and chemical decay, is described as *weathering*.

Sooner or later the products of weathering are removed from their place of formation. Blowing over the lands the wind becomes armed with dust and sand, carrying them far and wide and often becoming a powerful sand-blasting agent as it sweeps across areas of exposed rock. Glaciers, similarly armed with debris, grind down the rocks over which they pass during their slow descent from ice fields and high mountain valleys. Rainwash and landslips feed the rivers with fragments, large and small, and these are not only carried away, but are used by the rivers as tools to excavate their floors and sides. And in

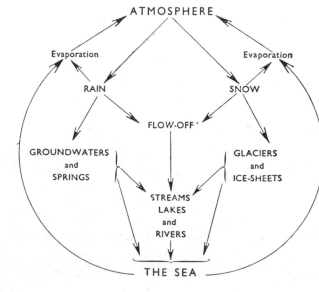

FIG. 2–1
The circulation of meteoric water. Evaporation takes place from all exposed surfaces of water and ice as well as from the sea. Part of the water ascends from the depths by way of volcanoes and reaches the surface for the first time; such water is called *juvenile* water to distinguish it from the *meteoric* water already present in the hydrosphere and atmosphere.

FIG. 2—2
Frost shattering of
Ordovician igneous rocks,
North peak of Tryfaen, North
Wales. (*G. P. Abraham Ltd,
Keswick*)

FIG. 2—3
Ice-transported boulder,
with crack enlarged by the
growth of tree roots,
Trefarthen, Anglesey. (*H.M.
Geological Survey*)

addition to their visible burden of mud and sand, the river waters carry an invisible load of dissolved material, extracted from rocks and soils by the solvent action of rain and soil water, and by that of the river water itself. Winds, rivers, and glaciers, the agents that carry away the products of rock waste, are known as *transporting agents*. All the destructive processes due to the effects of the transporting agents are described as *erosion* (L. *erodere*, to gnaw away).

It is convenient to regard weathering as rock decay by agents involving little or no transport of the resulting products, and erosion as land destruction by agents which simultaneously remove the debris. Both sets of processes co-operate in wearing away the land surface, and their combined effects are described by the term *denudation* (L. *denudare*, to make bare).

DEPOSITION OF SEDIMENT

The sediment carried away by the transporting agents is sooner or later deposited again. Sand blown by the wind collects into sand dunes along the seashore or in the desert (Fig. 2–4). Where glaciers melt away, the debris gathered up during their journey is dumped down unsorted (Fig. 2–5), to be dealt with later by rivers or the sea. When a stream enters a lake the current is checked and the load of sand and mud gradually settles to the bottom. Downstream in the open valley sand and mud are spread over the alluvial flats during floods, while the main stream continues, by way of estuary or delta, to sweep the bulk of the material into the sea. Storm waves thundering against rocky coasts provide still more rock waste, and the whole supply is sorted out and widely distributed by waves and currents. Smooth and rounded water-worn boulders collect beneath the cliffs. Sandy beaches accumulate in quiet bays. Out on the sea floor the finer particles are deposited as broad fringes of sediment, the finest material of all being swept far across the continental shelves before it comes to rest. All these deposits are examples of sedimentary rocks in the making.

We have still to trace what happens to the invisible load of dissolved mineral matter that is removed from the land by rivers. Some rivers flow into lakes that have no outlet save by evaporation into the air above them. The waters of such lakes rapidly become salt

FIG. 2–4
A stage in the landward drift (from upper right towards lower left) of the Culbin Sands, Moray, Scotland. Most of this area has now been stabilized by plantations. (*H.M. Geological Survey*)

FIG. 2—5
Öraefajökull Glacier, Iceland, from its source in an upland ice-cap to its snout, where it is melting away amidst the moraines of rock waste which it transported and deposited before shrinking to its present size. (*Thorvardur R. Jonsson*)

because, as the famous astronomer Halley realized more than two centuries ago, "the saline particles brought in by the rivers remain behind, while the fresh evaporate". Gradually the lake waters become saturated and rock salt and other saline deposits, like those on the shores and floor of the Dead Sea, are precipitated. Most rivers, however, reach the sea and pour into it the greater part of the material dissolved from the land. So, as Halley pointed out, "the ocean itself is become salt from the same cause". But while, on balance, the salinity of the sea may be slowly increasing, much of the mineral matter contributed to the sea is taken out again by living organisms. Cockles and mussels, sea-urchins and corals, and many other sea creatures, make shells for themselves out of calcium carbonate abstracted from the water in which they live. When the creatures die, most of their soft parts are eaten and the rest decays. But their hard parts remain, and these accumulate as the shell banks of shallow seas (Fig. 2–6) the coral reefs of tropical coasts

FIG. 2—6
Limestone in the making: a deposit of shell gravel (mainly cockles). (*S. H. Reynolds*)

and islands, and the grey globigerina ooze of the deep-sea floor. All of these are limestones in the making. Life, as a builder of organic sediments, is a geological agent of first importance.

THE IMPORTANCE OF TIME AND RATES OF DENUDATION

It will now be realized that while the higher regions of the earth's crust are constantly wasting away, the lower levels are just as steadily being built up. Evidently denudation and deposition are great levelling processes. In the course of a single lifetime their effects may not be everywhere perceptible. Nevertheless they are not too slow to be measured. There are two methods by which the average rate of denudation can be approximately determined. One is by estimating the weight of materials transported by rivers from a source area within a particular span of time. The other is by estimating the weight of sediment, for which the source area can be inferred, that has been deposited within a restricted catchment area or basin during a particular span of time. A third method is applicable when the original form of a land mass can be reconstructed and dated radiometrically (see p. 62). This method has been used to estimate the rate of denudation of volcanic structures, the original form of which can readily be reconstructed and dated by the radiometric age of the volcanic rock.

An estimate of 8,000 million tons, for the materials annually transported to the sea by rivers, is based on data available for drainage basins having a total area of 40 million square miles. Averaged over this area the annual loss of rock waste corresponds to 200 tons per square mile, which is equivalent to about 1 foot in 9,000 years, or 1 metre in 30,000 years. Rates of denudation vary from place to place, however, because they are related both to relief and climate. For example, there is a loss of 1 foot in 400 years in the Irrawaddy-Chindwin basin for which the mountainous region of Burma forms the source area, and a loss that varies from about 1 foot to 3 feet in 1,000 years in mountainous regions in the humid tropics, while for the low-lying areas draining into Hudson Bay the rate falls to 1 foot in 47,000 years. In Britain, about half an inch has already been worn from the outer surface of the Portland stone with which St Paul's Cathedral was built over 250 years ago. Portland stone has justified Wren's confidence in its suitability to withstand the London atmosphere, for the land of Britain as a whole is being worn down rather faster—at an average rate of about one foot in three or four thousand years. At this rate a million years would suffice to reduce the varied landscapes of our country to a monotonous plain. Evidently slowly acting causes are competent to produce enormous changes if only they continue to operate through sufficiently long periods.

Now, geologically speaking, a million years is a comparatively short time, just as a million miles is a short distance from an astronomical point of view. One of the triumphs of geology and physics is the demonstration that the age of the earth cannot be less than 4,500 million years. Geological processes act very slowly, but geological time is inconceivably long. The effects of slow processes acting for long periods have been fully adequate to account for all the successive transformations of landscape that the earth has witnessed.

EARTH MOVEMENTS

It follows that there has been ample time, since land and sea came into existence, for Britain, and indeed for the highest land areas, to have been worn down to sea level over and over again. How then does it happen that every continent still has its highlands and mountain peaks? There are two possibilities: either the lands, together with adjoining parts of the sea floor, may have been uplifted from time to time, or the level of the sea may have fallen, leaving the land relatively upraised.

Relative movements between land and sea are convincingly proved by the presence in Islay and Jura, and in many other places, of typical sea beaches, now raised far above the reach of the waves (Fig. 2–7). Behind these *raised beaches* the corresponding cliffs, often tunnelled with sea caves, are still preserved (Fig. 2–8). In Scandinavia and Peru old strand lines can be traced which rise from near sea level in the south to heights of hundreds of feet in the north. Such tilting of the shores shows that the movements involved actual upheaval of the crust and not merely a change of sea level. The former uplift of old sea floors can be recognized in the Pennines, where the grey limestones contain fossil shells and corals that bear silent witness to the fact that the rocks forming the hills of northern England once lay under the sea. The most spectacular example of uplift is provided by Mount Everest, the summit of which is carved out of sediments that were originally deposited on the sea floor of a former age.

FIG. 2—7
100-foot raised beach, west of Rhuvaal Lighthouse, Islay, Argyll, Scotland. (*H.M. Geological Survey*)

FIG. 2—8
25-foot raised beach with sea cave in the quartzite cliff behind, Loch Rarbet, Jura, Argyll, Scotland. (*H.M. Geological Survey*)

FIG. 2—9
Submerged Forest, Leasowe
foreshore, Cheshire.
(*C. A. Defieux*)

FIG. 2—10
Displacement of a road and
production of a fault scarp
by a sudden movement on
the White Creek Fault which
was responsible for the
Murchison earthquake of
1929, South Island, New
Zealand. The uplifted block
rose 15 feet relative to
the foreground. (*New
Zealand Geological Survey*)

Relative movements between land and sea may also bring about submergence of the land, as shown, for example, by the local occurrence around our shores of submerged forests (Fig. 2–9). These are groups of tree-stumps still preserved with their roots in the original position of growth, but now uncovered only at the lowest tides. In Mount's Bay, near Penzance, what is probably the same submergence is indicated by the occurrence, beneath the sea, of a Stone Age axe-factory, dating from about 1,800–1,500 B.C.

When earth movements take place suddenly, they are recognized by the passage of earthquake waves. In certain restless belts of the crust, for example in Japan, there may be several shocks in a single day, occasionally with disastrous consequences. In Yakatut Bay, Alaska, in 1899, an exceptionally great upward jerk of 47 feet occurred; but usually these sudden movements are on a much smaller scale (Fig. 2–10).

Where crustal movements have been uniformly vertical, the beds of sediment uplifted from their original positions on the sea floor lie nearly horizontally (Fig. 2–11). In many places, however, they have been corrugated and buckled into folds like a wrinkled-up tablecloth that has been pushed along the table (Fig. 2–12). A familiar small-scale domestic model that corresponds more closely to the mode of formation of many such fold-structures is provided by the skin that forms on hot milk. If the containing vessel is tilted a little, the skin slumps into a series of folds, some of which are likely to overlap their down-slope neighbours. Many an Alpine precipice displays great sheets of rock which have been "overfolded" in much the same way, so that parts of them lie upside down (Fig. 13–4). In other places layers of rock have been folded tightly together, like the pleats of a closed concertina. All the great mountain ranges of the world have been carved out of rocks that have been folded and crumpled and overthrust.

Although there must have been long periods when much of the land lay under the sea, it is probably thousands of millions of years since most of the land was submerged simultaneously. Earth movements and volcanic additions to the surface have evidently been fully competent to restore the balance of land and sea whenever that balance was threatened by the levelling processes of denudation. Most of the sediments originally deposited on the shallow sea floor, sometimes hardened and cemented into firm and durable rocks, sometimes bent and twisted into intricate folds, sometimes accompanied by lavas and volcanic ashes, have sooner or later emerged to form new lands, either by upheaval or by withdrawal of the sea.

VOLCANIC AND IGNEOUS ACTIVITY

Earth movements are not the only manifestations of the earth's internal activities. Volcanic eruptions provide a most spectacular proof that the earth's interior is so hot that locally even the crustal rocks pass into a molten state. A volcano is essentially a fissure or vent, communicating with the interior, from which flows of lava, fountains of incandescent spray, or explosive bursts of gases and volcanic "ashes" are erupted at the surface. The fragmental materials produced during volcanic eruptions are collectively known as *pyroclasts* (Gr. *pyro-*, fire; *klastos*, broken in pieces).

The general term for the parental materials of these hot volcanic products, as they occur in the depth before eruption at the surface, is *magma*, a Greek word originally meaning any kneaded mixture, such as dough or ointment. In its geological application the property of high temperature is also implied. So far as can be judged from their products, magmas may consist of hot liquids, gases, and solids in variable proportions and combinations, which are capable of penetrating into or through the crustal rocks. As a highly gas-charged magma ascends and the overhead pressure gradually falls, the gases begin to be liberated. Sooner or later the growing gas pressure overcomes the resistance—the soda-water bottle bursts, so to speak, or blows off its cap—and an explosive eruption breaks out (Fig. 2–13).

In the more familiar volcanoes the magma ascends through a central pipe, around which the lavas and pyroclasts accumulate to form a more or less conical volcanic mountain. Magma may also reach the surface through long fissures from which lava-flows spread over the surrounding country, filling up the valleys and forming widespread volcanic plains or plateaux. Thus volcanic activity is a constructive process whereby new materials are brought to the surface, and new topographic forms built up.

Volcanic activity is only the surface manifestation of the movement through the earth's crust of magma generated in the mantle or in exceptionally heated regions of the crust itself. The new rocks formed in the crust from magma that failed to reach the surface are called *intrusive* rocks, to distinguish them from lavas, which are called volcanic or *extrusive* rocks. In many places intrusive rocks are exposed to observation, as on Dartmoor, as a result of the removal of the original cover by denudation (Fig. 3–4). All rocks which owe their origin to the solidification of magmas in depth (intrusive rocks) or of lavas at the surface (extrusive rocks) are described as *igneous* rocks (L. *ignis*, fire).

METAMORPHISM OF ROCKS

When crustal rocks are buried and come under the influence of (*a*) the intense pressure or stress accompanying severe earth movements; (*b*) the increased temperature associated with igneous activity; or (*c*) chemically active gases and liquids, they respond by changes in structure and mineral composition, and so become transformed into new types of rocks. All such changes are described as *metamorphism*, and examples of them will be considered in the following chapter. Here the term is introduced to draw attention to the fact that rocks respond to the earth's internal activities not only by crumpling or by fusion, but also by recrystallization. It must be carefully noticed that metamorphism is the very antithesis of weathering. Both processes bring about great changes in pre-existing rocks, but weathering is destructive while metamorphism is constructive. Instead of reducing a pre-existing rock to a decaying mass of rock waste and soil, metamorphism brings about its transformation, often from a dull and uninteresting-looking stone, into a durable crystalline rock of bright and shining minerals and attractive appearance.

SUMMARY OF THE GEOLOGICAL PROCESSES

It will now be clear from our rapid survey of the leading geological processes that they fall into two contrasted groups. The first group—denudation and deposition—includes the processes which act on the crust at or very near its surface, as a result of the movements and chemical activities of air, water, ice, and living organisms. Such processes are essentially of external origin. The second group—earth movements, igneous activity, and metamorphism—includes the processes which act within or through the crust, as a result of the physical and chemical activities of the materials of both crust and mantle. Such processes are essentially of internal origin.

Both groups of processes operate under the control of gravitation (including attractions due to the sun and moon), co-operating with the earth's bodily movements—rotation about its axis and revolution around the sun. But if these were all, the earth's surface would soon reach a state of approximate equilibrium from which no further changes of geological significance could develop. Each group of processes, to be kept going, requires some additional source of energy. The processes of external origin are specifically maintained by the radiation of heat from the sun. Those of internal origin are similarly maintained by the liberation of heat from the stores of energy locked within the earth.

Throughout the ages the face of the earth has been changing its expression. At times its features have been flat and monotonous. At others—as to-day—they have been bold and vigorous. But in the long struggle for supremacy between the sun-born forces of land destruction and the earth-born forces of land renewal, neither has permanently gained the mastery.

CLASSIFICATION OF GEOLOGICAL PROCESSES

PROCESSES OF EXTERNAL ORIGIN

1. Denudation (Weathering, Erosion, and Transport)
Sculpturing of the land surface and removal of the products of rock decay mechanically and in solution.

2. Deposition
(*a*) of the debris transported mechanically (*e.g.* sand and mud);
(*b*) of the materials transported in solution:
(*i*) by evaporation and chemical precipitation (*e.g.* rock-salt);
(*ii*) by the intervention of living organisms (*e.g.* coral limestone);
(*c*) of organic matter, largely the remains of vegetation (*e.g.* peat).

PROCESSES OF INTERNAL ORIGIN

1. Earth Movements
Uplift and depression of land areas and sea floors; mountain building with associated folding and overthrusting of rocks; earthquakes.

2. Metamorphism
Transformation of pre-existing rocks into new types by the action of heat, pressure, stress, and hot, chemically active, migrating fluids.

3. Igneous Activity
Emplacement of intrusions; emission of lavas, gases, and other volcanic products.

FIG. 2–11
Horizontal strata exposed by river erosion; looking up Bright Angel Canyon, a tributary of the Grand Canyon of the Colorado River. (*United States Geological Survey*)

FIG. 2–12
Folded strata of Jurassic age. The Stair Hole, west of Lulworth Cove, Dorset. (*F. N. Ashcroft*)

FIG. 2—13
Paricutin, Mexico, erupting early in April 1943, six weeks after the first appearance of the volcano. (*Three Lions Inc., New York*)

EXTERNAL PROCESSES AND ISOSTASY

It will now be realized that external processes bring about changes that must inevitable upset the ideal state of isostatic balance which gravitation tends to establish (see p. 10). When a mountain range is carved into peaks and valleys and gradually worn down by the agents of denudation, the load on the underlying column of the crust is reduced by the weight of the rock waste that has been carried away. At the same time a neighbouring column, underlying a region of delta and sea floor, where the rock waste is being deposited, receives a corresponding increase of load. Unless a complementary transfer of material occurs in depth, the two columns cannot remain in isostatic equilibrium. At the base of the crust the pressure exerted by the loaded column is increased, while that exerted by the unloaded column is decreased. In response to this pressure difference in the mantle a slow flowage of material occurs (Fig. 2–14). The loaded column sinks and the unloaded one rises. This process, whereby isostasy is restored, is called *isostatic readjustment*.

Certain processes disturb the pre-existing isostatic balance much more rapidly than it can be restored by deep-seated flowage in the mantle. For example, when the last of the thick European and North American ice sheets melted away, say 11,000 and 8,000 years ago, these regions were quickly relieved of an immense load of ice. The resulting uplifts which then began are still actively in progress. Far above the shores of Finland and Scandinavia there are raised beaches which show that a maximum uplift of nearly 900 feet (274 m) has already occurred, and every twenty-eight years another foot is added to the total all around the northern end of the Gulf of Bothnia. The region is still out of isostatic balance, and it can be estimated that it has still to rise another 700 feet (213 m) or so, before equilibrium can be reached.

THE PARADOX OF SOLIDS THAT FLOW

For the re-establishment of equilibrium around the Gulf of Bothnia, continued inflow of the mantle, beneath the sialic crust, is necessary (Fig. 2–14). In this respect the mantle behaves like an extremely viscous fluid, but it is not liquid because, like the crust, it transmits earthquake vibrations of a kind that can travel only through rigid materials that can be sheared, not through liquids (S waves, p. 244). Judged by this test alone the mantle is undoubtedly solid. Since the mantle may be transmitting earthquake waves and also, at the same time, be imperceptibly flowing to restore isostatic equilibrium, it is clearly both rigid and viscous simultaneously. It has a double personality, so to speak, being at the same time an elastic solid and a viscous fluid. It is not, however, a viscous liquid. The earth acts as a rigid solid

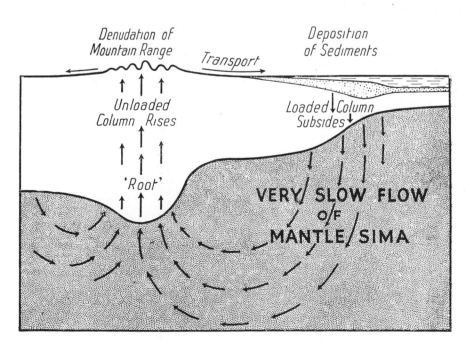

FIG. 2–14 Schematic section to illustrate isostatic readjustment, by slow sub-crustal flow in the mantle, in response to unloading by denudation and loading by deposition. Vertical scale greatly exaggerated.

to short-lived phenomena like earthquake waves (each lasting a second or so), and tides (half a day), but it behaves as a viscous fluid to all phenomena of long duration (from ten thousand years upwards). Indeed, its very shape is that of a fluid body (see p. 9).

Fortunately there are several familiar rocks that display this double personality in periods of time that are well within human experience. For example, a lump of pitch is easily broken into angular fragments by a tap from a hammer, but the same lump when left to itself at ordinary temperatures flattens out under its own weight into a thin sheet. To a sharply applied force it behaves as a brittle solid, while in response to the long continued but much smaller stress of its own weight it flows as a viscous fluid. Ice is another material that, with a sharp blow, breaks as a brittle solid, but over longer periods demonstrably flows in glaciers and ice sheets. The term *rheid* has been introduced to describe a substance—like pitch and ice— in the state when it flows. A rheid differs from a liquid in being below its melting point

and in having a certain amount of strength. It flows by virtue of the relatively long duration of the deforming stress. A whole new border-line science, known as rheology (Gr. *rheo*, flow), is now devoted to the investigation of these phenomena.

Unlike pitch, ice in bulk is a crystalline rock. So sluggish is the flow of ice that it is no wonder we have an intuitive difficulty in understanding how it manages to flow at all. But flow it does, as Fig. 2–15 demonstrates in no uncertain fashion. Were it not for comparable but much more sluggish flow in the mantle, and for corresponding flow of the deep-seated rocks of the crust of the earth, we should not be here to discuss the matter. The continents would long ago have disappeared beneath the sea, washed away by rain and rivers, and worn down still further by waves and currents. Only a few volcanic islands and coral reefs might diversify the otherwise monotonous seascape. That the earth has avoided this uninteresting fate is due to processes at work in the depths.

FIG. 2–15
Contortions of ice and morainic debris resulting from competition for space between glaciers advancing into the same valley at different but comparable rates of flow, Alaska. (*Bradford Washburn*)

3
Materials of the Earth's Crust

ELEMENTS, MINERALS, AND ROCKS

The vast majority of rocks are aggregates of minerals. Of the remainder, some, like pumice, are made of volcanic glass, whilst others, like coal, are composed of the products of organic decay. All these materials in turn are made of atoms of the chemical elements, of which 102 are known. Of these only about 90 occur naturally in detectable amounts, the others having been synthesized by nuclear reactions. Of the 90 naturally occurring elements, eight are so abundant that they make up more than 99 per cent by weight of all the many thousands of rocks that have been analysed. Many of the others, such as gold, tin, copper, and uranium, though present only in traces in rocks, are locally concentrated in mineral veins and other ore deposits that can be profitably worked.

Some of the elements, for example gold, copper, sulphur, and carbon (as diamond and graphite) make minerals by themselves, but most minerals are compounds of two or more elements. Oxygen is by far the most abundant element in rocks. In combination with other elements it forms compounds called oxides, some of which occur as minerals. As silicon is the most abundant element after oxygen, it is not surprising that silica, the oxide of silicon, SiO_2, should be the most abundant of all oxides. Silica is familiar as *quartz*, a common mineral which is specially characteristic of granites, sandstones, and quartz veins. The formula, SiO_2, is a very simple way of expressing the fact that for every atom of silicon in quartz there are two atoms of oxygen. Quartz has therefore a definite composition. The formulae for other minerals can be similarly interpreted. The most abundant minerals of the earth's crust are the *feldspars*: orthoclase ($KAlSi_3O_8$) and plagioclase. Plagioclase is a group name for a continuous series of minerals ranging from albite ($NaAlSi_3O_8$) at one end to anorthite ($CaAl_2Si_2O_8$) at the other. The intermediate members of the series contain both sodium and calcium.

In the cavities of mineral veins, quartz can

FIG. 3–1
Quartz crystals from La Gardette, Isère, France. (*British Museum, Natural History*)

be found as clear transparent prisms, each with six sides and each terminated by a pyramid with six faces. The ancient Greeks gave the name crystal (*krustallos*, clear ice) to these beautiful forms, and to this day water-clear quartz is still known as rock crystal (Fig. 3–1). Most other minerals can also develop into symmetrical forms bounded by flat faces, and all of these are now called crystals. The study of crystals with X-rays has revealed that the symmetrical shape is the outward expression of an organized internal structure. The atoms composing a crystal are arranged in an orderly fashion, the different kinds of atoms being built into a definite pattern which is repeated over and over again, as in the design of a wall-paper, except that in crystals the design is in three dimensions (Fig. 3–2). It follows that any crystalline mineral has a chemical composition that is either fixed (as in quartz), or varies (as in feldspars) within limits that depend on the degree to which the atoms of certain elements can substitute for those of other elements without changing the pattern of the atomic framework.

Although about 2,000 minerals are known, most common rocks can be adequately described in terms of a dozen or less, as the following table indicates.

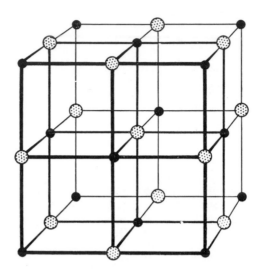

FIG. 3–2
Lattice structure of a crystal of common salt, NaCl. Relatively small Na^+ ions (black) and larger Cl^- ions (dotted) are arranged alternately at the corners of a set of cubes.

AVERAGE MINERAL COMPOSITIONS OF SOME COMMON ROCKS

MINERALS	IGNEOUS ROCKS		SEDIMENTARY ROCKS		
	Granite	*Basalt*	*Sandstone*	*Shale*	*Limestone*
Quartz	31·3	—	69·8	31·9	3·7
Feldspars	52·3	46·2	8·4	17·6	2·2
Micas	11·5	—	1·2	18·4	—
Clay minerals	—	—	6·9	10·0	1·0
Chlorite	—	—	1·1	6·4	—
Hornblende	2·4	—	—	—	—
Augite	rare	36·9	—	—	—
Olivine	—	7·6	—	—	—
Calcite and dolomite	—	—	10·6	7·9	92·8
Iron ores	2·0	6·5	1·7	5·4	0·1
Other minerals	0·5	2·8	0·3	2·4	0·3

The few references to rocks that have already been made suffice to show that rocks may be divided into three major groups—igneous, sedimentary, and metamorphic—according to the processes that were concerned in their origin.

IGNEOUS ROCKS

GRANITE

Granite forms the cores or backbones of mountain ranges, where it is the character-istic rock of many of the high peaks. But the mountains of former geological ages have been worn down by denudation, as in Cornwall and Devon (Fig. 3–3), and so it happens that granite can be more comfortably examined in the tors and valleys of less elevated regions (Fig. 3–4), or in the cliffs of headlands where, for a time, it resists the attack of the sea (Fig. 4–18). In most towns it can be seen as hewn blocks or decorative slabs and columns, and it provides one of the best materials for piers and lighthouses.

Granite is a medium- to coarse-grained rock composed essentially of quartz, feldspar, and mica. In some examples (Fig. 3–5) the interlocking minerals are uniformly distributed, and all are about the same size.

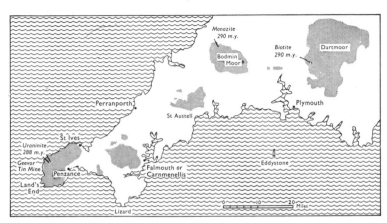

FIG. 3–3
Granite stocks of Cornwall and Devon. The ages of some radioactive minerals that have been dated are indicated in millions of years (m.y.).

FIG. 3–4
Saddle Tor, Dartmoor, Devon: part of a large granite intrusion. Three sets of joints have controlled the erosion forms: (a) those roughly parallel to the page, (b) those roughly parallel to the average ground surface; and (c) those at right angles to the page. (*Dorien Leigh Ltd*)

FIG. 3–5
Polished surface of bluish grey granite from Rubislaw, Aberdeenshire. Half natural size. (*Granite Supply Association, Aberdeen*)

Feldspar, mostly orthoclase, is the most abundant mineral. Gleaming plates of mica (black or bronze-like biotite, accompanied in some varieties by silvery white muscovite) can easily be recognized. Between the feldspars and micas the remaining spaces are occupied by translucent, glassy-looking quartz.

Instead of being uniformly granular, certain granites (*e.g.* from Cornwall and Shap Fells, Fig. 3–6) have a distinctive pattern or *texture*, clearly seen on polished slabs, due to the development of orthoclase as conspicuous, isolated crystals which are much larger than those of the granular groundmass in which they are embedded. This texture is technically described as *porphyritic*, a term derived from an old Greek word meaning "purple". The Romans, prospecting for decorative stones in Egypt two thousand years ago, came upon a deep purple rock—which they called *porphyrites lapis*—of such attractive appearance that they quarried it for columns, vases, and slabs. In the course of time the same name came to be applied to other rocks which contain large crystals embedded in a finer groundmass, even though they lack the purple hue of the original porphyritic rock.

In a less common variety of granite, large crystals of quartz and feldspar are intergrown in such a way that, when seen on a flat surface, they look like Hebrew writing. The rock is then called *graphic granite*.

IDENTIFICATION OF GRANITE FROM ITS MINERALS

Orthoclase, whether it occurs as porphyritic crystals or in the matrix of granite, can be recognized as a cream, pink, or grey mineral. When it is broken across, the surfaces are smooth and glistening. Orthoclase does not just break anyhow: it "cleaves" along parallel cleavage planes in the crystal structure across which cohesion is comparatively weak. Just as in many wall-papers the repetition of the unit pattern gives rise to a parallel series of "open" lines, so in the atomic pattern of a crystal there may be similar "open" planes, and it is along these that the crystal splits most readily. Orthoclase has two such sets of cleavage planes, and the mineral takes its name from the fact that they are exactly at right angles (Gr. *orthos*, rectangular; *clastos*, breaking).

Plagioclase is also present in the groundmass of granite. It is cream or grey in colour, like orthoclase, but not pink. If it is examined with a lens, it can sometimes be distinguished from orthoclase because some of its surfaces are striped with narrow parallel bands. This striped appearance is due to a phenomenon known as twinning: it is as though alternate slices of the crystal have been rotated round through 180°, and as a result reflect light differently from the intervening slices. Like orthoclase, plagioclase also has two cleavages, but in this case, though nearly at right angles, they are not exactly so. Hence the name (Gr. *plagios*, oblique).

Microcline, rather than orthoclase, forms the large crystals in some porphyritic granites. This is another variety of potash feldspar ($KAlSi_2O_8$) and its name, meaning "little slope", refers to the fact that the angle between its two cleavages departs by half a degree from a right angle. With a lens, microcline can be distinguished from orthoclase by its cross-hatched appearance; it shows the same striping as plagioclase but in two directions making a high angle with one another.

Mica, in granite, in the form of black or bronze *biotite* or silvery white *muscovite*, can be recognized by its brilliant lustre and excellent cleavage. It cleaves in only one direction and, if the crystals are big enough, it is an easy matter to cleave them into small shining flakes.

Quartz fills in the interspaces between the other minerals in granite, except in graphic granite when it is intergrown with orthoclase. It can be recognized by its translucent glassy appearance, its lack of cleavage, and—if the irregular-shaped crystals are large enough—by its conchoidal fracture, like that of bottle glass.

GRANITE AS A FIELD TERM

The name granite can be used in two different ways. Technically a granite is rich in potash: that is, it contains more orthoclase (or microcline) than plagioclase. If a granitic rock contains more plagioclase than orthoclase it is called quartz diorite or diorite, depending on whether quartz is present or not. Granitic rocks intermediate in composition between these two extremes are called granodiorite (Fig. 3–7).

FIG. 3–6
Polished surface of Shap granite (Westmorland) showing porphyritic crystals of orthoclase in a groundmass of quartz, plagioclase (oligoclase), orthoclase, and biotite. Natural size. (*The Shap Granite Company Ltd*)

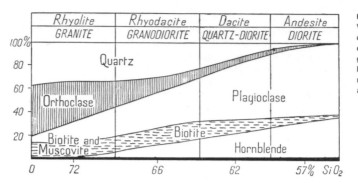

FIG. 3–7
Variation in mineral
composition and silica
content of the rock series
granite-diorite. The black
line at the base represents
minerals present in accessory
amount.

As will be seen from Fig. 3–7, throughout the mineralogical series from granite to diorite, mica progressively decreases and at the same time hornblende appears and increases. *Hornblende* is a dark green mineral with a prismatic form. It has two well-developed cleavages both of which are parallel to the direction of elongation, and make an angle of about 124° with one another.

Because it is not always easy in the field to distinguish between the varieties of granitic rocks, the term granite is commonly used as a field term to include them all. But when using the name in this way it is important to make this clear. In this book the name granite is used in this broad sense, as a field term, because all the varieties are related structurally and consequently give rise to similar scenic features.

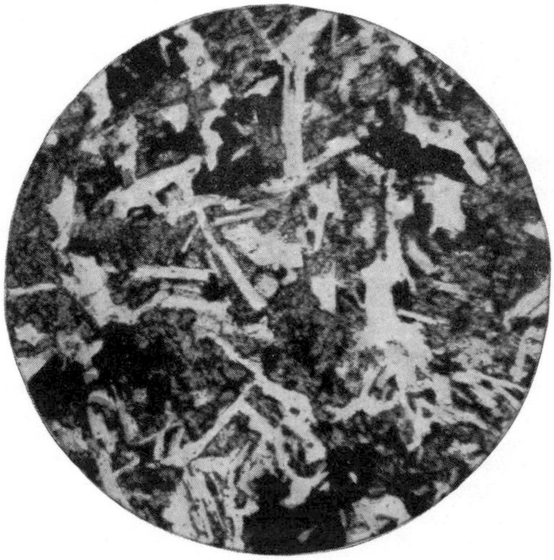

FIG. 3–8
Basalt as seen in thin
section under the microscope,
showing plagioclase (white),
augite (grey), and ilmenite
(black). 50 times natural
size. (G. O'Neill)

BASALT

Basalt is a dark-coloured, very fine-grained rock, which is of widespread occurrence as lava flows of all geological ages, and is still the most abundant type of lava erupted from the volcanoes of today.

It is only by examining basalt in a thin section under the microscope (Fig. 3–8) that its mineralogical composition can be determined. Lath-like crystals of a clear colourless mineral, which is calcic plagioclase, form an irregular open network which extends throughout the rock. The grey mineral, which is greenish or brownish as seen through the microscope, is augite. Many basalts also contain olivine, sometimes abundantly. The black opaque mineral is magnetite or ilmenite. It is the high proportion of iron in basalt which is responsible for the dark colour of the rock, and for the rusty-looking material (limonite) that encrusts its surface when it has been exposed to the weather.

Basalt is not always wholly made up of crystals. Varieties that solidified very rapidly, as a result of sudden chilling, had no time to crystallize completely. In consequence, the part that remained uncrystallized had no alternative but to solidify into black volcanic glass. Crystals may already have grown in the magma before its eruption as lava. In this case the resulting basalt is a porphyritic variety, with relatively large crystals in a very fine-grained or glassy groundmass. At the top of a basalt flow the lava may be blown into a cinder-like froth by the expansion of escaping gases. Even in the more compact basalts, gas-blown cavities of various sizes may occur. These may be empty; or lined with crystals, often beautifully developed; or even completely filled with minerals. The filled "bubbles" sometimes look like almonds, and so the name *amygdale* is given to them (from the Gr. *amygdalos*, an almond). Basalts which are studded with numerous amygdales are called *amygdaloidal* basalts. One of the commonest minerals found in amygdales is *agate*, banded in concentric layers of different tints. Agate is a variety of silica, and sometimes, inside a lining of agate, crystals of quartz or of amethyst (purple quartz) may be found projecting into the hollow space within.

TEXTURES AND CLASSIFICATION OF
COMMON IGNEOUS ROCKS

Granite and basalt, and types closely related to them, are by far the most abundant of the igneous rocks. Granite is an example of the coarse-grained rocks that crystallized slowly in large masses within the crust. Such rocks are described as *plutonic*, after Pluto, the god of the underworld. Basalt, on the other hand, is an example of the very fine-grained or glassy rocks that cooled quickly from lavas that flowed over the surface. These are *volcanic* rocks, after Vulcan, the god of fire. Between the two extremes there are rocks of intermediate grain that cooled and crystallized at intermediate rates, generally in small

intrusions like the dykes and sills described on pages 64–8. Such rocks are distinguished as *hypabyssal* (intermediate depths). Many of the hypabyssal rocks of sialic composition are remarkable for a very conspicuous development of porphyritic texture, in consequence of which they are known by the familiar rock name *porphyry*.

The simple relationship between mode of occurrence and grain size indicated above does not completely cover all the possibilities, because (a) the outer skin of a thin dyke or sill may be chilled against cold wall rocks almost as quickly as the upper layers of a lava flow against the air; and (b) the rate of cooling in the interior of a thick lava flow may be as slow as it is within the smaller dykes and sills. However, provided that such inevitable exceptions to the general rule are not forgotten, the following correlations serve as a useful basis for the classification of igneous rocks:

MODE OF OCCURRENCE		TEXTURE	
EXTRUSIVE	Lava flows	Volcanic	{ Glassy / Very fine-grained	and porphyritic
INTRUSIVE	{ Minor intrusions / Major intrusions	Hypabyssal / Plutonic	Fine-grained / Coarse-grained	varieties of each

According to this scheme, the rocks of any given composition may have any one of eight different textures. In the case of rocks of granitic composition, the eight textural types are distinguished by the following names:

VOLCANIC	{ Glassy / Stony	Obsidian and Pumice (frothy) / Rhyolite	Porphyritic Obsidian / Porphyritic Rhyolite
HYPABYSSAL	Fine-grained	Felsite	Quartz-porphyry
PLUTONIC	Coarse-grained	Granite	Porphyritic Granite

In the case of rocks of basaltic composition the corresponding types are: VOLCANIC—basalt and tachylyte (the glassy form of basalt), HYPABYSSAL—dolerite, COARSE-GRAINED—gabbro; but gabbro is not a plutonic rock like granite, it is intruded in smaller masses and at higher levels in the crust. There are also porphyritic varieties of each of these rock types of basaltic composition.

SEDIMENTARY ROCKS—DETRITAL

SANDSTONE, CONGLOMERATE, AND SHALE

Sandstone is perhaps the most familiar of all rocks, for it is easily quarried, and it is used more than any other kind of natural stone for building purposes. Examined closely, using a lens if necessary, a piece of sandstone is seen to consist of grains of sand identical in appearance with those that are churned up by the waves breaking on a beach. Most of the grains consist of more or less rounded grains of quartz, but there are others of cloudy, weathered-looking feldspar, and generally a few shining spangles of mica can be seen (Fig. 3–9).

Clearly, sandstone is made of second-hand materials, of worn fragments derived from the disintegration of some older rock, such as granite, which contained the same minerals. It differs from deposits of modern sands only in being coherent instead of loose. Calcite is a common cementing material. Brown sandstones are cemented by limonite and red varieties by hæmatite. In pure white, extremely hard sandstones, the cement is quartz. These materials were deposited between the grains

FIG. 3–9
Torridon sandstone, as seen under the microscope magnified thirty times. North-West Highlands of Scotland. (*G. S. Sweeting*)

FIG. 3–10
Bedding and joining in Carboniferous sandstone, Muckross Head, Co. Donegal, Ireland. (*R. Welch*)

by groundwater which percolated through the sand when it was buried under later sheets of sand or other formations.

In the steep face of a quarry or cliff, successive beds or layers can be seen, differing from one another by variations in colour or coarseness of grain (Fig. 3–10). At intervals there may be strongly marked bedding planes, along which the sandstone is easily split, due perhaps to the presence of a thin layer packed with flat-lying flakes of mica, or to the intervention of a thin band of clay or shale. Evidently the beds or strata have been formed by the deposition of layer after layer of sediment. The resultant bedding or *stratification* is a primary structure of sedimentary rocks.

Along the beach, and especially near the cliffs, boulders and pebbles are heaped up by storm waves. Then come the sands, and beyond them on the sea floor lie still finer deposits of mud, made up of minute flaky shreds of clay minerals and their micaceous and chloritic associates (products of chemical weathering), together with finely comminuted grains of quartz and altered feldspar. Each of these different types of deposit can be recognized among the stratified rocks. Sooner or later, a sheet of sandstone thins out and passes laterally into clay or shale. Traced in the other direction, it may become coarser in grain and pass into a massive boulder bed or conglomerate (Fig. 3–11). The term *conglomerate* is applied to cemented fragmental rocks containing rounded fragments such as pebbles; if the fragments are angular or sub-angular, the rock is called *breccia*.

The very fine-grained sedimentary rocks, corresponding to mud, are described as clay, mudstone, or shale. Mudstone is compact, but shale can easily be divided into thin laminæ. This fissility is due to a structure resembling stratification on a fine scale, which is distinguished by the term *lamination*. The micas

FIG. 3–11
Conglomerate of Old Red Sandstone age, deposited during the interval of time represented by the unconformity shown in Figs. 4–28 and 4–30. Gorge of the River North Esk, Angus/Kincardine boundary.
(*H.M. Geological Survey*)

FIG. 3–12
The Great Scar Limestone
(Carboniferous) above
Malham Cove, Yorkshire,
showing joints widened by
chemical weathering.
(*H.M. Geological Survey*)

and clay minerals all occur as minute films which lie with their flat surfaces parallel to the bedding, and in consequence the shale readily divides along the lamination planes.

SEDIMENTARY ROCKS—ORGANIC AND CHEMICAL

LIMESTONES

Limestones of suitable quality are widely used as building stones, because of the ease with which they can be worked, and some varieties, the aristocrats of a very mixed group, have become famous through their lavish use in great public buildings. Portland stone, for example, has been a favourite choice for many of London's greatest buildings, ever since Wren selected it for the rebuilding of St Paul's Cathedral after the Great Fire of 1666. The towers and steeples of the London churches, the government offices in Whitehall, the front of Buckingham Palace, and the home of London University, all display its use in varied styles of architecture.

The natural architecture of limestones can be studied in the quarries of Portland and the Cotswolds, in the grey scars of the Pennines (Fig. 3–12), and in the white gashes cut by lime-works in the green slopes of the chalk downs. Some of the limestones of the Pennines are packed with the remains of corals and

FIG. 3–13
Weathered surface of crinoidal
limestone (Carboniferous).
(*W. W. Watts*)

marine shells, and the bead-like relics of the stems of sea-lilies (animals like starfishes on long stalks—Fig. 3–13). The yellow Cotswold limestones, more open and porous, are often crowded with fossil shells, while belemnites, looking like thick blunt pencils, and the coiled forms of ammonites add further interest and variety. The fine-grained and friable limestone known as chalk contains smooth white shells and sea urchins. But besides these visible fossils there are innumerable little coiled or globular shells of foraminifera, visible only under the microscope, embedded in an extremely fine-grained matrix of highly comminuted shell debris. Moreover, spicules of opaline silica, that formed the hard parts of vanished sponges, have contributed most of the silica that is now segregated in the bands of nodular flints (Fig. 3–14).

Evidently many limestones are accumulations of organic remains, vast cemeteries in which the teeming life of the sea has been entombed. It is easy to prove with dilute acid that shells and corals and limestones are all composed of calcium carbonate. They effer-vesce briskly when the acid is applied and give off carbon dioxide, while a drop of the resulting solution held on a clean platinum wire in the flame of a bunsen burner colours the flame with the brick-red tint due to calcium. Soft-bodied organisms abstracted the calcium carbonate from sea water and deposited it around or within themselves, to form a protective covering or a supporting framework.

The limestones of Portland and Bath also contain shells, but they are mainly composed of rounded grains that look like insects' eggs. For this reason they are called *oolites* or oolitic limestones (Gr. *oon*, an egg). Under the microscope each granule is found to be made of concentric layers of calcium carbonate, often with a bit of shell at the centre (Fig. 3–15). Along coral strands, where the conditions are favourable, oolitic grains are forming to-day around such nuclei by the deposition of calcium carbonate from sea water. Rolled about by the surf, the grains tend to grow equally on all sides, and so to become round.

Limestones are thus seen to be deposits

FIG. 3–14
Chalk with characteristic bands of flint nodules, Beachy Head, Sussex. (*Dorien Leigh Ltd*)

formed from disolved material: generally, but not always, from sea water. They usually accumulate outside the stretches of sand and mud that in most places border the lands, but where the sea is uncontaminated by muddy sediment, and especially where the cliffs themselves happen to be made of older limestones, they may form close up to the land. Beaches may locally be composed of sand made up, not of quartz grains, but of shell debris (Fig. 2–6). Similarly, the sands associated with coral reefs and atolls consist largely of coral debris, ground down by the waves.

Limestones are distinctly fragmental, whether formed from organic remains or from oolitic grains. Others are extremely fine-grained and compact, and most of these represent chemical precipitates from waters rich in calcium carbonate. The double carbonate of calcium and magnesium (dolomite) may also be precipitated; either directly, or by the action of warm sea water on limestone already in process of accumulation on the floor of the sea. In these ways *magnesian* or *dolomitic limestones*, grading into pure *dolomite rocks*, have been formed. Dolomite was selected as the building stone for the Houses of Parliament. Unfortunately, the stone was subjected for years to the attack of sulphurous fumes from the potteries that used to be situated on the other side of the Thames. Sulphuric acid and rain corroded the delicate carving of the buildings, turning the magnesia of the stone into easily soluble epsom salts, so that very extensive repairs, especially to the riverside facade, had eventually to be carried out. But where dolomite is not exposed to such abnormal weathering conditions it makes an excellent building stone.

EVAPORITES

Mineral matter carried in solution in rivers, and derived by denudation from the rocks of the catchment area, eventually reaches either the sea or, in areas of inland drainage, a lake with no outlet. In arid or semi-arid climates where evaporation is high in relation to intake of fresh water, the water of such lakes or of essentially land-locked gulfs of the sea, becomes increasingly brine. Eventually the water may become oversaturated with certain salts which are precipitated in order of increasing solubility—that is, the least soluble is precipitated first. Great thicknesses of salt deposits, known as *evaporites*, may eventually be formed in this way. The best

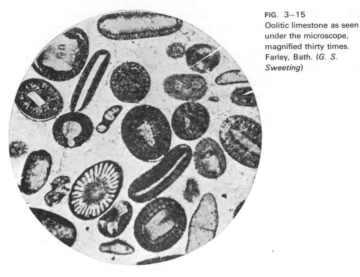

FIG. 3–15
Oolitic limestone as seen under the microscope, magnified thirty times. Farley, Bath. (*G. S. Sweeting*)

known salt of the evaporites is rock salt, halite (NaCl). Beds of halite are commonly associated with others of anhydrite and gypsum, calcium sulphates without and with water respectively. Amongst the most valuable evaporites are those rich in potash which are used as fertilizers.

Amongst the places where evaporites are forming at the present day (see p. 184) are Salt Lake, Utah, and the Gulf of Kara Bogaz, a shallow embayment of the Caspian Sea. It is evaporites of past geological ages, however, that provide the greatest sources of mineral wealth. Amongst these are the Stassfurt deposits of Germany and the salt mines of Wieliczka (near Cracow) in Poland. The latter have been worked for over a thousand years and have long been celebrated as a tourist attraction because of the underground houses, churches, roads, railways, and restaurants, excavated far below the surface in a layer of salt 1,200 feet (365 m) thick. The Stassfurt deposits of Germany are less thick, but they are commercially more important because valuable potash salts have been preserved under a protective cover of impervious clays and marls that prevent their removal by solution in groundwater. In the British Isles rock salt used to be mined but it is now dissolved and pumped to the surface from the Triassic rocks near Carrickfurgus in Co. Antrim, Northern Ireland, and in Cheshire. From the Permian of east Yorkshire, evaporites rich in potash are mined.

Rock salt, like ice, is a rheid (p. 26). When the load of strata overlying a deep-seated bed of rock salt varies from place to place, the rock salt flows, extremely slowly, away from the sites of greatest down pressure and towards those where the overlying load is lightest. Here it flows upwards and forms *salt domes* (Fig. 3–17*e*). A rising salt dome updomes and commonly pierces through the overlying strata, and a piercement fold or *diapir* (Gr. *dia*, through; *peiro*, piercing) results (Fig. 3–17*e*). The rate of uprise of salt domes beneath the Gulf of Mexico has been found to be of the order of 1 mm per annum (M. and J. Ewing, 1962).

COAL

In water-logged environments such as bogs and swamps, the decay of dead plant debris by bacteria and fungi is controlled by the paucity or absence of oxygen. Under these conditions the accumulations of plant remains become relatively rich in carbon and form peat, on the surface of which new generations of bog-plants flourish. The vegetation which contributes to peat formation ranges from mosses to trees and the environment may be a swampy lowland or a water-logged upland with imperfect drainage. The climate must therefore be humid and the conditions such that growth exceeds wastage. In the bogs of cool humid regions the rate of decay lags behind because of the low temperature, whereas in the densely forested swamps of tropical regions the phenomenal rapidity of growth more than keeps pace with the high rate of decay. Under ideal circumstances peat may accumulate to depths of several feet, or even tens of feet, and it may cover an area of many square miles.

As peat gradually accumulates the entrapped water is squeezed out of the lower layers and the peat shrinks and consolidates. It becomes still further compacted if, as a result of subsidence, it becomes buried beneath deposits of clays and sands. As the overhead pressure increases water and gases continue to be driven off, their composition being such that the residue is progressively enriched in carbon, until the peat is transformed into a variety of coal. The essential conditions for the development of a coal seam are therefore: (*a*) long-continued accumulation of peat; and (*b*) subsidence of the area and burial of the peat beneath a thick accumulation of sediments. Coal of the highest rank, called *anthracite*, occurs in certain localities (*e.g.* South Wales) where unusually high pressure due to deep burial and subsequent earth movements, combined with a moderate increase of temperature, has caused nearly all the volatile constituents to be driven off.

The peak period of coal formation in Britain was the Upper Carboniferous and the coal seams of this system are members of a characteristic succession of sediments which is commonly repeated dozens of times. A coal seam is usually roofed with shales in which fossil leaves may occur and occasional bands of freshwater mussels. Higher up in the succession the shales become sandy and pass into sandstones, sometimes with shaly interruptions. Then follows seat earth that underlies the next coal seam. The sequence is clearly one that implies repeated alternations of subsidence and comparative rest. Eventually subsiding regions developed into basins separated by tracts of rising country which supplied the basins with sediments. The elevated regions, subjected to denudation, lost their original covering of Coal Measures, whilst the depressed regions have been preserved as the isolated coalfields of today, where Coal Measures may be exposed at the surface or, like the coalfield of Kent, concealed beneath younger sedimentary rock (Fig. 3–16).

PETROLEUM AND GAS

Petroleum (Gr. *petra*, rock; L. *oleum*, oil) is the general term for all the natural hydrocarbons—whether gaseous, liquid, or solid—found in rocks. In common usage, however, it refers more particularly to the liquid oils, gaseous varieties being distinguished as *natural gas*. Highly viscous to solid varieties are called *bitumen* or *asphalt*, but the latter term has a wider application being used, for example, for artificial paving materials with a bituminous cement.

Unlike coal, petroleum retains within itself no visible evidence of the nature of the material from which it was formed. Various lines of chemical and physical evidence, however, lead to the conclusion that it originates from the organic matter of muddy sediments, deposited in depressed regions of the sea floor, where the water was stagnant and deficient in oxygen. Under such conditions anaerobic bacteria would be expected to abstract oxygen from the organic matter, for example, the remains of algae and diatoms, transforming it, molecule by molecule, into fatty and waxy substances. It will be noticed that coal and petroleum develop in quite different environments and are not related to one another.

Sediments in which petroleum originated

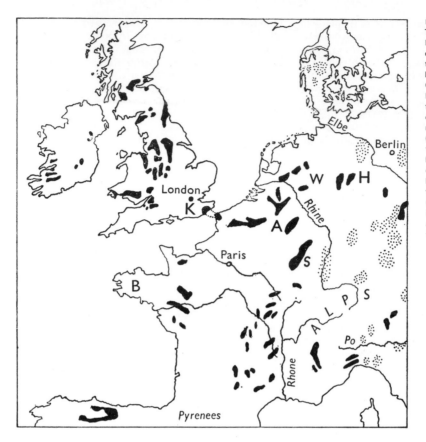

FIG. 3–16
The Coalfields of Western Europe, some of which are concealed by later strata, e.g. the Kent coalfield (K). Carboniferous coalfields, black; Cretaceous coalfields, dotted. In middle Carboniferous times the northern front of a Hercynian mountain range extended from Brittany (B) through the Ardennes (A) to the Harz Mts (H) and beyond. Coal measures were deposited (a) in a series of basins to the north, extending from South Wales and Kent (K) to Westphalia (W), including the Ruhr, and (b) in a series of intermontane basins to the south (e.g. the Saar, S).

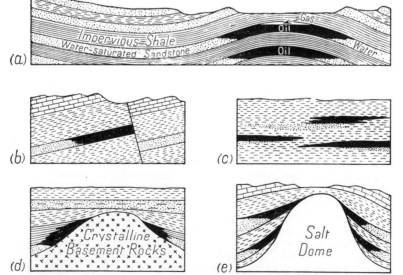

FIG. 3–17
Sections illustrating various types of structural traps favourable to the accumulation of oil and gas. (Gas is omitted except in (a).)

are called the *source rocks*, to distinguish them from the *reservoir rocks* in which *oil* and *gas* are found on a commercial scale. In response to pressure differences set up by variations from place to place in the overhead load or, more effectively, by earth movements, oil and gas migrate upwards from the source beds into porous (sandy) or fissured reservoir rocks. They rise to the highest possible level and collect within the rock pores or fissures, forming an *oil pool* beneath a cover or barrier of impervious beds which impede further migration (Fig. 3–17).

Gas, if present in excess of the amount that the oil can hold in solution, bubbles to the top and forms a *gas cap* over the oil pool (Fig. 3–17a). If the pressure and gas content are sufficiently high, the oil gushes out like an effervescent fountain when the pool is tapped by drilling. But where the pressure is too low to drive the oil to the surface—or becomes so as the initial pressure falls off—pumping is necessary to bring it up.

NORTH SEA GAS

The North Sea has for long been regarded as an epicontinental sea: a flooded portion of the continental area (Fig. 3–18). Since the rocks of the adjacent land areas are far from rich in oil there was, until recent years, no reason to suspect that the North Sea might be rich in either oil or gas. Even the German oilfields, the richest of the adjacent land

Great interest was at once aroused in the possibility that there might be similar gas reservoirs beneath the North Sea. Dr T. F. Gaskell (1967), of the British Petroleum Co., has recounted the geophysical investigations (summarized below) on which the decision to drill through the floor rocks of the North Sea was based. At the outset, magnetic measurements, made from aircraft above the North Sea, revealed the correctness of the inference that the sea is underlain by a series of sedimentary rocks, and showed them to be several miles thick. Gravimetric measurements followed in a search for low gravity areas. The reason for this was that at Groningen the impervious cover which prevents the gas from escaping is a thick layer of evaporites, which forms an area of low gravity. Gravimetric measurements over the North Sea revealed a similar gravity low to the south of the Dogger Bank. The seismic reflection method (echo sounding, p. 246) was then used to locate sites most favourable for drilling. The object being to locate anticlinal structures in the Permian sandstone, similar to that forming the gas reservoir at Groningen (Fig. 3–18 and Fig. 3–17).

For echo sounding, a specially equipped ship drops explosive charges into the sea at fixed points. The sound waves from the explosions travel outwards in all directions: some of them are refracted across the boundary planes between rock layers of different density through which they travel with different velocities; whilst others are reflected,

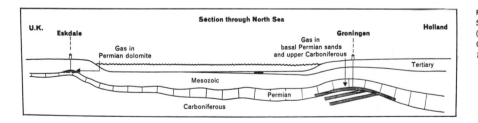

FIG. 3–18
Section across the North Sea. (T. F. Gaskell, "North Sea Gas", *Endeavour, vol xxvi, 1967, p. 7*)

areas, could not be profitably worked if they lay beneath the sea.

In 1959, however, the picture was completely changed by the discovery at Groningen, in Holland, of one of the world's largest gas fields. There, in an anticlinal structure at a depth of about 9,000 feet (2,743 m) porous Permian sandstone forms the reservoir rock for these vast accumulations of gas (Fig. 3–18) but, as we shall see directly, this gas is derived from the underlying Coal Measures and is not related to oil.

that is echoed, back to the surface from the boundary planes. Hydrophones floating in known positions behind a receiving ship record the times at which the reflected sound waves (echoes) reach them. From these times the distances travelled by the reflected sound waves and so the depths of the boundary surfaces can be calculated. From the results of such echo sounding over wide areas, the profiles of rock layers can be plotted, and the positions of anticlines (upbulges) and synclines (depressions) determined.

To the layman it has seemed nothing short of miraculous that the first drilling by British Petroleum hit a gas-bearing structure, and that this discovery was so rapidly followed by others. The success, however, serves to emphasize the exactness of the various geophysical techniques that were used to locate the sites, and the expertness of the geophysicists who used them.

The application of a further technique revealed the origin of the gas at Groningen and beneath the North Sea. Plants, including those from which coal is formed, derive their carbon dioxide from the atmosphere, whilst marine organisms, from which petroleum and related gas are formed, derive their hydrocarbons from sea water. Since the ratio between the isotopes of carbon, $C^{12} : C^{13}$, in the atmosphere is different from that in the carbon dioxide dissolved in sea water, it is possible, by determining the carbon isotope ratios to distinguish between gas derived from coal and gas derived from petroleum. In this way the gas from Groningen and that from the North Sea were found to be derived from coal. Moreover, the greater part of the gas is methane, like the coal gas largely responsible for explosions in coal mines. The most probable source rock for the North Sea gas is therefore the Coal Measures of the Carboniferous, underlying the Permian sandstone which forms the reservoir rock (Fig. 3–18).

ments, and permeating solutions have mottled the stone in tints of red and filled the cracks with white veins of calcite. This example illustrates the ease with which limestone becomes changed by natural processes into "marbles" of endless variety. Limestone is chemically a very sensitive rock, and the walls of many of Lyons' restaurants show in spectacular fashion how readily it has responded to the effects of heat, pressure, and percolating waters.

To the geologist, however, the term marble is restricted to limestones which have been completely recrystallized by metamorphic processes during their burial in the earth's crust. Under the influence of heat from igneous intrusions the calcium carbonate of shells and finer particles alike is gradually reconstructed into crystals of calcite of roughly uniform size. All traces of fossils are destroyed, and the rock, when pure, becomes a white granular rock like the well-known statuary marble from Carrara in Italy. The great sheets of basalt in Antrim lie over a surface of chalk (Figs. 1–3 and 4–34), and the chalk, instead of being soft and friable like that of southern England, has become hard and indurated by the heat from the overlying lavas. And against the channels through which the lava reached the surface, the chalk is transformed locally into saccharoidal marble.

It may be asked how it is that carbon

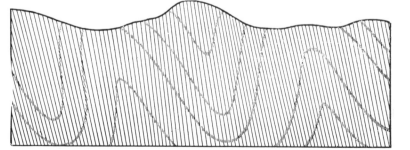

FIG. 3–19
To illustrate the relation of slaty cleavage to bedding and folding. The cleavage planes are approximately parallel to the axial planes of the folds (see Fig. 4–5).

METAMORPHIC ROCKS

MARBLE AND CRYSTALLINE LIMESTONES

Limestones are known commercially as "marble" when they can be effectively polished and used for decorative purposes. Corals and the stems of sea-lilies give a variegated pattern commonly seen on polished slabs cut from the grey limestones of the Pennines. The pink and grey limestones of Torquay have been fissured by earth move-

dioxide did not escape under such conditions, as it does when limestone is heated to make lime. The explanation is that when the heating takes place under pressure, as when the limestone is confined under a load of overlying rocks, the carbon dioxide is not liberated as a stream of gas, but only as dispersed molecules, temporarily freed. These mobile molecules may be thought of as acting like tiny ball-bearings, lubricating the crystal boundaries and so facilitating the process of recrystallization.

SLATE

The world-famous roofing slates that are quarried from the rugged hills around Snowdon owe their value to a structure whereby they can be split along planes that are not parallel to the bedding, like the lamination of shales, but inclined to it, often at a high angle. This structure is neither stratification nor lamination, but a fissility or cleavage, often of great perfection. It is distinguished as *slaty cleavage* (Fig. 3–19). It must not be confused with the cleavage of crystals, for the latter is a property depending on the orderly arrangement of atoms, whereas slaty cleavage depends on the orderly arrangement of minute flaky minerals such as mica, clay, and chlorite within the rock. A thin section of slate cut at right angles to the cleavage shows all the flaky minerals lying parallel to the cleavage planes. It is due to this orientation that the rock splits along these planes and along no others.

Traces of the original bedding planes can be made out in the quarry face wherever bands of contrasted colour or more gritty material are present; such bands are often badly crumpled and contorted. If, by a rare chance, a fossil is found, it, too, is deformed and squeezed out of shape, being shortened in the direction at right angles to the cleavage and correspondingly elongated parallel to the cleavage.

A majority of slates have been formed from shales, but they are sometimes formed from volcanic ash. The silvery green slates of the Lake District, for example, have been formed from beds of fine volcanic ashes. Their cleavage and silvery sheen is due not merely to the flattening of the original particles, but also to the development of new minerals from the volcanic materials. Microscopically small shreds of mica and wisps of chlorite have grown in the rock, all with their film-like surfaces lying parallel to the cleavage direction.

KINDS OF METAMORPHISM

Slate is thus an example of a rock on which a new "grain" has been impressed, mainly by

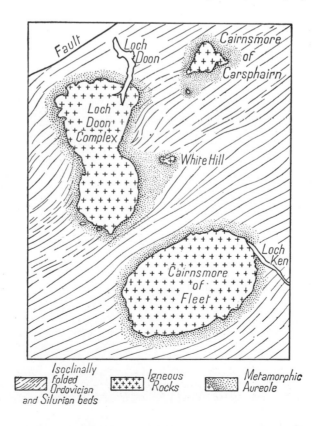

FIG. 3–20
Aureoles of contact metamorphism around granitic intrusions (batholiths and stocks). Galloway, south-west Scotland.

the effect of compression in a direction at right angles to the cleavage. To some extent chemical changes promoted by heat and solution have co-operated in facilitating the growth of new minerals. The original shale or volcanic ash has responded by becoming a slate, a new type of rock. Since the main process is dynamic, slate is said to be a product of *dynamic metamorphism*.

The change from limestone to marble, on the other hand, is mainly brought about by the action of heat. It illustrates the effects of *thermal metamorphism*. The rocks in contact with igneous intrusions are commonly metamorphosed by heat and migrating fluids, and metamorphism of this kind is distinguished as *contact metamorphism*. The zone of altered rock surrounding the intrusion is described as the metamorphic *aureole* (Fig. 3–20), and the recrystallized and hardened rocks within the aureole are called *hornfels* (plural, *hornfelses*). Within hornfels, lamination and cleavage may be obliterated, and if these structures can still be recognized the rock no longer breaks along them.

When all the agencies of metamorphism operate together, as they do in the heated depths of a crustal belt where mountain building movements are in progress, the rocks throughout an extensive region are characteristically transformed, and the metamorphism is then described as *regional*.

CRYSTALLINE SCHISTS

When shale or slate is recrystallized by regional metamorphism the effects of heat and migrating fluids lead to the development of mica and other new minerals on a visible scale, as in contact metamorphism. At the same time the effects of shearing or flowage give the rock a new structure, due to the streamlined arrangement of the platy and elongated minerals along planes of gliding. This structure is called *foliation*, a term based on analogy with leaf-mould composed of tightly packed leaves. Foliation may develop along an earlier cleavage, but more commonly it follows the stratification of sediments that have not been cleaved, and in some cases, when the shearing or flowage failed to coincide with the earlier parting planes, it follows a new direction altogether. The surfaces along which a foliated rock can be divided may be plane to undulating, wavy, or contorted. When the foliation is closely spaced throughout the body of the rock, so that almost any part of it can be split into flakes or flat lenticles, the rock is called a *schist* (Gr. *schistos*, divided) (Fig. 3–21). The schistosity of the rock—that is, the pro-

FIG. 3–21
Crumpled schist, north of Fearna Nah, Kyles of Bute, Argyllshire. (*H.M. Geological Survey*)

perty whereby it can be easily split—is somewhat akin to slaty cleavage, but on a coarser, rougher, and less uniform scale.

Schists are named after the chief mineral responsible for the foliation in any given case. When this is mica, as frequently happens, the rock is called *mica-schist*, this being the type that develops from shales and slates. Another type is *hornblende-schist*, which develops from basaltic rocks, the hornblende being formed at the expense of the original augite. Sandstone and limestone rarely form schists, and then only crudely, the reason being that quartz and calcite are naturally granular minerals. The usual metamorphic equivalents of these rocks are quartzite and marble, respectively, both granulitic rocks.

and composition. Many gneisses, indeed, have the mineral composition of granite or granodiorite, and thus they further differ from schists in containing feldspar as an important mineral, especially in their granular portions.

Gneisses were at one time thought to be strongly crushed granites, and indeed some gneisses are. The most typical gneisses, however, appear to represent transitions between schist and granite. If we examine areas where gneisses are well exposed, such as the low, wave-swept islands of southern Finland we can see that the older schists seem to have been impregnated by granite in every conceivable way. In some places veins and tongues of granite magma appear to have run between the folia of the schists, like water seeping

FIG. 3–22
Biotite-gneiss, Uxbridge, Mass., U.S.A. (*Ward's Natural Science Establishment, Inc.*)

GNEISSES AND MIGMATITES

One of the most characteristic types of metamorphic rocks is that known by the old Saxon miners' term *gneiss*. Like schist, gneiss is a foliated rock, but its foliation is open and interrupted (Fig. 3–22). Highly micaceous layers, or layers rich in hornblende, alternate with bands or lenticles or "eyes" that are granular, and more like granite in their texture·

between the pages of a book. Close by, the schists are strewn with crystals of feldspar, again suggesting that granite magma soaked into the rocks (Fig. 3–23). Such mixed gneisses are called *migmatites* (Gr. *migma*, a mixture). However, the first idea that migmatites result from the mixing of schist and granite magma is open to doubt. Both the

FIG. 3—23
Large boulder of migmatite associated with the Galway granite, Ireland. Hornblende schist is partly replaced by granite adjacent to which pink crystals of feldspar have grown within the schist. (*Doris L. Holmes*)

veined and the "eyed" varieties of migmatite pass into types with larger and more abundant feldspars, so that the rock looks like a granite, except for a shadowy background representing vague remnants or "ghosts" of the original schists. Finally, even the "ghosts" vanish, and only granite remains. The schists have somehow been transformed into granite. This is a complex process that is still being investigated. Under the influence of migrating fluids, new ingredients have been added to the schists, whilst others have been carried away. As a result the schists are changed in composition, migmatites are formed, and the final product is granite.

Gneisses are found associated with schists and granites, and all these rocks occur in the Highlands of Scotland and North-West Ireland.

4
Architectural Features of the Earth's Crust

FOLDS

Stratification is a primary structure of sedimentary rocks, due to the deposition of layer after layer of differing or alternating types of sediment. Most sediments were originally deposited on flat, very slightly inclined surfaces. But in many regions we find that great thicknesses of strata have been tilted, so that they now lie in inclined positions, sometimes for many miles. The tilted beds generally represent one side of a very broad fold. The attitude, or position in the ground of any inclined bed, is accurately described by what is called its *dip* (Fig. 4–1). The dip is both the direction of the maximum slope down a bedding plane and the angle between the maximum slope and the horizontal. The direction is measured by its true bearing, as so many degrees east or west of north, the compass reading being suitably corrected for magnetic variation. The angle is measured with a

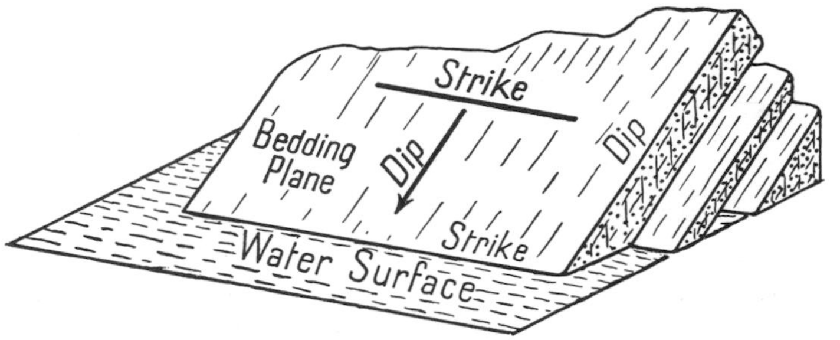

FIG. 4–1
Illustration of the meaning of the terms *dip* and *strike*.

FIG. 4–2
Sea cliff of Torridonian Sandstone strata showing dip and strike. Cailleach Head, Ross-shire, north-west Scotland.
(*H.M. Geological Survey*)

47

FIG. 4–3
Anticline in Coal Measures,
Sandfoot, Pembrokeshire,
south Wales. (*H.M.
Geological Survey*)

FIG. 4–4
Syncline in Coal Measures,
north of Bude, Cornwall.
(*H.M. Geological Survey*)

clinometer. The *strike* of an inclined bed is the direction of any horizontal line along a bedding plane; the direction, for example, of the intersection of the bed with still water or level ground. It is at right angles to the dip direction (Figs. 4–1 and 4–2).

When beds are upfolded into an arch-like form the structure is called an *anticline*, because the beds then "incline away" from the crest on either side (Fig. 4–3). When the beds are down-folded into a trough-like form the structure is called a *syncline*, because in this case the beds on either side "incline together" towards the keel, (Fig. 4–4). The two sides of a fold are described as its *limbs*, the limb which is shared between an anticline and an adjacent syncline being called the middle limb. The plane which bisects the angle between the two limbs is called the *axial plane*, and the line of intersection of this plane with a bedding plane gives the direction of the axis of the fold at that place (Fig. 4–5). So long as this direction remains unchanged, which may be for a few inches or for many miles, the axis can be thought of as a line that would generate the form of the fold if moved parallel to itself. It should be noted that an axial plane has a definite position in space, whereas the axis is only a direction, although it is commonly thought of, and drawn on geological maps, as though situated in the axial plane. If the axial plane is vertical and the axis horizontal, as in Fig. 4–5, the fold is said to be upright and symmetrical. If the axial plane is inclined, as in Fig. 4–6, the fold is also inclined, and is described as an *over-fold*.

The axes of folds are commonly tilted; the folds are then said to *pitch* or *plunge*. The angle of plunge is the angle between the axis and a horizontal plane. In Fig. 4–7, which depicts an anticlinal mountain, the plunge is towards the bottom left-hand corner in front; but towards the top right-hand corner in the background, 11 miles away, it is in the opposite direction. Fig. 4–8 illustrates the way in which the V-shaped outcrops of a denuded plunging anticline "close" or "point" in the direction of plunge. Conversely, the outcrops of a denuded plunging syncline open out like a horseshoe in the direction of plunge.

The Asmari Mt anticline of Fig. 4–7 can be described as an elongated dome, and the Weald in South-East England is a structural dome elongated from east to west (Figs. 4–9 and 8–8). In an ideal *structural dome* the beds dip radially outwards from the centre. In a similarly perfect *structural basin* the beds dip radially inwards towards the centre. From

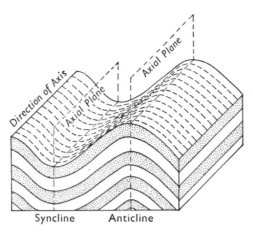

FIG. 4–5
Upright symmetrical folds, to illustrate the meaning of the terms *axial plane* and *axis*. The upper surface shown is not that of the ground but of one particular bed in a series of folded strata.

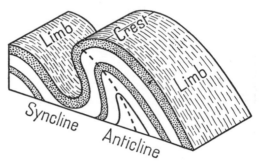

FIG. 4–6
Inclined folds, with the upper strata removed to show the surface of one particular bed. The trace of an axial plane is marked by the broken line.

more or less elongated domes to anticlines that extend for very long distances there is every gradation, and there are similar transitions between basins and synclines. Such structures must not be confused with hills and valleys, for they refer solely to the forms and attitudes of the bedrocks: not to the relief of the surface. Here and there landscape forms may coincide with the underlying structure for a time, as they do in the Jura Mts (Fig. 4–10), and as they are seen to do in Fig. 4–7. But in the long run, when landscapes have been carved out of uplifted tracts of folded rocks by long-continued denudation, this relationship is sooner or later reversed (Fig. 4–31). Snowdon in North Wales is a well-known mountain with a synclinal structure, and Fig. 4–8 shows the core of an anticline in the Canadian Arctic being dissected by a stream and its tributaries, whilst Fig. 8–8 illustrates the landforms (escarpments) that have been carved by denudation from the Weald dome during the last three or four million years. As can be seen from Fig. 4–31, after denudation, the oldest beds outcrop in the core of a dome or anticline. On the other hand the youngest beds outcrop in the core of a denuded basin or syncline.

FIG. 4–7
Air view from the NW of Asmari Mountain, Persia (16 miles long by 3 miles across in the middle). A relatively short anticline or elongated "dome" of the Asmari Limestone. (*British Petroleum Company Ltd*)

FIG. 4–8
Air view of a plunging anticline, Bathurst Island, Canadian Arctic. The core of the anticline is being dissected by a stream and its tributaries, and a small delta is being built out into Peel Inlet. (*National Air Photo Library, Department of Energy, Mines and Resources, Canada*)

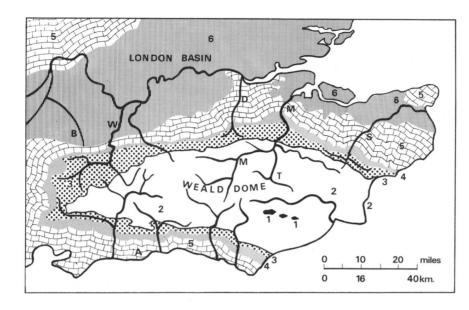

FIG. 4—9
Sketch map showing the structure of the Weald dome and the relationship of some of the rivers to the structure. Jurassic rock (1), outcropping in the core of the dome, is overlain by Cretaceous rocks (2, Wealden beds; 3, Lower Greensand; 4, Gault Clay and Upper Greensand; 5, Chalk) which dip northwards on the northern side of the dome, and southwards on its southern side. See Fig. 8—8 for a section across the dome. Tertiary rocks (6) form the core of the London Basin.

The names of some of the rivers referred to in Chapter 8 are indicated by letters: M = Medway; T = Teise; W = Wey; B = Blackwater; A = Arun; D = Dart.

FIG. 4—10
Anticline in the Moutier Gorge, Jura Mts, Switzerland an example of concordant morphology and structure. (*Peter Christ*) Left to right: Professor A. Buxtorf, Professor Arthur Holmes, Professor M. Reinhard.

Folds range in intensity from broad and gentle undulations like those of the Jura Mts (Fig. 4–10) and The Weald (Fig. 4–9) to tightly compressed plications in which the dips of the limbs are almost parallel. Folding of this latter style is described as *isoclinal* and is exemplified in the Southern Uplands of Scotland and in North Wales. In the Lake District and North Wales, the puckers and smaller folds are superimposed on broad anticlinal and synclinal folds of a much larger order. An anticlinal complex of folds of different orders is called an *anticlinorium*, and the complementary synclinal complex a *synclinorium* (Fig. 4–11).

When a pack of cards is flexed, into, say an anticlinal form, each card slips a little over the one beneath. Similarly, when bedded rocks are folded by flexing, slipping along bedding planes occurs, and the resultant folds, like those of the Jura Mts (Fig. 4–10) are described as *flexure folds*. At depths of several kilometres, and under intense pressure, the folding of bedded rocks is accompanied by, and may result from, slipping along closely spaced shear planes inclined to the bedding planes. As a result of innumerable minute displacements along the shear planes, the bedding planes gradually assume fold-forms and the shear or cleavage planes (see p. 42) are orientated parallel to the axial planes of the growing folds (Figs. 3–19 and 4–11). Folds of this kind are known as *shear folds*.

An overfold (p. 49) has one of its limbs more or less inverted. When the inverted limbs approach the horizontal the overfold is described as *recumbent*; the beds of the middle limb (the lower limb of the anticline and the upper limb of the underlying syncline) are then upside down (Fig. 4–12). Parts of the Gram-

pian Highlands of Scotland are denuded out of gigantic recumbent folds. In structures of this kind, part of the middle limb may be sheared or squeezed out altogether. Further development of the structure then results in the rocks of the upper limb being pushed bodily forward along the plane of shearing. The latter has become a *thrust plane* and the structure an *overthrust fold* or a *fold-thrust* (Fig. 4–12).

JOINTS

If we examine a quarry or cliff section of sandstone or limestone, we find that in addition to the bedding planes the rock is traversed by fractures, known as joints, that are generally approximately at right angles to the stratification, and therefore nearly vertical when the beds are flat (Figs. 3–10 and 4–13). They frequently occur in sets consisting of two series of parallel joints (Fig. 4–13). In many rocks, however, and especially in the older formations, subordinate joints cut across the main sets, dividing the rocks into irregular angular blocks.

Most joints are the result of either shearing or tension. Shear joints tend to be clean-cut, and in unweathered rocks they are tightly closed. Tension joints, on the other hand have rough and irregular faces. Tension joints are characteristic of the stronger beds in dome structures where the upper strata have been extended over the lower during the updoming. The extension fractures the strata along two sets of joint planes, essentially at right angles to the bedding planes and making a high angle with one another (Fig. 4–14). If updoming continues (Fig. 4–14), tension joints open and

FIG. 4–11
Schematic section through an anticlinorium bordered on each side by a synclinorium. The broken lines represent axial plane cleavage arranged in cleavage fans.

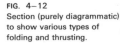

FIG. 4–12
Section (purely diagrammatic) to show various types of folding and thrusting.

FIG. 4–13
Flat-bedded Permian sandstone cut by two sets of well-developed vertical joints nearly at right angles. The "Tessellated Pavement" at Eaglehawk Neck, southern Tasmania. (*Dorien Leigh Ltd*)

provide easy passage-ways for natural waters from which minerals may be deposited, coating the sides or developing into mineral veins. The fissure-like spaces occupied by many dykes probably began as tension joints.

The polygonal cracks seen on dried-out mud flats (Fig. 4–15) and the characteristic jointing of columnar basalt (Fig. 4–16) provide other examples of tension joints. The mud cracks result from shrinkage due to loss of water by evaporation from the surface layers. The polygonal cracks or joints of basalt sheets result from contraction during cooling (Fig. 4–16).

When a hot homogeneous rock cools uniformly across a plane surface, the contraction is equally developed in all directions throughout the surface. This condition is mechanically the same as if the contraction acted towards each of a series of equally spaced centres. Such centres (*e.g.* C, 1, 2, 3, etc. in Fig. 4–17a) form the corners of equilateral triangles, and theoretically this is the only possible arrangement. At the moment of rupture the distance between any given centre C and those nearest to it (*e.g.* 1–6) is such that the contraction along lines such as C-1 is just sufficient to over-

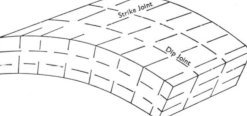

FIG. 4–14
Tension joints resulting from extension of strata over the arch of a dome-like anticline.

come the tensile strength of the rock. A tension crack then forms half-way between C and 1 and at right angles to the line C-1. As each centre is surrounded by six others (1 to 6 in Fig. 4–17a), the resultant system of cracks is hexagonal. Once a crack occurs somewhere in the cooling layer the centres are definitely localized, and a repeated pattern of hexagonal cracks spreads almost simultaneously throughout the layer (Fig. 4–17b). As cooling proceeds into the sheet of rock the cracks grow inwards at right angles to the cooling surface, and so divide the sheet into a system of hexagonal columns.

Neither the physical conditions nor the rocks are usually sufficiently uniform to ensure perfect symmetry, and the actual result

FIG. 4—15
Mud cracks on the dried-out floor of Loughaveema, the "vanishing lake" between Cushendun and Ballycastle, Co. Antrim. The lake drains underground through the Chalk and rises and falls with the rainfall, vanishing after long dry spells. (*R. Welch*)

FIG. 4—16
Columnar jointing in the basalt of the Giant's Causeway, Co. Antrim, showing concave and convex cross-joints. (*J. Allan Cash*)

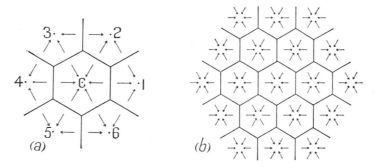

FIG. 4–17
The formation of an ideal hexagonal pattern of joints by uniform contraction towards evenly spaced centres.

is a set of columns with from three to eight sides, six, however, being by far the commonest number. Vertical contraction is relieved by cross joints, which may be either concave or convex, and the columns are thus divided into short lengths. The resulting appearance of well-trimmed masonry is often remarkably impressive, as in the tessellated pavement of the Giant's Causeway (Fig. 4–16) and the amazing architecture of Fingal's Cave in Staffa (Fig. 11–14). Comparable, but usually cruder and less regular columnal jointing develops during the cooling of sills and dykes. In a dyke the cooling surfaces are the vertical walls, and the resulting columns are therefore horizontal.

In granite masses there are generally three sets of joints. Two of these are upright or vertical, and the third is approximately parallel to the surface, the undulations of which it tends to follow (Fig. 3–4). This third set of joint planes is responsible for the *sheet structure* that is commonly seen in exposures of granite.

At and near the surface the presence of joints of any kind makes a rock more susceptible to the attack of weathering agents (see p. 80); they are readily opened up by the work of rain, frost, wind, and plant roots. It is due to this opening of joints and bedding planes that cliffs and mountain scarps often resemble roughly hewn masonry (Fig. 4–18). Along the shore, waves attack the rocks selectively along joints and the influence of the joint pattern is often clearly shown in the outlines of inlets, caves, and skerries. The joint pattern may also control the course of rivers, the joint planes themselves commonly forming the walls of steep-sided gorges and canyons.

FAULTS

A fault is a fracture surface along which the rocks have been relatively displaced. Vertical displacements up to thousands of feet and horizontal movements up to many miles are well known, but in no case is there any reason to suppose that the total displacement occurred in a single catastrophic operation. Earthquakes commonly result from sudden movements along faults that are still active, but the fault movements are rarely more than a few feet at a time (pp. 21 and 240).

The sides of a clean-cut fault plane may be polished or striated by friction between the moving blocks; such surfaces are known as *slickensides*. Sometimes, instead of a single fracture, there are two or more, forming a strip consisting of a sheet of crushed rock of variable thickness. This is distinguished as a *fault zone*, and the shattered material within is called a *fault breccia*.

Three types of faults occur most commonly, but the details given below by no means exhaust the possibilities, which may be tantalizingly complex.

(*a*) *Normal Faults* (Figs. 4–19, 4–20, and 4–21).—The fracture, known as a *fault plane* is generally inclined at an angle of more than 45°. The beds abutting against the fault on its upper face or "hanging wall" are displaced downwards relative to those against the lower face or "footwall". The terms "downthrow" and "upthrow" for the two sides (Fig. 4–19) are of course, purely relative; in some examples both sides have been uplifted, but one more than the other. The inclination of the fault plane, its *dip*, is expressed by the angle between it and the horizontal, but its inclination may also be expressed as its *hade*—that is, the angle between the fault plane and the vertical.

In faults recently active, the footwall may be exposed at the surface as a *fault scarp* (Fig. 2–10), but such scarps have usually been removed by erosion. Sometimes, however, differential erosion of weak and strong beds, brought into juxtaposition by the fault, results in the gradual development of a scarp,

FIG. 4–18
Jointing of granite illustrated
by the castellated cliffs of
Land's End. Part of a large
intrusion of granite (see
Fig. 3–3) now exposed
to weathering and marine
erosion. (*Aerofilms Ltd*)

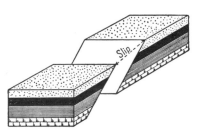

FIG. 4–19
The relative movement
involved in a normal fault.
Part of the fault plane is
left unshaded.

FIG. 4–20
Oblique-slip normal fault,
illustrating the meaning of
the term *slip*. Here the
movement has involved both
dip-slip and strike-slip,
the former being the greater.

which may closely resemble a fault scarp. Because such scarps are erosional as opposed to structural features they are distinguished as *fault line* scarps.

Normal faults result in lengthening of the crust across the fault, indicating horizontal tension at the time of faulting, a condition that exists, for example, when crustal rocks are extended by upheaval (Fig. 4–14). Regions that are divided by faults into relatively elevated and depressed blocks are said to be *block faulted* (see pp. 231 and 232).

(*b*) *Reverse or Thrust Faults* (Fig. 4–22).— The rocks of the hanging wall—that is, on the upper side of the fault plane—are displaced up the slope of the fault plane relative to those below. Shortening of the crust, across the fault, results.

When the dip of the fault plane is low, the reverse fault is described as a *thrust*, and the upper block may have moved forward for many miles. The celebrated Moine and associated thrusts of the North-West Highlands are classic examples of low-angle thrusts

FIG. 4–21
A normal fault, Ballygally Head, Co. Antrim. Tertiary basalt, overlying Chalk in depth, has been downthrown against Chalk from which most of the overlying basalt has been removed by erosion.

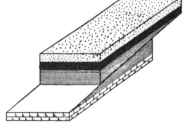

FIG. 4–22
Reverse or thrust fault.

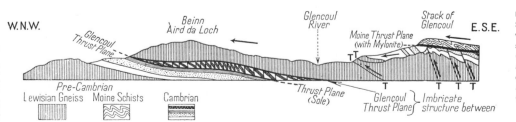

W.N.W.

Beinn
Àird da Loch

Glencoul
River

Stack of
Glencoul

E.S.E.

Glencoul
Thrust Plane

Moine Thrust Plane
(with Mylonite)

Pre-Cambrian
Lewisian Gneiss   Moine Schists   Cambrian

Thrust Plane
(Sole)

Glencoul
Thrust Plane

Imbricate
structure between

FIG. 4–23
Section across the north-west highlands of Scotland, showing the Moine and Glencoul low-angle thrusts, and imbricate structure due to closely spaced high angle thrusts beneath the Glencoul thrust.

(Figs. 3–16, 4–23, and 4–24). Along the sole of a major thrust severe crushing and grinding of the rocks occurs. A layer of hard, streaky or banded rock, composed of pulverized materials, may be formed in this way which, because of its highly characteristic structure and mode of origin, is called *mylonite* (Gr. *mylon*, a grinding mill).

(c) Tear, Transcurrent, or Wrench Faults (Fig. 4–25).—The relative movement along the fault plane is predominantly horizontal, the fault plane being vertical or nearly so. Along some of the more spectacular wrench faults the cumulative horizontal displacement may amount to tens and even hundreds of miles.

The best known of all wrench faults is the great San Andreas "fault" of California, which has a known length of over 800 miles

(Fig. 12–9). Displacements of Cretaceous and late Jurassic rocks, of from 320 to 350 miles, indicate that this fault zone may have been active for some hundreds of millions of years. Systematically repeated surveys carried out during the last few decades on both sides of the fault zone show that it is moving continuously at a rate of about 2 inches a year, which is equivalent to 30 miles in a million years. Sooner or later the growing strain of this deformation will add yet another great earthquake to the hundreds of thousands that must already have occurred along this restless stretch of the crust.

An ancient wrench fault, still not entirely dead, cuts straight across Scotland from coast to coast. This is the fault zone of the Great Glen, a broad shatter belt of intensely crushed rocks along which erosion has been relatively

FIG. 4–24
Inclined sole of the Moine thrust exposed by stream erosion near Knockan, Sutherland. Precambrian rocks above the stream on the right (Moine) have been thrust over Cambrian magnesian limestone.
(*H.M. Geological Survey*)

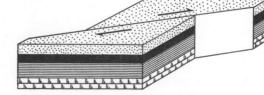

FIG. 4–25
Tear, wrench, or transcurrent fault.

FIG. 4—26
The shatter belt of the Great Glen wrench fault, viewed from Loch Oich, with Loch Ness in the distance. (*Robert M. Adam*)

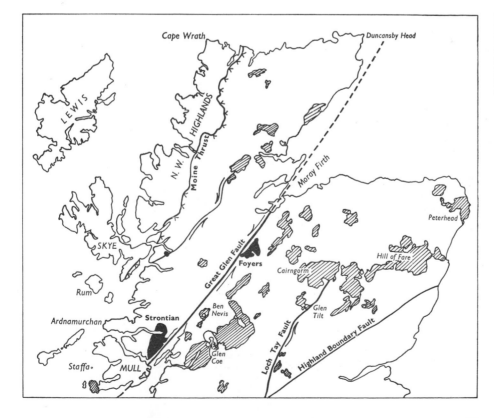

FIG. 4—27
Map of the Great Glen wrench fault. Before movement occured along the fault the Strontian and Foyers granites probably formed parts of the same plutonic mass.

easy, so that it has become the site of a string of lochs (Fig. 4–26). Horizontal displacement of about 65 miles is indicated by the various geological features that can be matched on the two sides. These include the Strontian and Foyers granite masses, which probably originated as a single plutonic mass during the Caledonian orogeny (Fig. 4–27). Although most of the displacement occurred during late Devonian and early Carboniferous times about 350 million years ago, the fault zone is still a line of weakness. Its continued response to the straining earth is indicated by the fact that about sixty minor earthquakes have originated along the zone during the last two centuries.

THE SUCCESSION OF STRATA

The stratified rocks have accumulated layer upon layer, and where a continuous succession of flat-lying beds can be seen, as on the slopes of Ingleborough (Fig. 4–28), where there has been no inversion of beds by overfolding or repetition of beds by overthrusting, it is obvious that the lowest beds are the oldest, and those at the top of the series the youngest. Where a series of beds has been tilted, as between the Welsh borders and London, the worn-down edges of layer after layer come in turn to the surface and it becomes possible to place a long succession of beds in their proper sequence (Fig. 4–29).

Around Ingleborough the great limestone platform of the Pennines can be traced over a wide stretch of country, but where the streams have cut through to its base, the limestone is found to lie on the upturned edges of strongly folded and crudely cleaved beds, as shown in Figs. 4–28 and 4–30. Here there is evidently a sudden break in the continuity of the record. Such a break, which may represent a very long interval of geological time, is called an *unconformity*. The beds in continuous succession above the break in the sequence are said to be *conformable*. The lowest of the conformable beds rests *unconformably* on the underlying rocks (Figs. 4–28 and 4–30). After the latter had been deposited on the sea floor as newly formed sediments, they were uplifted and folded, deep in the heart of an ancient mountain system that extended throughout the length of Norway and across much of the British Isles. Because much of Scotland is carved out of these hard and contorted rocks this is known as the Caledonian mountain system or, more technically, as the Caledonian *orogenic* belt (Gr. *oros*, mountain, see p. 222). By denudation the folded grits and slates were gradually uncovered and ultimately reduced to an undulating lowland. Then the worn-down surface was submerged beneath the sea, to become the floor on which the horizontal sheets of the Pennine limestones were deposited. Successive stages of the events which occurred during

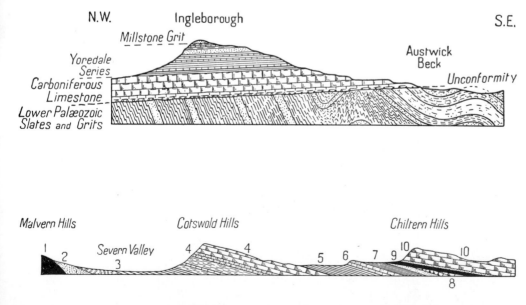

FIG. 4–28
Section across Ingleborough and its foundations, Yorkshire, showing the unconformity between the Carboniferous beds above and the intensely folded Lower Palaeozoic strata below. Length of section about 4 miles.
(*After D. A. Wray*)

FIG. 4–29
Section from the Malvern Hills to the Chiltern Hills: 1. Precambrian and Cambrian; 2. Triassic; 3–8. Jurassic (3. Lias; 4. Lower Oolites; 5. Oxford Clay; 6. Corallian; 7. Kimmeridge Clay; 8. Portland Beds); 9–10. Cretaceous (9. Gault and Upper Greensand; 10. Chalk).

FIG. 4–30
Unconformity: Carboniferous
limestone lying on an erosion
surface of steeply inclined
Silurian slates. Arco Wood
Quarry, four miles north of
Settle, Yorkshire. (*S. H.
Reynolds*)

Deposition of
Sediments

Gentle Folding

More intense Folding

Uplift and
Sculpturing of
Surface by Denudation

Reduction of Surface to
a Plain by Denudation

Subsidence and Deposition
of a new series of Sediments
----*UNCONFORMITY*

FIG. 4–31
Successive stages in the
development of an
unconformity.

the time gap represented by the unconformity are shown by the diagrams of Fig. 4–31.

Another type of unconformity is shown in Fig. 1–1. The sands of the Sahara rest unconformably on the surface of a rocky landscape that is mostly buried out of sight, but of which the highest peaks still stand above the surrounding sands. The Sphinx was chiselled out of such a hillock of limestone that rose abruptly above the desert sands.

In general terms, every unconformity is an erosion surface, representing a lapse of time during which denudation (including erosion by the sea) exceeded deposition at that place. The time gap is likely to be represented by strata somewhere else (see Fig. 3–11) and these strata, if they are fossiliferous, can be recognized from the particular assemblage of fossils they contain. Towards the end of the eighteenth century, William Smith, who had collected fossils from his boyhood days, found that while some fossils in any particular bed might be the same as some of those from the beds above or below, others were definitely distinct. Each formation has, in fact, a suite of fossils peculiar to itself, and the relative age, or position in the time sequence, of a formation can thus be ascertained from its distinctive fossils. By piecing together information gathered from many areas, the complete succession of strata has thus been established for the last 600 million years, that is, since organisms (now fossils) became abundant upon the earth.

RADIOMETRIC DATING

Apart from the relative geological age to be read from the order of superposition of strata and the assemblages of fossils they contain, there have been many attempts to measure geological time by reference to the estimated rate at which physical processes are now going on. For example, estimates of the age of the oceans have been made by reference to the amount of sodium in the sea, and the estimated amount added annually by rivers. Quite apart from the inevitable inaccuracy of the estimates involved, such geological methods are based on the quite unjustified assumption that the rates of denudation and deposition have been the same as at present throughout geological time.

All such methods have been superseded; the age of a rock can now be directly measured if it contains either the radioactive elements uranium or thorium, or radioactive isotopes of the common elements potassium or rubidium. Radioactive elements spontaneously emit radiations of particles, some positively and others negatively charged, and as a result they themselves are transformed into other elements. Uranium, for example, found in pitchblende, is the progenitor of a large family of elements, including radium, all of which are radioactive, except the end products helium and lead. Thorium is similarly a parent element which is ultimately transformed into the stable daughter elements lead and helium.

The radioactive isotope of rubidium (Rb^{87}), found in biotite and potash feldspar, decays in a relatively simple way and is directly transformed into an isotope of strontium (Sr^{87}). The radioactivity of potassium is more complex: the radioactive isotope is K^{40} and, of the atoms that disintegrate, about 89 per cent disintegrate to calcium (Ca^{40}), whilst the remaining 11 per cent disintegrate to argon. For age determination only the generation of argon is of interest, since calcium is a very common element and is mostly Ca^{40}.

The rate of decay of all radioactive elements corresponds with a very simple law that was discovered by Rutherford and Soddy as long ago as 1902. The number of atoms, n, which decay during a given unit of time (*e.g.* a second or a year, as may be convenient) is directly proportional to the number of atoms, N, of the radioactive element present in the sample concerned. It is important to notice that the rate of decay is quite independent of the length of time the atoms have existed. Unlike human beings, amongst whom the chance of dying increases with old age, the atoms of a radioactive isotope are just as likely to decay or disintegrate whatever their age may be. Their rate of decay is purely statistical. Out of ten million atoms (N) of radium, for example, 4,273 (n) decay every year. The fraction n/N is called the disintegration or decay constant. It is generally easier to think of the half-life period, T, which is the time taken for any initial number of atoms to be reduced to half.

The number of atoms of a parental radioactive element now present in a given sample that crystallized t years ago (t being the age of the mineral), and the number of atoms of the end product (the stable daughter element) generated in the sample during time t, can be determined by very exact methods of analysis. Then knowing the rate of disintegration of the parent element—that is, the disintegration constant, the time required for the generation of the number of daughter atoms can be calculated.

The parental radioactive elements considered above have half-lives comparable with the age of the earth, and are therefore suitable for measuring long intervals of geological time. For measuring shorter intervals, such as those of historical and archaeological interest, no similar methods were available until 1951, when Libby discovered that minute amounts of a radioactive isotope of carbon, C^{14}, exist in air, natural water, and living organisms. Carbon consists mainly of two stable isotopes: C^{12} (98·89 per cent) and C^{13} (1·11 per cent); C^{14}, in modern wood, forms only 0·000000000107 per cent.

Radioactive carbon is continually being produced in the atmosphere by reactions caused by cosmic rays, and its rate of decay is such that its half-life is 5,570 years. The newly born atoms of radioactive carbon, C^{14}, are speedily oxidized to CO_2 which becomes uniformly distributed by wind, rivers, and ocean currents, so that the ratio C^{14}/C^{12} remains theoretically constant. Living creatures, both plants and animals, continually assimilate C to replenish their living tissues, and consequently the proportion of C^{14} in their carbon remains constant. When the organisms die, however, the amount of radioactive carbon present in their remains begins to diminish, in accordance with its rate of decay, since it is no longer replenished by intake of fresh C. As a result, if the carbon from prehistoric wood, for example, is found to contain only half as much radioactive carbon as that of living plants, it can be estimated that the wood is 5,570 years old. In practice, however, precautions have to be taken, because, in recent years, human activities have upset the balance. For example, radioactive carbon is a by-product from testing of nuclear missiles and in a few years has increased the abundance of C^{14} by about 1 per cent. On the other hand the burning of coal and oil decreases the proportion of radioactive carbon in the atmosphere by adding CO_2 from which all trace of radioactive carbon was long ago lost.

THE STRATIGRAPHIC SEQUENCE

The stratigraphic sequence, that is the succession of the geological systems, is shown in Fig. 4–32; the length of each geological period—that is, the length of time during which each system was deposited—can be judged from the radiometric ages expressed in millions of years. The names and approximate times of mountain building movements, since the beginning of the Cambrian period, are also shown. The names of the geological eras, Palaeozoic, Mesozoic, and Cainozoic,

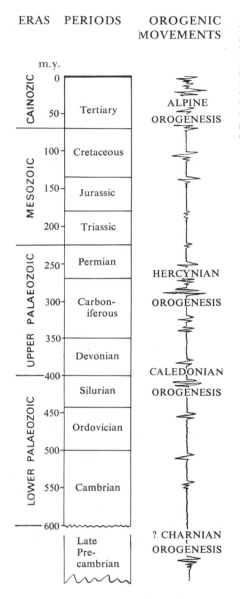

ERAS   PERIODS   OROGENIC MOVEMENTS

FIG. 4–32
The Stratigraphic Column.
(m.y. = millions of years)
The names of the rock systems are also used to indicate the periods of time during which the systems were respectively deposited. The thick line at the top of the column represents the Pleistocene or Glacial period and Recent times; jointly called the Quaternary period.

respectively mean, ancient life (Gr. *palaios*, ancient; *zoe*, life), middle life (*mesos*, middle), and recent life (*kainos* or *cenos*, recent). Underneath the oldest Palaeozoic beds there are enormously thick groups of sedimentary strata, overlying crystalline rocks, both metamorphic and igneous. Only rare and obscure forms of life have been found in the less altered strata of these ancient rocks of no value for defining world-wide systems. The only collective name for these very old rocks is *Precambrian*. It should be noticed, however, that the duration of time represented by the Precambrian rocks, as dated by radiometric methods, was five or six times as long as the 600 million years that have elapsed since the beginning of the Cambrian period. Precambrain rocks form the shield areas of the Baltic, Canada, and Africa. The "grain" of these shields depicts the trends of many belts of Precambrian fold mountains, but it is intersected and disrupted by more recent block fault movements (pp. 229–32).

MODES OF OCCURRENCE OF IGNEOUS INTRUSIONS

Dykes and Sills. The forms and attitudes of igneous rocks which have been injected into the stratified rocks largely depend on their relation to the parting planes of the invaded formations. This is seen most clearly where the strata have remained horizontal or have been only gently tilted or folded. One of the commonest signs of former igneous activity

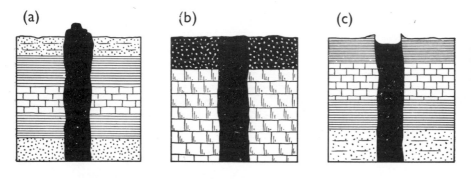

(a)   (b)   (c)

FIG. 4–33
(a) Dyke more resistant to erosion than wall rocks.
(b) Dyke and wall rocks equally resistant.
(c) Dyke less resistant than wall rocks.

FIG. 4–34
Dyke of dolerite (a basaltic rock) cutting the Chalk and the overlying Tertiary plateau basalt lavas. Cave Hill, Belfast. (*R. Welch*)

is provided by the wall-like intrusions called *dykes* (Figs. 4–33 and 4–34). Here the magma has ascended through approximately vertical fissures, forcing the walls apart as it rose, and so, on cooling, becoming a vertical sheet of rock with roughly parallel sides cutting across the bedding planes. Such intrusions are said to be *transgressive* or *discordant*. In certain circumstances the magma may open up a passage-way along a bedding plane, making room for itself by uplifting the overlying rocks. The resulting tabular sheet of rock (Fig. 4–35) is called a *sill* (Anglo-Saxon, *syl*, a ledge). Intrusions that are parallel to the adjacent stratification are said to be *concordant*.

Dykes vary greatly in thickness, from a few inches to hundreds of feet, but widths of five to twenty feet are most common. There is also great variation in length, as seen at the surface, from a few yards to many miles. Dykes

FIG. 4–35
Arthur's Seat, Edinburgh, a Lower Carboniferous volcano that was active more than 300 million years ago. The bold escarpment of Salisbury Crags is the outcrop of a later sill. (*Air-views Ltd*)

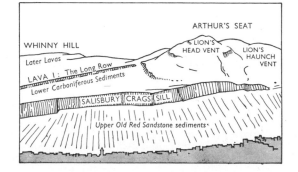

65

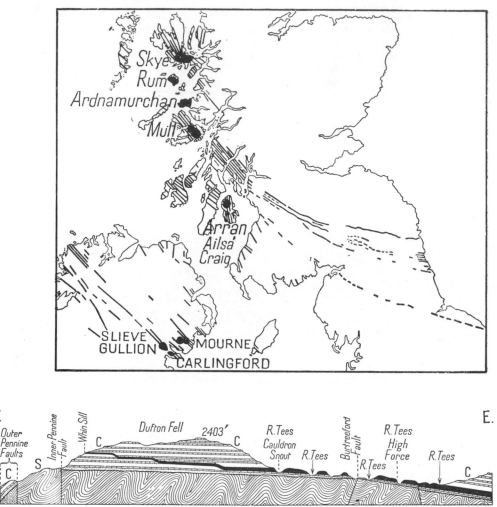

FIG. 4–36
Map showing the Tertiary dyke swarms of the British Isles and their relation to the intrusive centres of igneous activity.

FIG. 4–37
Section across the northern Pennines to show up-stepping and thinning of the Great Whin Sill towards the west: T = Triassic; C = Carboniferous; S = Silurian and Ordovician.

are very numerous in some regions of igneous activity. Along a fifteen-mile stretch of the coast of Arran, for example, a swarm of 525 dykes can be seen, the total thickness of the dykes being 5,410 feet. Here the local extension of the crust has been more than one mile in fifteen. Farther north, focussed on Mull, there is another great swarm of dykes, some of which can be traced at intervals across southern Scotland into the north of England (Fig. 4–36). Most of these dykes are dolerites of various kinds, though along the margins the rock is generally of finer grain, owing to chilling by the walls, and may be basalt or even tachylyte. The wall rocks themselves show the effects of thermal metamorphism. When a dyke is more resistant to weathering and erosion than its walls, it projects as a prominent ridge, sometimes running across the country like a wall. On the other hand, if the walls are more resistant, the dyke is worn away (*e.g.* by sea waves) into a long narrow trench or cleft. In its ordinary usage, the word "dyke" may refer to either a ditch or a wall (Fig. 4–33).

The classic example of a *sill* is the Great Whin Sill of the north of England (Figs. 4–37 and 4–38). *Whin* or *whinstone* is a quarryman's term for any dark-coloured rock, such as basalt or dolerite, which can be used as road-metal. Beginning in the north of Northumberland, the surface outcrop of the edge of the Whin Sill swings round to the crags of Bamburgh, surmounted by the castle, and seawards to the Farne Islands. Appearing again on the coast below the ruins of Dunstanburgh Castle, it can be followed across Northumberland towards the River North Tyne. Then for miles its tilted and weather-worn scarp boldly faces the north (Fig. 4–39), and here, with an eye

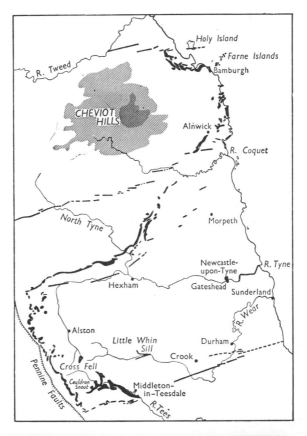

FIG. 4–38
The Great Whin Sill, and four echelon series of contemporaneous dykes (late Carboniferous). The Cheviot Hills are carved from the remains of an ancient volcano of Lower Devonian age; the original volcanic conduit and some of the adjoining lavas and tuffs have been replaced by an intrusion of granite (darker shading).

FIG. 4–39
The Great Whin Sill and the Roman Wall. Cuddy's Crag, Northumberland.
(*J. Allan Cash*)

for the best defensive line, the Romans carried their famous Wall along its crest. To the south-west it outcrops in the valleys that notch the western margin of the Pennines. Inland from the exposed edge, the Upper Tees cuts through it in the waterfalls of Cauldron Snout and High Force. Near Durham it is encountered in depth, over a thousand feet below the surface. The thickness of the sill varies from a few feet, through a general average of nearly 100 feet, to more than 200 feet. In places it divides into two or more sills at different levels, and locally it betrays its intrusive character by breaking obliquely across the strata from one set of beds to another (Fig. 4–37). This observation proves that the Whin Sill is not a lava flow, and further evidence of this is provided by the fact that the rocks above it are metamorphosed, as well as those below.

Sills are commonly more resistant to weathering and erosion than their roof and floor rocks. As a result they characteristically form bold escarpments, as illustrated by Salisbury Crag sill (Fig. 4–35), and the Whin sill (Fig. 4–39).

Laccoliths. (Gr. *lakkos*, a cistern). Instead of spreading widely as a relatively thin sheet or sill, as basaltic magmas usually do, a more viscous magma may arch up the overlying strata into a dome-like shape (Fig. 4–40). Such intrusive forms were first described from the Henry Mts, Utah, by Gilbert, a famous American geologist.

Cone-Sheets and Ring-Dykes. Intrusions whose outcrops appear as arcs or rings, sometimes concentric, are characteristically developed in connection with the Tertiary volcanic centres in Mull and Ardnamurchan, in the west of Scotland, and in the Slieve Gullion area in Northern Ireland (Fig. 4–36). They are of two distinct kinds. One variety, known as *cone-sheets*, consists of dykes in the form of inverted cones that dip inwards towards a common focus (Fig. 4–41). A thick cone-sheet is of the order of 20 feet wide and rarely 50 feet. Cone-sheets are intruded along tension fractures which result from strong upward pressure by rising magma. Uplift of an inner cone relative to its neighbour makes space available for the intrusion of magma, usually basaltic, which was presumably under sufficient hydraulic pressure to produce the cone fractures in the roof rocks. Swarms of these intrusions are to be seen in Mull and Ardnamurchan.

The other variety of ring-intrusions, *ring-dykes*, similarly outcrops as rings or parts of rings, but ring-dykes are much wider than cone-sheets, measuring up to a mile across, and they are characteristically of granitic composition. They dip very steeply and encircle rocks, including layers of volcanic rocks, that have subsided many hundreds of feet. Subsidence of a cylinder would provide no space for the intrusion of a ring-dyke, whereas subsidence of a cone widening downwards could provide space for a narrow one.

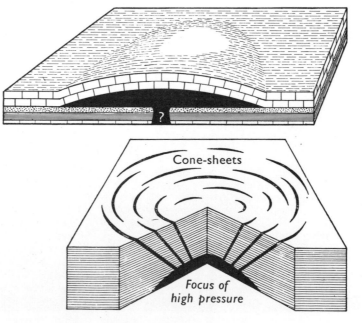

FIG. 4–40
Diagram to illustrate the form of an ideal laccolith.

FIG. 4–41
Block diagram illustrating the ideal form of a series of cone-sheets and their probable relationship to an underlying focus of high magmatic pressure.

Cone-sheets

Focus of
high pressure

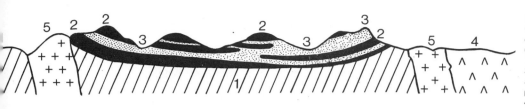

FIG. 4–42
Glen Coe, Argyll. A ring-dyke
of Old Red Sandstone age
(after Bailey and Maufe,
1916): 1 = schists; 2 and
3 = volcanic rocks (2 =
andesite, basalt, and
pyroclasts; 3 = rhyolite);
4 = granite; 5 = ring-dyke.
The length of the section
is about 10 miles (16 km).

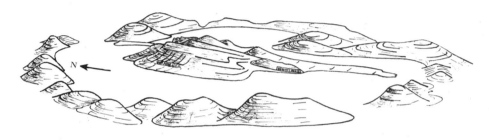

FIG. 4–43
Sketch of Slieve Gullion
(1,894 feet; 577·3 m), Co.
Armagh, Ireland, showing
its trap topography depicting
its layered structure. The
encircling ring of hills is
formed by the related
Tertiary ring-dyke. The
ring structure has a diameter
of about 7 miles.
  Slieve Gullion illustrates
crag and tail structure
(p. 149), the tail at its
southern end is formed of
solid rock overlain by
glacial deposits.

This geometrical aspect of the problem led to a belief that the dip of a ring-dyke must always be outwards. Ring complexes have now been mapped in many parts of the world (*e.g.* Oslo district, Norway; New Hampshire, U.S.A.; South-West Africa; Nigeria; the Sudan) and wherever outcrops are adequate they have been observed to dip steeply and commonly vertically. Not infrequently they encircle subsided layers of volcanic rocks which, like piles of saucers, dip inwards from the ring-dyke (Fig. 4–42). Such marginal dips indicate that the foundered rocks had to accommodate themselves (*e.g.* by folding, faulting, and differential sliding) to the narrowing space within downward-converging ring-fractures. It can be inferred that ring-fractures, like cone-fractures, converge downwards, but much more steeply, and that they are probably also tension phenomena resulting from upward pressure and consequent updoming of the crustal rocks. However, whereas in the case of cone-sheets the central keystone was punched up, in the case of ring-dykes the central keystone subsided relative to the main dome-structure. The subsidence is analogous to that resulting in rift valley formation, where an arch becomes fractured and pulled apart as a result of extension due to updoming. Hans Cloos' experimental models of rift valley formation help to make this mechanism clear (pp. 238 and 239; Figs. 13–30 and 13–31). In Ardnamurchan the outward dips of the Mesozoic country rocks provide evidence of updoming prior to intrusion of Tertiary ring-dykes and cone-sheets, and in the Slieve Gullion area the fault pattern depicts updoming prior to the intrusion of the Tertiary ring-dyke. Space for the emplacement of a narrow ring-dyke would be available at an early stage of updoming when the ring fracture was formed in response to tension. In some examples further space has been provided by replacement of the pre-existing rocks, either mechanically, *e.g.* by blowing out by volcanic eruption, or chemically, or both.

Ring-dykes sometimes form spectacular scenic features, rising above the level of the adjoining rocks as rings of hills—for example, the Slieve Gullion ring-dyke (Fig. 4–43).

Volcanic Plugs and Necks. Lava, which fills the conduit of an extinct volcano, forms a more or less pipe-like intrusion, called a *plug*. When the less resistant rocks of the cone and possibly part of the foundation rocks on which it rested have been removed by erosion, the plug may remain as a highly conspicuous feature of the landscape. A well-known example is that of Castle Rock on which Edinburgh Castle stands (Fig. 9–14).

The term *neck* is of more general application than plug and includes volcanic pipes filled with fragmental material. When lava is associated with the fragmental infillings, necks—like plugs—form prominent hills. Two such necks are represented by Arthur's Seat, Edinburgh, one forming the Lion's Head and the other the Haunch (Fig. 4–35).

Batholiths (Gr. *bathos*, depth). These are gigantic intrusions of granite and related rocks, including migmatite (see p. 45). They have dome-like roofs and walls that dip steeply, but there is no general agreement as to the actual form of the intrusions, which are commonly depicted as in Fig. 4–44. Sometimes the walls dip steeply inwards, suggesting that the form is funnel-like, or it might be mushroom-like (Fig. 4–45c) whilst other batholiths are known to be tongue-shaped like the migmatite bodies in Fig. 4–45(*b*) and (*d*). Whatever their form may be, however, batholiths occur in the heart of fold mountain ranges (orogenic belts) of all geological ages and, in plan, they are characteristically elongated parallel to the general trend of the mountain system in which they are found. Some of the batholiths of western America have been exposed over lengths of many hundreds of miles, the width being usually about a tenth of the length or less. The largest batholith in the British Isles is the Leinster granite which extends SSW from the Wicklow Mountains, in South-East Eire for a distance of about 75 miles.

The term batholith is restricted to intrusions with outcrops at the surface of 40 square miles or more. Smaller intrusions of similar type, but less elongated and with dimensions of only a few square miles or less, are called *stocks*. Many of these are probably offshoots from underlying batholiths of which only the highest parts have been exposed by denudation. The results of gravity surveys have revealed that the granite stocks of Devon, Cornwall, and the Scilly Isles (Fig. 3–3) rise upwards from an elongated batholith that forms the anticlinal core of an ancient fold mountain range of Hercynian age (Fig. 4–46).

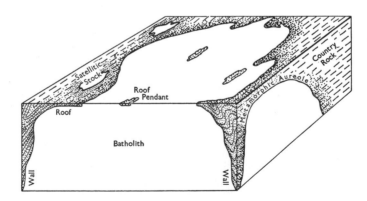

FIG. 4–44
Block diagram to illustrate some characteristic features of a batholith.

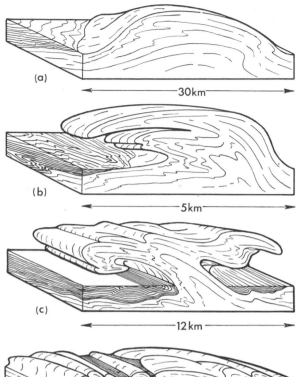

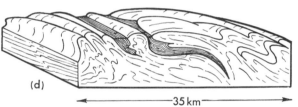

(a)

30km

(b)

5km

(c)

12km

(d)

35km

FIG. 4—45
Block diagrams illustrating
the forms of intrusive
batholiths of migmatite
as seen on the high fjord
walls in eastern Greenland:
(*a*) dome; (*b*) tongue; (*c*)
mushroom; (*d*) migmatite
complex. (*John Haller*)

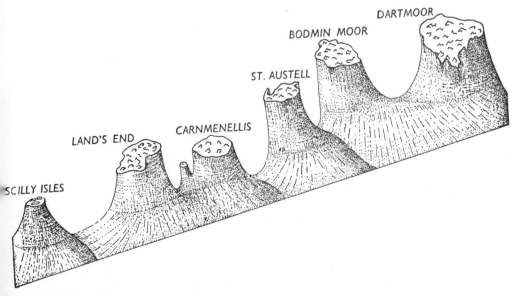

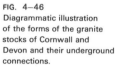

SCILLY ISLES

LAND'S END

CARNMENELLIS

ST. AUSTELL

BODMIN MOOR

DARTMOOR

FIG. 4—46
Diagrammatic illustration
of the forms of the granite
stocks of Cornwall and
Devon and their underground
connections.

Part 2
External Processes: Earth Sculpture

5
Rock Weathering and Soils

WEATHERING AND CLIMATE

Weathering is the total effect of all the various sub-aerial processes that co-operate in bringing about the decay and disintegration of rocks, provided that no large-scale transport of the loosened products is involved. The work of rainwash and wind, which is essentially erosional, is thus excluded. The products of weathering are, however, subject to gravity, and there is consequently a universal tendency on the part of the loosened materials to fall or slip downwards, especially when aided by the lubricating action of water. It is, indeed, only through the removal of the products of weathering that fresh surfaces are exposed to the further action of the weathering processes. No clean-cut distinction between weathering and erosion can therefore be attempted.

The geological work accomplished by weathering is of two kinds: (a) physical or mechanical changes, in which materials are disintegrated by temperature changes, frost action, and organisms; and (b) chemical changes, in which minerals are decomposed, dissolved, and loosened by the water, oxygen, and carbon dioxide of the atmosphere, and by organisms and the products of their decay. The physical, chemical, and biological agents actively co-operate with one another. Shattering requires stresses powerful enough to overcome the strength of the materials, but the latter is generally greatly reduced by the preliminary action of decomposition. Shattering in turn provides increased opportunities for the further penetration of the chemical agents. Everywhere full advantage is taken of the joints and bedding planes which, together with the cracks newly formed, admit air, water, and rootlets down to quite considerable depths. Thus, although the processes of weathering may be considered separately, it must not be forgotten that the actual work done is the resultant effect of several processes acting together in intimate co-operation.

The materials ultimately produced are broken fragments of minerals and rocks; residual decomposition products, such as clay; and soluble decomposition products which are removed in solution. The products of weathering differ widely in different places according to the climatic conditions and the relief and configuration of the surface. In general it may be said that disintegration is favoured by steep slopes and by the conditions characteristic of frost-ridden or desert regions, while decomposition and solution are favoured by low relief and by humid conditions, especially in tropical regions. In the temperate zones the weather is widely variable, and most of the leading processes are to be found in operation during one part of the year or another.

DISINTEGRATION BY TEMPERATURE CHANGES

Frost is an irresistible rock breaker. When water fills cracks and pores and crevices in rocks and then freezes, it expands by more than 9 per cent of its volume, and exerts a bursting pressure of about 2,000 lb to the square inch (140 kg/cm²). The rocks are ruptured and fragments are wedged apart, to become loose when thaw sets in. Steep mountain slopes and cliffs are particularly prone to destruction in this way, especially where joints are plentiful (Figs. 2–2 and 5–1). The frost-shivered fragments fall to lower levels, and accumulate there as *screes* of angular debris (Fig. 5–2). Above, the ragged skyline rises out of the ruins. The screes of Wastwater, the buttresses of Snowdon, and the great pyramid of the Matterhorn (Fig. 9–18) are familiar witnesses to the quarrying power of frost. For a time the screes protect the lower slopes, but their permanent accumulation is prevented by landslides and avalanches, transport by rivers and glaciers, and coast erosion by the sea.

In arid climates the rocks exposed to the blazing sun become intensely heated, and in consequence an outer shell expands and tends to pull away from the cooler layer a few inches within. If the rocks are appropriately bedded or jointed, actual separation of a curved shell readily takes place. If the rocks are massive, they must first be weakened by chemical weathering, but sooner or later rupture occurs. When the rocks cool down again, the resulting contraction is relieved by the development of cracks at right angles to the surface. This part of the process is facilitated by rapid chilling due to sudden rainstorms, for in the rare downpours of desert regions the rain may be near freezing point, and even hailstones are not unknown. Shells and flakes of rock are thus set free and

FIG. 5—1
The serrated skyline and the opening-up of joints and other parting planes illustrate the effects of weathering, dominated by frost-wedging. A peak of Torridonian Sandstone lying unconformably on Lewisian Gneiss. Stac Polly, Wester Ross, NW Highlands of Scotland. (*L. S. Paterson*)

FIG. 5—2
Screes of Doe Crag (Borrowdale Volcanic Series), Old Man of Coniston, English Lake District. (*G. P. Abraham Ltd, Keswick*)

broken down into smaller fragments. The disintegration of pebbles is often conspicuous (Fig. 5–3). Individual minerals swell and shrink and gradually crumble apart, especially in coarse-grained rocks like granite. Even in temperate regions the effect of the sun is far from negligible. Building stones exposed to the sun are found to decay much more rapidly than those facing north or otherwise in the shade.

In desert and semi-arid regions and in monsoon lands with a marked dry season a characteristic effect on the outlines of upstanding hillocks and peaks, especially where they are made of crystalline rocks, is produced by *exfoliation*, the peeling off of curved shells of heated rock. At edges and corners the ruptures are particularly curved, because there the increase of temperature penetrates more deeply into the rock than where flat surfaces are exposed. Sharp corners and projecting knobs are the first to fall away, rounded outlines are developed, and the hills become dome-shaped. On convex slopes, successive shells may be seen, overlapping like the tiles on a roof, each ready to fall away as soon as it is liberated by the formation of radial cracks. This effect is well seen in the *inselbergs* (isolated "island" mounts) of Mozambique and other parts of Africa (Fig. 8–16). Sometimes after sunset the loud report of a splitting rock and the noise of its fall down the mountain side can be heard.

THE ROLE OF ANIMALS AND PLANTS

Earthworms and other burrowing animals such as rodents and termites play an important part in preparing material for removal by rainwash and wind. Worms consume large quantities of soil for the purpose of extracting food, and the indigestible particles are passed out as worm casts. In an average soil there may be 150,000 worms to the acre, and in the course of a year they raise ten to fifteen tons of finely comminuted materials to the surface.

The growing rootlets of shrubs and trees exert an almost incredible force as they work down into crevices. Cracks are widened by expansion during growth (Fig. 2–3) and wedges of rock are forcibly shouldered aside. Plants of all kinds, including fungi and lichens, also contribute to chemical weathering, since they abstract certain elements from rock materials. Moreover, water, containing bacteria, attacks the minerals of rocks and soils much more vigorously than it could do in their absence. The dead remains of organisms decay in the soil largely as a result of the activi-

ties of bacteria and fungi. This liberates carbon dioxide and organic acids, together with traces of ammonia and nitric acid, all of which increase the solvent power of soil water. The chief organic product is a "complex" of brown jelly-like substances collectively known as *humus*. Humus is the characteristic organic constituent of soil, and water containing humic acids can dissolve small amounts of certain substances, such as limonite, which are ordinarily insoluble.

Another effect of vegetation, one which is of vital importance in the economy of nature, is its protective action. Rootlets bind the soil into a woven mat so that it remains porous and able to absorb water without being washed away. The destructive effects of rain and wind are thus effectively restrained. Grass roots are particularly effective in this way. Forests break the force of the rain and prevent the rapid melting of snow. Moreover, they regularize the actual rainfall and preclude the sudden floods that afflict more sterile lands. For these reasons the reckless removal of forests may imperil the prosperity of whole communities. Soil erosion is intensified, agricultural lands are impoverished and lost, and barren gullied wastes, like the "badlands" of North America, take their place (Fig. 7–1). Except after heavy rainfall, the rivers run clean in forested lands, but after deforestation their waters become continuously muddy. Destruction of the natural vegetation by land clearing and ploughing, and the failure to replace forests cut down for timber or destroyed by fire, have had disastrous economic consequences in many parts of Africa and America. Man himself has been one of the most prodigal of the organic agents of destruction.

CHEMICAL WEATHERING

The alteration and solution of rock material by chemical processes is largely accomplished by rain water acting as a carrier of dissolved oxygen and carbon dioxide, together with various acids and organic products derived from the soil. The degree of activity depends on the composition and concentration of the solutions so formed, on the temperature, on the presence of bacteria, and on the substances taken into solution from the minerals decomposed. The chief changes that occur during weathering are solution, oxidation, hydration, and the formation of carbonates. Few common minerals resist decomposition, quartz and muscovite (including sericite) being the chief examples. Others,

FIG. 5—3
Desert surface near the
Pyramids, Cairo, showing
pebbles shattered by
temperature changes. (*J. J.
Harris Teall*)

FIG. 5—4
Chemical weathering of Great
Scar Limestone (Carboniferous)
with formation of clints and
grikes. Above Malham Cove,
Yorkshire. (*Bertram Unné*)

like the carbonate minerals, can be entirely removed in solution. Most silicate minerals break down into relatively insoluble residues, such as the various clay minerals, with liberation of soluble substances which are removed in solution.

Limestone is scarcely affected by pure water, but when carbon dioxide is also present the $CaCO_3$ of the limestone is slowly dissolved and removed as calcium bicarbonate, $Ca(HCO_3)_2$. The harsh limestone platforms around Settle and Ingleborough have deeply grooved and furrowed surfaces which clearly show the effects of solution (Figs. 3–12 and 5–4). The joints are widened into "grikes" with intervening "clints" of bare rock. The surface is free from soil except where a little wind-blown dust has collected here and there in crevices. On steep or vertical exposures of limestone, deep grooves, like hemicylindrical pipes, may be formed by the solvent action of rain water that has been concentrated into narrow vertical channels,—for example, at joint intersections. These remarkable flutings are a special variety of "grikes", known internationally as *lapiés* (Fig. 5–6).

Clay minerals are the chief residual products of the decomposition of feldspars. Under the hydrolysing action of slightly carbonated waters the feldspars break down in the following way:

$$6H_2O + CO_2 + 2KAlSi_3O_8 =$$
Water   *Orthoclase*

$$= \begin{cases} Al_2Si_2O_5(OH)_4 \ (a \ clay \ mineral) \\ 4SiO(OH)_2 \ (silicic \ "acid") \\ K_2CO_3 \ (removed \ in \ solution) \end{cases}$$

From plagioclase the products are similar, except that Na_2CO_3 is formed from albite and $Ca(HCO_3)_2$ from anorthite (in place of K_2CO_3). Most of the clay is probably at first in colloidal solution, that is to say, it consists of minute particles dispersed through water, the particles being much larger than atoms but much smaller than any that can be seen with a microscope. The particles eventually crystallize into tiny scales or flakes. The alkalies easily pass into solution, but whereas soda tends to be carried away, to accumulate in the sea, potash is largely retained in the soil. It is withdrawn from solution by colloidal clay and humus, from which in turn it is extracted by plant roots. When the plants die the potash is returned to the soil. Analyses of river waters show that relatively little ultimately escapes from the lands.

The decomposition of the ferromagnesian minerals may be illustrated by reference to the simplest type of pyroxene:

Water + carbon dioxide + $Ca(Mg, Fe)(SiO_3)_2$
Diopside

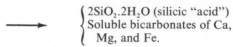

$$\longrightarrow \begin{cases} 2SiO_2.2H_2O \ (silicic \ "acid") \\ Soluble \ bicarbonates \ of \ Ca, \\ Mg, \ and \ Fe. \end{cases}$$

When Al_2O_3 and Fe_2O_3 are also present (as in biotite, augite, and hornblende) clay and chloritic minerals and limonite remain as residual products. In the presence of oxygen, limonite is also precipitated from solutions containing $Fe(HCO_3)_2$. For this reason weathered rock surfaces are commonly stained a rusty brown colour. Ordinary rust is, in fact, the corresponding product of the action of water and air on iron and steel.

Chemical weathering contributes to the disintegration of rocks (*a*) by the general weakening of the coherence between minerals, so that the rock more readily succumbs to the attack of the physical agents; (*b*) by the formation of solutions which are washed out by the rain, so that the rock becomes porous and ready to crumble (*e.g.* the liberation of the grains of a sandstone by solution of the cement); and (*c*) by the formation of alteration products with a greater volume than the original fresh material, so that (as in exfoliation) the outer shell swells and pulls away from the fresh rock within,

The separation of shells of decayed rock is called *spheroidal weathering* (Fig. 5–5). It is best developed in well-jointed rocks which, like many basalts and dolerites, are readily decomposed. Water penetrates the intersecting joints and thus attacks each separate block from all sides at once. As the depth of decay is greater at corners and edges than along flat surfaces, the surfaces of rupture become rounded. As each shell breaks loose, a new surface is presented to the weathering solutions, and the process is repeated again and again, aided according to the climate, by temperature changes with or without frost. Each successive wrapping around the fresh core becomes more nearly spheroidal than the one before, until ultimately the angular block is transformed into an onion-like structure of concentric shells of rusty and thoroughly rotted residual material, with perhaps a round and coherent core of fresher rock still left in the middle. Such cores may

FIG. 5—5
Spheroidal weathering of dolerite sill, North Queensferry, Fife. (*H. M. Geological Survey*)

FIG. 5—6
Lapiés formed by chemical weathering and erosion along vertical joint planes in impervious olivine-basalt, Oahu, Hawaii. (*H. S. Palmer*)

stand out like boulders when their soft outer wrappings have been washed away by the rain.

By no means all basaltic rocks leave rusty shells of residual materials behind when exposed to weathering. In some environments vertical joint faces of compact basalts and dolerites are found to be fluted with the hemi-cylindrical vertical gutters known as lapiés—solution forms already referred to in the simpler case of the weathering of lime-stones where only calcium carbonate is dissolved (see p. 78). Where lapiés are formed in basalts and dolerites everything has been dissolved, even the iron and aluminium compounds, leaving outcrops with fresh-looking surfaces. Lapiés of this kind were first described by Palmer (1927) from the Island of Oahu, Hawaii (Fig. 5–6). The Oahu lapiés vary in width from two to six inches and the depths of the vertical hemi-cylinders (measured in a horizontal plane) varies from one to ten inches. Subsequently similar lapiés were described by Bartrum and Mason (1948) from basalts in New Zealand, and by Doris Holmes (1961) from dolerite sills on Slieve Gullion, Co. Armagh, Northern Ireland. The lapiés from all three localities are remarkably similar in dimensions and all occur in essentially impermeable basaltic layers as a result of long-continued chemical erosion by water that drains away by trickling down vertical joint planes.

THE PROBLEM OF GRANITE TORS

Weathering along all three sets of joint planes in granite is well exemplified by the tors of granite moorlands. On Dartmoor, for example, tors consisting of piles of gigantic blocks, still *in situ* but with their corners more or less rounded off, suggest cyclopean fort-resses (Fig. 3–4). These tors occur near the summits or on the upper slopes of hills, which are themselves carved out of the granite, and it is obvious that enormous volumes of granite have been removed by denudation from the intervening spaces. Since the tors are now being modified or destroyed, they cannot have been formed under present conditions of weathering. Moreover the windward surfaces of the boulder-like forms have been pitted, roughened, grooved, and fluted subsequent to the rounding.

Linton (1955) has suggested that the tors were formed in two stages (Fig. 5–7). Accord-ing to his hypothesis the tors were sculptured during the first stage by sub-surface chemical weathering along joint-planes and the rounded blocks of the present day tors represent the residual sound granite core stones. Linton envisages the tors as having been exhumed during the second stage when the region was elevated, the rivers rejuvenated, and the friable products of chemical weathering denuded away. He suggests that the melt waters from the ice and last snows of the

(a)　　　　　　　　(b)　　　　　　　　(c)

FIG. 5–7
Stages in the evolution of a granite tor according to Linton (1955):
(a) Section through fresh granite with varied spacing of joints.
(b) The same granite after a period of subsurface chemical weathering by percolating ground water, down to the level of permanent saturation; decomposed rock, black.
(c) After elevation, the decomposed rock is removed, leaving a tor.

The chemical weathering of granite gives rise to boulder-like forms. In the humid tropics rain water, acidified by its passage through the soil, sometimes attacks sub-surface granite along joint planes, rounding off the corners of the joint blocks and even-tually leaving rounded cores of solid rock, (variously described as core stones or core boulders) embedded within "rotten" rock disintegrated by chemical weathering. In County Armagh, Northern Ireland, jointed Caledonian granite (the Newry granite) locally exhibits sub-surface chemical weathering of this kind down to a depth of twenty feet or more; it is possible, however, that this chemical weathering occurred mainly at a time when the climate was warmer and wetter.

glacial period may have been the active agents in washing away the decomposed material. The flat or gently inclined surfaces of bed-rock from which the granite tors rise, Linton interprets as representing the level of the water table, during the period of rock de-composition, above which the granite would be subjected to sub-surface chemical weather-ing. Supporting evidence for the hypothesis includes the fact that quarrying operations have revealed small tor-like forms still embedded in incoherent rotten rock, but not yet naturally exhumed because of their low-lying position in the landscape.

Attractive as Linton's hypothesis is, it is not accepted by all geomorphologists. Palmer and Neilson (1962), for example, regard the granite tors as residual masses of sound rock that were left behind when the surrounding granite was mechanically disintegrated by frost action during the ice age, when Dartmoor lay not far from the ice-covered region to the north. According to this hypothesis the rounding of the corners of the granite joint blocks results from atmospheric weathering—predominantly chemical—during inter-glacial and post-glacial times. The holders of both hypotheses are agreed that solifluction (p. 101) in front of the ice-covered regions would be a highly effective process for the removal of loose material from uplands and slopes.

The granite tors of Dartmoor are amongst the most spectacular, but tors are not confined to granite terrains. They are known to be formed of various kinds of well-jointed rock, and the Millstone Grit of the Pennines provides another example of tor scenery.

WEATHERING RESIDUES

In dry climatic regions on steep rock slopes, and over massive crystalline rocks, the coating of chemically weathered rock material may be no more than a thin film. But where rain and soil water can soak deeply into the rocks, weathering may proceed to a considerable depth. In regions where the rainfall is heavy and evenly distributed, granite may be converted into soft friable earth to depths of from 50 to 100 feet. In humid temperate regions the depth of weathered rock is usually intermediate between these two extremes.

The weathering residues are commonly clays of various kinds. When granite and gneiss are weathered, the initial quartz remains as grains associated with newly formed clay minerals derived from the feldspars (see p. 78). The weathering of basalt gives rise to clay minerals, more or less stained with the iron oxide limonite, and the weathering of clay rocks similarly gives rise to clay residues.

As already described, limestones may be slowly dissolved and removed during weathering (p. 78). When they contain impurities such as quartz and clay, these minerals remain and accumulate as weathering residues. The red earths, known as *terra rossa*, that cover the white limestone of the Karst, a plateau behind the Adriatic coast of Yugoslavia, are weathering residues rich in insoluble iron hydroxides derived by long accumulation from the minute traces of iron compounds in the original limestone.

In tropical regions which have a heavy rainfall during the wet season, succeeded by a dry season with high temperature and rapid evaporation, a reddish brown deposit accumulates on rocks of all types. During the hot dry season soil water is removed by plants, and water is drawn up from below to make good the loss so long as the supply lasts. The weak solutions produced by leaching of the rocks during the wet season thus become concentrated by evaporation and the dissolved materials are deposited, the least soluble being the first to be precipitated. The products include hydroxides of aluminium and iron, silica, and various carbonates and sulphates. Most of these are redissolved by the rains of the next wet season. The hydroxides of aluminium and iron, however, are left in a highly insoluble state, at or near the surface, and gradually accumulate as the reddish brown deposit known as *laterite* (L. *later*, a brick). The reason for the name is that in certain regions, as in parts of India, laterite is found to be quite soft below a hard and slag-like crust. The soft laterite can be readily cut into bricks which set hard on exposure to the sun. This easily worked and valuable building material was called laterite not because it resembles brick, but because bricks are made from it.

Quartz and clay minerals that have not suffered the ultimate loss of silica remain cemented in the laterite in various proportions, and concretionary structures form within the laterite. In depth this weathering residue is variegated and paler in colour, and it is here that alumina tends to be specially concentrated. At greater depths the bedrocks may be intensely decomposed, with abundant development of clay minerals. There are two important varieties of laterites: those rich in iron and those rich in aluminium. The latter, when of high grade, constitute *bauxite*, the only ore of aluminium from which it is practicable to extract the metal on a commercial scale. In Co. Antrim, in Northern Ireland, both laterite and bauxite were at one time mined, the former for iron ore and the latter for bauxite. The laterite and bauxite are here weathering residues formed in Tertiary times during the interval between the outpourings of the lower and upper plateau basalts. They represent the weathered upper surface of the lower plateau basalts and can be seen in the cliff at the Giant's Causeway just above the path that skirts round the amphitheatres (Fig. 1–3).

THE MANTLE OF ROCK WASTE (Continental deposits)		
Mode of Origin		Characteristic Deposits
SEDENTARY		
Essentially inorganic	*Residual*	Gravel, sand, silt and mud. *Terra rossa*, lateritic earths and laterite
Inorganic and organic	*Soils*	Including soils on bedrock and on mantle deposits
Essentially organic	*Cumulose*	Vegetation residues: swamp deposits and peat
TRANSPORTED		
By gravity	*Colluvial*	Screes and landslip deposits
By wind	*Æolian*	Sand dunes, sand wastes, and loess
By ice	*Glacial*	Boulder clay, moraines, and drumlins
By melt water from ice	*Glaciofluvial*	Outwash fans, kames, and eskers
By rivers (deposited in lakes)	*Lacustrine*	Alluvium and saline deposits
By rivers	*Fluviatile*	Alluvium, passing seawards by way of *estuarine* or *deltaic* deposits into *marine* deposits

THE MANTLE OF ROCK WASTE

The superficial deposits which lie on the older and more coherent bedrocks form a mantle of rock waste of very varied character. In many places the waste mantle lies directly on the bedrock from which it was formed by weathering. In this case quarry sections and cuttings of all kinds generally show a surface layer of *soil*, passing gradually downwards through a zone of shattered and partly decomposed rock, known as the *subsoil*, to the parental bedrock, still relatively fresh and unbroken by weathering agents. In the soil, vegetable mould and humus occur to a varying extent, and under appropriate conditions they accumulate to form thick beds of peat which must also be regarded as part of the waste mantle. Soils develop, however, not only on bedrock, but also on a great variety of loose deposits transported into their present positions by gravity, wind, running water, or moving ice. Although these deposits will not be considered in detail till later, it is convenient to summarize them here, according to their mode of origin, together with the untransported or *sedentary* deposits of the waste mantle.

THE GROWTH AND NATURE OF SOILS

The purely mineral matter of the residual or transported deposits is first colonized by bacteria, lichens, or mosses. By the partial decay of the dead organisms, mould and humus begin to accumulate; lodgment is afforded for ferns and grasses; berries and winged seeds are brought by birds and the wind; and finally shrubs and trees may gain a footing. The rootlets work down, burrowing animals bring up inorganic particles, and the growing mass becomes porous and sponge-like, so that it retains water and permits the passage of air. Frost and rain play their parts, and ultimately a mature soil, a complex mixture of mineral and organic products, is formed. But though the soil is a result of decay, it is also the medium of growth. It teems with life, and as the source of supply of nearly all food it is for mankind one of his most valuable and indispensable assets.

Soil may be defined as the surface layer of the mantle of rock waste in which the physical and chemical processes of weathering co-operate in intimate association with biological processes. All these processes depend on climate, and so it is found that soils vary with the climate in which they develop. Other factors are also involved: particularly the nature of the bedrock or other deposit on which the soil is generated, the relief of the land, the age of the soil (that is, the length of time during which soil development has been in progress), and the superimposed effects of cultivation.

The influence of the parental material is easily understood. Sand makes too light a soil for many plants, as it is too porous to retain water. Clay, on the other hand, is by itself too impervious. A mixture of sand and clay avoids these extremes and provides the basis of an excellent soil called *loam*. A clay soil may also be lightened by adding limestone, and the natural mixture, known as *marl*, is also

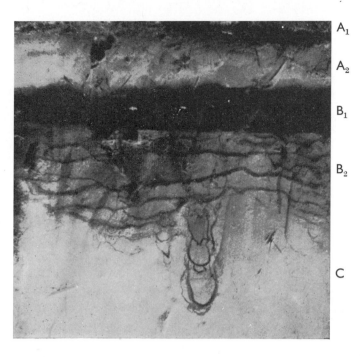

A₁
A₂
B₁
B₂
C

FIG. 5–8
Section through soil of podsol type formed from buff-coloured sandy alluvium C by descending soil water enriched in humus by its passage through A₁, (vegetable mould and humus) here provided by a cover of heather; near Endhaven, Netherlands. (*U.S. Department of Agriculture, photograph by Roy W. Simonson*)
A_2 is the zone of bleached grey soil from which the podsol type takes its name; iron hydroxides have been leached out as ferro-humus materials and fixed, with washed down clay particles, in the dark and more compactzone, B_1, which may eventually develop into hardpan. Continued downward migration leads to periodic precipitation of ferruginous materials in zone B_2, which is generally mottled, but sometimes banded, as here. Where there are favourable passageways, localized tongues of B_2 may invade the parental rock material C.

a favourable basis. Limestone alone, as we have seen, cannot make a soil unless it contains impurities. In most climates granite decomposes slowly and yields up its store of plant foods very gradually. Basaltic rocks, on the other hand, break down much more quickly. Volcanic ashes and lavas provide highly productive soils which, even on the flanks of active volcanoes, such as Etna, compensate the agriculturist and vine-grower for the recurrent risk of danger and possible destruction.

Differences due to the bedrock are most marked in young soils and in temperate regions. As the soil becomes older, and especially when the climate is of a more extreme type, the influence of long continued weathering and organic growth and decay makes itself felt more and more. Certain ingredients are steadily leached out, while others are concentrated. Humus accumulation depends on the excess of growth over decay, and this in turn depends on climatic factors. The composition of the evolving soil thus gradually approaches a certain characteristic type which is different for each climatic region. The black soil of the Russian steppes, for example, is equally well developed from such different parent rocks as granite, basalt, loess, and boulder clay. Conversely, a single rock type, like granite, gives grey soils in temperate regions (*podsol*), black soils in the steppes (*chernosem*), and reddish soils in

tropical regions of seasonal rainfall (*lateritic earths*). The colours of soils are almost wholly due to the relative abundance (or paucity) of various iron compounds and humus.

Deeply cultivated soils may be more or less uniform throughout, but this is not the case in purely natural soils. A vertical cutting through an old natural soil reveals a layered arrangement which is called the *soil profile* (Fig. 5–8). The successive layers of one type of profile are clearly developed in the grey soils of the more or less forested north-temperate belt of Canada, northern Europe, and Asia. As the drainage is dominantly descending, iron hydroxides, and humus derived from the surface layer of vegetable mould, are carried down in colloidal solution. Thus a bleached zone develops, and for this reason the soil type is called *podsol* (Russian, ashy grey soil). By the accumulation of the ferro-humus material at a depth of a few inches or a foot or so, accompanied by particles of silt and clay washed down mechanically, a deep brown or nearly black layer of variable thickness is formed. This may develop into a hard, well-cemented band, impervious to drainage, which is known as *hardpan*. One of the objects of ploughing is to prevent the growth of hardpan. Otherwise, water-logged conditions may set in, and there will then be a marked tendency for peat to accumulate.

Farther south in the grasslands of the steppes and prairies, summer drought and winter frosts favour the accumulation of humus, largely provided by the grass roots which die each year. During the dry season groundwater is drawn towards the surface, and calcium carbonate is precipitated, often in irregular nodules, at a depth of two or three feet. Under the influence of the ascending calcareous solutions the humus becomes black and insoluble. Iron hydroxides are therefore not leached out as in the podsol. The upper layer of the soil profile is black, becoming brown in depth where the humus content is less. For this reason the soil type is called *chernosem* (Russian, black earth). The black cotton soils of India and the "black bottoms" of the Mississippi flood plains are of similar origin.

In the tropical monsoon lands, where laterite forms the weathering mantle, rain forests protect the iron-rich soil from the hardening effect of the sun's rays. When the ground is cleared, however, and the land ploughed in the hope of increasing food production, the lateritic soil hardens into a brick-like pavement within a few years.

CLIMATIC SOIL TYPES AND ASSOCIATED RESIDUAL DEPOSITS

	Climatic Regions	Characteristic Natural Vegetation	Mainly Organic	Mixed Organic and Inorganic	Mainly or Entirely Inorganic
ARCTIC	Glacial	—	—	—	—
	Tundra (short mild summer)	Mosses and Lichens	Peat Soils Peat	Frost-shattered Stony Soils	
TEMPERATE HUMID	Boreal (cold winter)	Coniferous Forests	Peat Soils Peat	*Podsol* (Grey)	
	Temperate (mild and humid)	Coniferous and Deciduous Forests	Peat Soils Peat	*Podsol* (Grey) Grey Forest Earths	
	Mediterranean (short mild winter)	Evergreen Shrubs and Trees		Brown Forest Earths	*Terra Rossa*
ARID and SEMI–ARID	Steppes (dry summer)	Grasses		*Chernosem* (Black) Chestnut-brown Soils	
	Deserts	Marginal Scrub —		Grey Marginal Soils	White Salt Encrustations Desert Sands
		Marginal Scrub		Grey Marginal Soils	White Salt Encrustations
TROPICAL RAINY	Savannahs (wet and dry seasons)	Grasses and Scattered Trees		Brown Soils Black Soils	*Laterite*
	Monsoon Lands (wet and dry seasons)	Forests: Mixed, Open to Sub-tropical Evergreen	Swamp Soils Peat	Brown Lateritic Earths Red Lateritic Earths	*Laterite* (Red—Reddish and Brown)
	Equatorial (continuously humid)	Evergreen Tropical Rain Forests	Swamp Soils Peat	Brown Earths Grey Bleached Earths	

6
Underground Waters

SOURCES OF GROUND WATER

There is abundant evidence for the existence of important underground supplies of water. At least from the time of the Babylonians there was a widespread and firmly held belief that not only springs and wells, but also rivers, were fed and maintained by water from vast subterranean reservoirs. The underground streams of limestone caverns supported this belief, and so did the spurting up of "the fountains of the deep" through fissures riven in alluvial flats by earthquakes. Moreover, in arid countries like Mesopotamia and Egypt it was far from obvious that rivers could be maintained by rainfall. The author of Ecclesiastes remarked that although "the rivers run into the sea, yet the sea is not full," and inferred that the balance was restored by a return circulation, underground from the sea floor, back to the sources of the rivers. How the sea water rose to such high levels was not explained, and how it lost its salt before emerging as springs of fresh water remained an unsolved problem. It was only late in the seventeenth century that it first came to be realized, notably by Halley, that the circulation from sea to rivers was not underground, but through the atmosphere by way of evaporation and rainfall. Aristotle's erroneous conviction that the rainfall was quite inadequate to supply the flow of rivers was not dispelled until accurate measurements took the place of mere opinion. In 1674 Pierre Perrault completed the first quantitative investigation of the relation between rainfall and stream flow. He found that in the upper valley of the Seine the rainfall was actually several times greater than the stream flow, and so demonstrated for the first time a relationship that in humid climates seems now to be almost a matter of common sense.

The scheme at the bottom of the page shows the various ways in which rainwater is distributed (see also Fig. 2–1).

Ground water supplied by rain or snow or by infiltration from rivers and lakes is described as *meteoric*. Fresh or salt water entrapped in sediments during their deposition is distinguished as *connate*. During burial and compaction of the sediments, much of this fossil water is expelled, and during metamorphism most of it is driven out, carrying with it dissolved material which helps to cement the sediments at higher levels. Steam and hot mineral-laden water liberated during igneous activity, and believed to reach the surface for the first time, are known as *juvenile* water. It is possible, however, that such water includes water of connate origin.

THE WATER TABLE

Below a certain level, never far down in humid regions, all porous and fissured rocks are completely saturated with water. The upper surface of this ground water is called the *water table*. The water table is arched up under hills, roughly following the relief of the ground, but with a more subdued surface. In general, three successive zones may conveniently be recognized (Fig. 6–1):

RUN-OFF   Direct flow down surface slopes   ⎰

Superficial flow through soil and sub-soil to streams   ⎱ STREAM FLOW

PERCOLATION ⎰ Downward infiltration into bedrocks to replenish the ground water and maintain its circulation ⎱ GROUND WATER

Absorption by soil and vegetation, subsequently evaporated ⎱ EVAPORATION

DIRECT EVAPORATION

(During weathering a relatively trifling amount of water is fixed by hydration in clay minerals and other weathering products.)

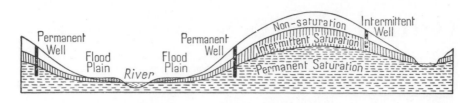

FIG. 6–1
Diagrammatic illustration of the relation of the water table to the surface, and the variation of its level from the top to the bottom of the zone of intermittent saturation after prolonged periods of wet and dry weather respectively.

(*a*) *The zone of non-saturation*, which is never completely filled, but through which the water percolates on its way to the underlying zones. A certain amount of water is retained by the soil, which yields it up to plant roots.

(*b*) *The zone of intermittent saturation*, which extends from the highest level reached by ground water after a period of prolonged wet weather, down to the lowest level to which the water table recedes after drought.

(*c*) *The zone of permanent saturation*, which extends downwards to the limit beneath which ground water is not encountered. The depths in mines and borings at which the rocks are found to be dry vary very considerably according to the local structures, but a limit of the order 2,000 to 3,000 feet is not uncommon. Juvenile and expelled connate water may, of course, ascend from much greater depths.

Wherever the zone of permanent saturation rises above ground level, seepages, swamps, lakes, or rivers occur. When the zone of intermittent saturation temporarily reaches the surface, floods develop and intermittent springs appear. Conversely, many springs and swamps, and even the rivers of some regions, go more or less dry after long periods of dry weather when the water table falls below its usual level.

THE STORAGE AND CIRCULATION OF GROUND WATER

Rocks through which water can pass freely are said to be *pervious*. They may be porous and *permeable*, like sand and sandstone; or they may be practically non-porous and impermeable, like granite, but nevertheless pervious because of the presence of interconnected open joints and fissures through which water can readily flow. Impervious rocks are those through which water cannot easily soak; they may be of two kinds: porous, like clay, or relatively non-porous, like massive unfissured granite. It should be noticed that although porosity is essential in order that a formation can be readily permeable by water, it is not a sufficient condition. The size and arrangement of the openings must also be such that continuous through-channels for the free passage of water are available (Fig. 6–2). In clays there are no continuous passage-ways wide enough to permit the flow of water, except by slow capillary creep.

Ordinary loose sand or gravel has a porosity of about 35 per cent (*i.e.* the material in bulk is made up of 35 per cent of "voids" and 65 per cent of "solids"), but this drops to about 15 per cent in common sandstones, according to the degree of compaction and the amount of cementing material. Clay, although it is impermeable, may have a porosity of over 45 per cent. By compaction under pressure and the squeezing out of water the porosity drops gradually, falling to as little as 5 per cent in some shales, and to 3 per cent in slates. In limestones the porosity ranges from 30 per cent in friable chalk to 5 or less in indurated and recrystallized varieties. Limestone, however, may carry a great deal of water in joints and other channels (including caves) opened out by solution. The porosity of massive igneous and metamorphic rocks is generally less than 1 per cent, but here again water may circulate in appreciable quantities through the passage-ways afforded by interconnected joints and fissures.

Alternations of pervious and impervious strata, especially when folded, faulted, and jointed, form underground reservoirs and natural waterworks of great variety. Where the catchment area is sufficiently high the

FIG. 6–2
Diagrams to illustrate how pore space varies according to the way the grains (here idealized as spheres) are packed together in a porous sediment:
(*a*) the most open packing—each sphere touches six others (in three dimensions) and the porosity is 47·6;
(*b*) the closest packing—each sphere touches twelve others and the porosity is 26.

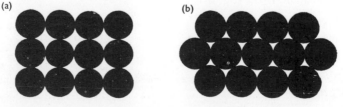

water slowly migrates through the most pervious formations towards places at a lower level where the water can escape to the surface. It may emerge through natural openings (seepages and springs) or through artificial openings (wells), or it may feed directly into rivers or lakes or even discharge through the sea floor. The sustained flow of rivers which, like the Nile, successfully cross wide stretches of desert is to some extent due to supplies received from underground sources.

SPRINGS AND WELLS

When rain water sinks into a permeable bed, such as sandstone, it soaks down until it reaches an underlying impermeable bed, such as clay or shale. If the surface of the junction is inclined, the water flows down the watertight slope, to emerge where the junction is intercepted by a cliff or valley side (Fig. 6–3a). A general oozing out of the water along the line of interception is called a seepage. More commonly a line of localized springs appears. The other diagrams of Fig. 16–3 illustrate various examples of other structures favouring

the development of springs. In (b) a fault brings pervious sandstone against shale which, being impervious, holds up the water. Springs are localized along the line of the fault, and the low ground on the left is marshy. In (c) water enters the joints in a massive rock, such as granite, and issues in appropriate places. In (d) water impounded by a dyke escapes along the outcrop of the junction. In (e) the upper spring is thrown out by a conformable bed of shale, as in (a); the lower spring appears at the outcrop of an unconformity, the underlying folded rocks being impervious. In (f) water enters jointed limestone, widens the joints by solution, forming caves and underground channels down to the impervious base of the formation. The latter holds up the water and lets it drain out, sometimes as an actual stream, where a valley has been excavated through the limestone into the underlying rocks.

Wells are simply holes dug or bored or drilled into the ground to a depth at which waterbearing permeable formations or fissured rocks are encountered. Shallow wells, as shown in Fig. 6–1, may dry up at certain seasons, unless they tap the zone of permanent

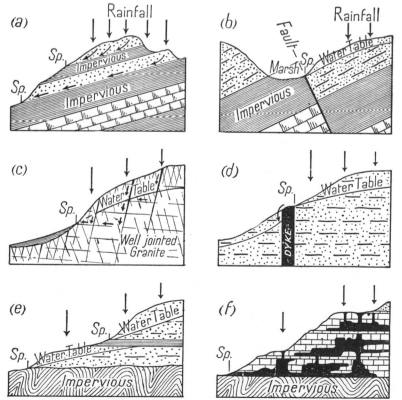

FIG. 6–3
Diagrams to illustrate various conditions giving rise to springs (see text).

saturation. Ground water percolates into the bottom of the well, and rises to a level that depends on the head of pressure behind it. Pumping or lifting may be necessary to bring the water to the surface. In selecting sites for shallow wells special precaution is necessary to preclude contamination by germ-laden water which might drain into the source of supply from farmyards and cesspools. The ground water from more deep-seated formations is preferable for human consumption, as it is more likely to be free from the dangers of surface contamination.

Artesian wells are those in which the water encountered in depth is under a sufficient hydraulic pressure to force it to overflow at the surface (Fig. 6–4). The necessary conditions are: (*a*) an inclined or broadly synclinal waterbearing formation, or *aquifer*, enclosed on both sides by watertight beds; (*b*) exposure of the rim of the aquifer over a catchment or intake area at a sufficient height to provide a hydraulic head at a level above the ground where the wells are sunk; (*c*) a sufficient rainfall to furnish an adequate supply of water; and (*d*) absence of a ready means of escape of the water except through the wells. The term *artesian* is sometimes extended to include deep wells in which the water approaches the surface but does not actually reach it.

The London Basin (Fig. 6–5) exemplifies these conditions very clearly. The aquifer is the Chalk, with sandy beds above and, locally, below. The enclosing impervious formations are the London clay above and the Gault clay below. Water falling on the Chalk, where it is exposed along the Chilterns to the north, and the North Downs to the south, sinks into the basin and accumulates there— or did so until the original resources became impoverished by the insatiable thirst of London. The water in the Chalk is tapped in the London area by more than a thousand wells sunk to depths of 600 or 700 feet. Up to a century ago the Chalk was saturated, and when the fountains in Trafalgar Square were first constructed the water gushed out well above the surface. In more recent years the enormous supplies which have been drawn from the Chalk reservoir have far exceeded replenishment by rainfall on the rims of the basin. The level of the water in the Chalk under London has therefore fallen—as much as 400 feet in places—and water can now be raised to the surface only by pumping.

In North and South Dakota an important aquifer dips off the edge of the Black Hills, and carries a copious supply of water beneath the plains to the east. Over an area of 15,000 square miles the water can be tapped by artesian wells. The largest artesian basin in the world is that of Queensland and adjoining parts of New South Wales and South Australia. The catchment area is in the Eastern Highlands where porous Jurassic and Cretaceous sandstones come to the surface. These sandstones, with their accumulated stores of water,

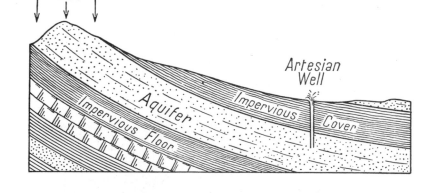

FIG. 6–4
Diagram illustrating the structural conditions favourable to artesian wells.

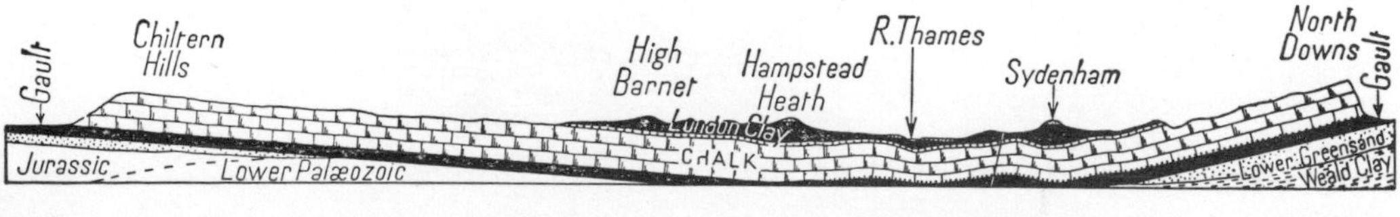

FIG. 6–5
Section, 58 miles (93 km) long, through the London Basin. (For map see Fig. 4–9)).

underlie an area of about 600,000 square miles. Without the artesian wells, some of which are a mile deep, much of this vast region would be a barren waste. The Desert Basin in the north of Western Australia and the Murray Basin in Victoria also provide invaluable supplies of artesian water.

Many of the *oases* of the Sahara and other deserts owe their existence to the local emergence of artesian water at the surface. Fertilized by the escaping underground water, vegetation flourishes amazingly and makes "a paradise in a setting of blazing sand and glaring rocks." Between the Chad basin and the Libyan Desert the highlands from Tibesti to Darfur constitute an important catchment area. There the occasional rains are readily absorbed by bare sandstones which continue underground far across Libya and Egypt. Many a traveller has died of thirst in the heart of the desert with water only a few hundred

feet beneath him. Oases occur where this usually inaccessible water emerges through fissures or artesian wells, or is brought to the surface by anticlines (Fig. 6–6), or where the desert floor itself has been excavated by the wind down to the level of the ground water (Fig. 6–7). South of Aswan, artesian water contributes to the flow of the Nile where the river has cut its channel into an aquifer locally brought up by an anticline.

The general rate of flow of ground water beneath the Libyan Desert has been found to be about 50 metres a year, and since some of the Egyptian oases are 1,500 km from the intake area they must now be fed with water that has taken 30,000 years to reach them. Irrigation of this desert region and of the Sahara farther west must be carried out with due regard to the resources available. An international study of the underground water supplies throughout the vast region between

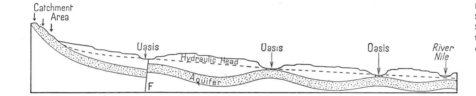

FIG. 6–6
Schematic section across the Sahara to illustrate conditions favourable to the development of oases.

FIG. 6–7
Part of the great oasis of Colomb Bechar in the NW of the Algerian Sahara, as it was about 1930. Since then the abundant supplies of gourndwater have been conserved by underground dams and reservoirs; coal has been discovered and not far away, ores of iron and manganese. Colomb Bechar has now become the centre of a rapidly expanding industrial area. (*Paul Popper Ltd*)

D

the Red Sea and the Atlantic is being made.

SWALLOW HOLES AND LIMESTONE CAVERNS

The solution of limestone by rain water charged with carbon dioxide has already been described (page 78). In limestone districts water readily works its way down through joints and along bedding planes until it reaches an impervious layer, which may be within the limestone formation or beneath it. The water then follows the natural drainage directions until it finds an exit, perhaps many miles away from the intake. Once a through drainage is established, but not until then, dissolved material is carried away and fresh supplies of water, coming in from above, continue the work of solution, localized along joints and bedding planes, until a labyrinth of interlacing channels and caves is dissolved out of the limestone (Fig. 6–3*f*).

The surface openings become gradually enlarged in places where the contours of the ground favour a special concentration of the flow-off, and funnel-shaped holes, known as *swallow holes* or *sink holes*, are developed. By continued solution beneath these, and the falling in of loosened joint blocks, the holes may be enlarged into roughly cylindrical shafts or chasms communicating with great vaulted chambers, perhaps hundreds of feet below.

One of the most impressive of these giant swallow holes in Britain is Gaping Ghyll (Fig. 6–8), on the south-east slopes of Ingleborough. The shaft goes down for 365 feet into a chamber 480 feet long and 110 feet high. The water escapes through an intricate system of passages into Ingleborough Cave, whence it emerges as the Clapham Beck.

The "cavernous limestone" plateau of Kentucky has over 60,000 sink holes and hundreds of caves, including the great Mammoth Cave, which itself has over 30 miles of continuous passages. Another famous American cave, the Carlsbad Cavern of New Mexico, has a "Big Room" nearly 4,000 feet long, with walls over 600 feet apart, and a ceiling rising to a height of 300 feet. Cave explorers, known as speleologists, find a great fascination in the thrills and dangers of penetrating the realms of subterranean waters. Some of their greatest achievements have been in the French Pyrenees and, more recently, in the French Alps, where underground waterfalls, rivers, and lakes have been explored and mapped to depths of more than a kilometre from the surface.

In addition to the streams which flow through the underground network of passageways, there is generally a slow seepage of lime-charged water from innumerable joints and crevices in the roofs and walls of caves. Calcium carbonate is deposited when a hanging drop of such water begins to evaporate or to lose part of its carbon dioxide. When the drop falls on the dry floor of a deserted channel, the remaining calcium carbonate is deposited. Thus, long icicle-like pendants, called *stalactites*, grow downwards from the roof; and thicker columns, distinguished as *stalagmites*, grow upward from the floor (Fig. 6–9). In time stalactites and stalagmites unite into pillars, and these are commonly clustered together in forms resembling organ pipes and other fantastic shapes that are often given fanciful names. Where the water trickles out more or less continuously along a roof joint, a fluted curtain or wavy screen may grow across the cave. When the water comes through a bedding plane it builds up encrustations from wall to floor which look like frozen cascades. The internal decoration of caverns in which these varied structures have grown in profusion produces an underground scenery of unique and fascinating beauty.

Occasionally the roof of a cave collapses and leaves a corresponding depression at the surface. When the roof of a long underground channel falls in, a deep ravine, floored with

FIG. 6–8
Gaping Ghyll, south-eastern slopes of Ingleborough, Yorkshire. (*Flatters and Garnett*).

FIG. 6–9
Miniature stalactites and stalagmites in a cave at Ogof Ffynnon Ddu, South Wales. The "Ballet Dancer" and the "Bees Knees" are 12 to 18 inches high. (*Alan C. Coase*)

FIG. 6–10
Trow Ghyll, on the slopes of Ingleborough, Yorkshire, a dry valley due to roof collapse of a former limestone cavern. (*A. Horner and Sons, Settle*)

limestone debris, further diversifies the irregular limestone topography (Fig. 6–10). For a time one part of the roof may hold firm, thus forming a natural arch or bridge (Fig. 6–11). Limestone regions, such as those referred to above, having roughly etched surfaces pitted with depressions due to solution or roof collapse, and with underground drainage in place of surface streams, are said to have a *karst* topography, from the prevalence of these features in the Karst Plateau bordering the Adriatic coast of Jugoslavia.

HOT SPRINGS AND GEYSERS

Ground water that has circulated to great depths in deeply folded rocks becomes heated, and if a sufficiently rapid ascent to the surface should be locally possible, it will emerge as a warm spring. Such conditions are rare, however, and really hot springs generally occur in regions of active or geologically recent vulcanism.

There are three volcanic regions that have long been celebrated for their hot springs and geysers: Iceland; Yellowstone Park, Wyoming; and the North Island of New Zealand. Others on an imposing scale are now known in Morocco and Kamshatka. The waters are highly charged with mineral matter of considerable variety. The Mammoth Hot Springs of Yellowstone Park are rich in calcium bicarbonate, and calcium carbonate is deposited at the surface as mounds and terraces of *travertine* (Fig. 6–12). In all the regions mentioned many of the springs are alkaline and carry silica in solution; this is similarly deposited as *siliceous sinter* or *geyserite*. Various investigations indicate that 80 or 90 per cent of the water is ordinary meteoric groundwater. In Iceland, for example, much of it comes from melting snow. However, the minor constituents carried in solution include many of the rarer elements, a peculiarity which points to a juvenile source, and suggests that they may have been introduced by steam of juvenile origin. Borings through the volcanic flows (ignimbrites, see p. 252) of Yellowstone Park encountered vast quantities of high-pressure, superheated steam. In one case the temperature at a depth of 245 feet was found to be 205° C. In New Zealand, Italy, California, and Japan underground supplies of superheated steam are being increasingly tapped by bore-holes to provide heat and water for domestic and industrial purposes. At Wairakei the world's first geothermal

FIG. 6–11
Natural Bridge., Virginia. Part of the roof of a former limestone cavern. (*American Museum of Natural History, New York*)

FIG. 6–12
Terraces of travertine. Mammoth Hot Springs, Yellowstone National Park, Wyoming. (*Dorien Leigh Ltd*)

power station is now feeding electricity into New Zealand's supply system.

Geysers are hot springs from which a column of hot water and steam is explosively discharged at intervals, spouting in some cases to heights of hundreds of feet. The term comes from *Geysir*, the Icelandic name (meaning "spouter" or "gusher") for the Great Geyser, which is the most spectacular member of a group situated in a broad valley north-west of Heckla (Fig. 6–13). It will serve as a typical example. A mound of geyserite, built up by deposition from the overflowing water, surrounds a circular basin, about 69 feet across and 4 feet deep, filled to the brim with siliceous water at a temperature of 75° to 90° C. From the middle of the basin a pipe, also lined with geyserite, goes down about 100 feet. At the bottom the temperature of the water is well above that at which the water would boil if it were not for the pressure due to the weight of the water column above it.

Following Bunsen it had been supposed that continued accession of superheated steam through cracks in the pipe gradually raised the temperature until eventually the boiling point was reached far down in the pipe. Investigations have shown, however, that although the temperature of the water increases with depth, the maximum temperature reached at the depths where eruptions begin remains below the boiling point corresponding to the pressure of the overlying column of water. Thorkelsson's explanation is that the observed "boiling" results not so much from increase of temperature as from reduction of pressure. The waters of hot springs are charged with dissolved gases. Well below the surface these begin to be liberated as bubbles, and being in contact with hot water they necessarily become saturated with water vapour. When the water is near its boiling point the proportion of water vapour in the ascending bubbles becomes very large and some of the resulting hot foam overflows at the surface. This so relieves the pressure on the heated water in depth that it violently flashes into a vast volume of foam and spray, which surges up with irresistible force, hurling itself up to a height of as much as 200 feet. A similar height is commonly reached by Old Faithful Geyser in Yellowstone National Park. The world record for height was made in 1901 by a geyser that broke out on one of the volcanic fissures of the Tarawera rift in New Zealand. During a few months of intense activity some of its intermittent fountains of hot spray shot up to a height of 1,500 feet.

In some geysers the amount of water dis-

FIG. 6–13
Geysir, the Great Geyser of Iceland in eruption. (*Iceland Tourist Bureau; photo: Mats Wibe Lund, Jr*)

charged is many times greater than that contained in the pipe or basin. In these cases the pipe must therefore communicate with underground chambers into which continuous supplies of meteoric water and hot gases (including steam) have access. The cavities and tunnels which sometimes occur in basaltic lava flows would provide the sort of reservoir required (Fig. 6–14). During each period of quiescence the whole system of cavities, communicating channels, pipe, and basin rapidly fills up. Gas content and temperature gradually rise until the quiet phase of the cycle is disturbed by the ascent and expansion of bubbles, and terminated by a roaring eruption of hot spray and steam.

FROZEN GROUND WATER

In the tundra and adjacent parts of the northern boreal regions the ground is permanently frozen, except for a surface layer a few feet thick which thaws out during the summer. This frozen ground, known as

93

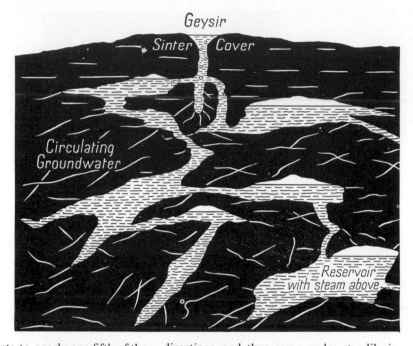

FIG. 6–14
Schematic section through *Geysir*, the Great Geyser of Iceland, to illustrate the conditions appropriate to intermittent eruption; showing subterranean reservoirs fed by groundwaters heated from below by the ascent of super-heated steam. (*After T. F. W. Barth*)

permafrost, amounts to nearly one fifth of the land areas and is probably a relic from the last glaciation. In Arctic Canada and Alaska thicknesses of frozen ground up to 1,300 feet have been penetrated, and in Siberia a maximum thickness of 2,300 feet is known. In Arctic Canada, Greenland, and northern Siberia sporadic mounds and cones, covered with deeply fissured layers of waste-mantle deposits, have been upheaved by intrusions of ground ice. These mounds rise up to 140 feet above the surrounding country, and many of them have a crater at the summit sometimes containing a shallow lake during the summer months. These remarkable structures are called *pingos* (an Eskimo name), and they have also been referred to as "hydro-laccoliths". They appear to form where unfrozen ground water (*a*) is trapped between an underlying zone of permafrost and an overlying frozen zone, or (*b*) has access to such a position from a high intake area which gives it a hydraulic head like that of artesian water.

East of the Mackenzie delta in North-West Canada, pingos of the first kind can be seen in various stages of development (Fig. 6–15). The zone of permafrost in this region is about 300 feet thick. Each pingo stands in the middle of the site of a former lake beneath which, it is thought, there was originally an extensive layer of ground water surrounded on all sides by permafrost. As the lake filled up with sediment and peat, the trapped ground water would be encroached upon by frost from all

directions and thus came under steadily increasing pressure as a result of the 9 per cent expansion. Relief could be gained only by upheaval of the roof, and this would occur where overhead pressure was least,—that is, at about the middle of the former lake. Water squeezed into this growing dome would be actively frozen from above, and by the time freezing was completed a considerable intrusion of ice would have formed. Drill cores from the margins of some of the ice bodies show that the roof and wall deposits have not only been upheaved and stretched, but also dragged up and penetrated by ice, indicating rheid flow of ice.

The east Greenland pingos grow from the freezing of ground water that originates from the summer melting of snow on high surrounding mountains, so that it has sufficient hydraulic head to penetrate the permafrost zone at lower levels. The mechanism then proceeds as described above. In this region numerous dykes and sills of ice have been found on the margins of pingos.

PATTERNED GROUND

In the northern hemisphere, on flat-lying regions of permafrost where the top layer of mud or stony mud thaws during the summer and is badly drained, polygonal patterns are developed (Fig. 6–16). In their origin these patterns are clearly related to contraction and expansion, but for two reasons the details are

Fig. 6–15
"Crater Summit" Pingo, 136 feet high, 950 feet across its base. East of the delta of the Mackenzie River (69° 50′N; 133°W). (*National Research Council, Division of Building Research, Canada*)

not well understood. First, contraction takes place not only when ice thaws into water, but also when it is cooled well below freezing point. At 0° C the density of ice is 0·92, but at −22° C it is 1·03, corresponding to a decrease in volume of 11 per cent. The second reason for uncertainty is that we cannot be sure that the polygons were initiated under conditions like those of the present day.

The recent discovery of polygonal patterns on flat surfaces of mud and stony mud (morainic material left by glaciers that have retreated) in some of the valleys in Victoria Land, Antarctica, throws new light on the problem (Fig. 6–17). Here there is perennial frost, with little or no thaw, and the cracks outlining the polygons are due to the contraction that accompanies the severe drop in temperature from summer to winter. Snow and perhaps a little thaw water and wind-blown sand fill up the cracks, and after freezing become ice-wedges that grow wider and deeper each year. Wedges up to 10 feet deep are known, surrounding roughly polygonal mounds up to 40 feet across. The annual expansion of the ice wedges in spring and summer is responsible for the domelike hummocks within each polygon (Fig. 6–17).

If we assume that the polygonal patterns

FIG 6–16
Mud polygons of two orders of size near Bruce City, Klaas Billen Bay, Spitsbergen. The mountain avens is growing in gutters that outline the larger polygons. The smaller polygons, outlined by mud cracks, are a seasonal result of summer desiccation and shrinkage. (*J. Walton*)

FIG. 6—17
Frost polygons developed in the moraine mantle covering the floor of a "dry valley" in Victoria Land, Antarctica. Those illustrated average about 30 ft across; they are outlined by peripheral troughs about 2 ft deep. (*P. N. Webb and B. C. McKelvey*)

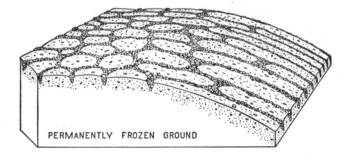

PERMANENTLY FROZEN GROUND

FIG. 6—18
Diagram illustrating the merging of stone rings on a flat surface into stone strips on a slope. (*C. F. Stewart Sharpe. 1938*)

in the regions of permafrost in the northern hemisphere began in the same way as those of Victoria Land, then the diagram (Fig. 4–17) illustrating the formation of columnar jointing as a result of contraction will serve to elucidate the development of the mud and stone polygons. At the present time, however, expansion is the dominant process in most of the northern regions: expansion of summer water to winter ice. Since the only direction of relief is upwards, the tops of the polygons bulge upwards, and in the surrounding gutters many Arctic flowering plants flourish in late spring and summer. If the hummocks temporarily

dry out as a result of summer desiccation, smaller polygons, outlined by mud cracks due to shrinkage, develop in the ordinary way (see Fig. 6–16).

So far the patterned top layer has been considered as consisting only of mud. More commonly, however, it is a mixture of fine and coarse debris and the polygonal hummocks are outlined by stones and known as *stone polygons*. The tendency of stones to work their way upwards to the surface in the stony soils of cool and temperate climates is well known to gardeners. Stones behave in this way because of the differences between their thermal properties and those of the wet soil or mud in which they are embedded. During freezing the under surface of a stone is chilled more quickly than the surrounding wet mud, and the first ice to form is beneath the stone. The expansion, due to ice formation beneath the stone, pushes it upwards. Uplift of stones, or of particles or fragments of any size, is called *frost-heaving*. During the next thaw some of the surface mud drains downwards and, on balance, the stone therefore continues to rise with every major frost and thaw.

In the tundra, frost-heaving is reinforced by the annual upward movement that results in the formation and maintenance of hummocks. When the wet surface mud freezes it expands and pushes upwards and outwards and, assisted by gravity, the stones slowly migrate towards the periphery of the hummocks. There they accumulate as rings or polygons of stones (Fig. 6–18).

On gently sloping ground the pattern made by the stones is roughly elliptical, elongated in the downhill direction. On steeper hillsides alternating stripes of stone and finer debris are formed (Fig. 6–18). The additional factors responsible for this modification are gravity and gullying by melt water. After thaw, water spilling over from the lowest parts of the slightly inclined gutters near the top of the slope forms a series of parallel rivulets into which the drainage is concentrated. Subsequent ice-wedging in the little gullies so formed, and general expansion of the ground between, heaves up the latter into hummocky ridges. As stones reach the surface they tend to migrate down the steepest slope into the gullies where they are concentrated as long stone stripes. These remarkable patterns are the cumulative effects of many thousands of years of frost and thaw.

7
River Action and Valley Development

RIVERS AND THEIR VALLEYS

The necessary conditions for the initiation of a river are an adequate supply of water and a slope down which to flow. As we have already seen, Perrault was the first to discover that an adequate supply is provided by the rainfall. From the result of his pioneer work in the valley of the upper Seine he justly concluded that "rain and snow waters are sufficient to make Fountains and Rivers run perpetually." Rivers are partly fed from ground waters, and some have their source in the melt waters from glaciers, but in both cases the water is derived from the meteoric precipitation. In periods of drought rivers may be kept flowing, though on a diminished scale, entirely by supplies from springs and the zone of intermittent saturation. When these supplies also fail, through the lowering of the water table, as commonly happens in semi-arid regions, rivers dwindle away altogether. However, even then water may still be found not far below the surface where the floors of such intermittent streams have a covering of alluvium.

The initial slopes down which rivers begin to flow are provided by earth movements or, more locally, by volcanic accumulations. Many of the great rivers of the world, *e.g.* the Amazon, Mississippi, and Congo, flow through widespread downwarps of the crust which endowed them with vast ready-made drainage basins from the start. The majority of rivers, however, originated on the sides of uplifted regions where, often in active competition with their neighbours, they gradually evolved their own drainage areas.

Most rivers drain directly into the sea. But in areas of internal drainage permanent or intermittent streams terminate in lakes or swamps which spread or contract so that evaporation just balances the inflow, the conditions being such that the water is unable to accumulate to the level at which it could find an outlet. Notable examples occur in Central Asia and Australia.

The development of a river valley depends on the original surface slope; on the climate, which determines the rainfall; and on the underlying geological structure, which determines the varied resistance to erosion offered by the rocks encountered. Where a newly emergent land provides an initial seaward slope, the rivers which flow down the slope, and the valleys which they excavate, are said to be *consequent*. The valley sides constitute secondary slopes down which tributaries can develop; these streams and their valleys are distinguished as *subsequent*. Later, of course, other generations of tributaries are added. A main river and all its tributaries constitute a river system, and the whole area from which the system derives water and rock waste is its drainage basin. Weathering continuously supplies rock waste, which falls or "creeps", or is washed by rain into the nearest stream. The latter carries away the debris contributed to it, and at the same time acquires still more by eroding its own channel. Valleys develop by the removal of material carried away by the streams which drain them. The load acquired by the main river is ultimately transported out of the basin altogether or deposited in its lower reaches. Deposits of gravel and sand are, of course, dropped on the way at innumerable places, but these are only temporary halts in the journey towards the sea. Rivers are the chief agents concerned in the excavation of valleys, not merely because of their own erosive work, but above all because of their enormous powers of transportation.

When a valley is formed principally by the down-cutting action of a river, it has the form of a vertical-sided cleft. Deep gorges approximating to this form are found where rivers intersect plateaux that have been raised high above sea level; the upward earth movement accelerates the downward cutting action and where the rocks are chemically resistant and mechanically strong a gorge is formed. Glenariff, one of the spectacular Glens of Antrim carved by easterly flowing rivers through the resistant basalt lava flows of the Antrim plateau provides an example (Fig. 7–16). But sooner or later the rate of deepening slows down and widening begins to catch up, and a cross-profile that approximates to a V-shape is produced. In less resistant rocks widening on a more conspicuous scale accompanies deepening from the start.

The valley widening that accompanies the

excavation of river floors obviously implies the wearing back or *recession* of the slopes that lead down to the sides of the river where erosion and transport are taking place. The slopes between two roughly parallel valleys necessarily approach each other as they recede from their respective valley floors. Eventually they meet and form a divide. The latter is then gradually lowered as the slopes continue to be worn back. Meanwhile, each main divide of this kind is itself being sub-divided by the slopes leading down to tributaries of the trunk rivers. Where there are several generations of tributaries, slope retreat comes into operation from several directions at once. Residual landforms are then developed in great variety: mountain peaks and hills; escarpments and ridges; inselbergs, tors, and isolated pinnacles. Each uplifted area is dissected bit by bit into a slowly changing landscape.

Somewhere or other every stage of land-scape development is to be seen, from plateaux representing uplifted plains or sea floors, through mountainous or hilly regions of maximum relief where the country is practic-ally all slopes, to those in which the land has again been reduced to a plain. By direct observation we are thus able to study how valleys gradually develop. We have to con-sider in turn how the lands are eroded and the rivers acquire their load of rock waste; how the rivers themselves erode their channels and transport and deposit their load; how valleys are lengthened, deepened, and widened; and how river systems develop and compete with their neighbours in the struggle for space.

RAIN EROSION

The chief mechanical effect of rain as it pelts down on the mantle of surface materials is to wash loose particles to lower levels. From each miniature crater, made by the impact of rain-drops hundreds of dislodged particles are scattered in a little fountain of spray, and on sloping ground most of these fall a little down-hill. Recent studies of splash erosion have revealed that during a heavy storm up to 100 tons of soil per acre may be shifted. This is less surprising when the energy involved is considered. In such a downpour thousands of millions of raindrops strike an acre of soil with velocities up to 20 miles an hour or so.

Present rates of erosion are excessive because of human interference with the natural cover of the soil—for example, by the widespread clearing of forests and the breaking-up of protective turf by ploughing.

But man is not always the culprit; he may be the victim. A localized cloudburst may con-centrate the run-off into a violent torrent that bites deeply into the turf on sloping ground, sweeping the underlying soil to the foot of the slope, and leaving a long gash in the hillside. The gash is gradually deepened into a gully by recurrent rains, and as soon as the water table is tapped it begins to carry water and becomes a rivulet. This is one of the ways in which tributaries originate or extend their headwaters backwards.

In semi-arid regions, where the occasional rains are often exceptionally violent, rain-gashing reaches spectacular proportions in sloping ground underlain by clay or soft earthly deposits. Such land is sculptured into an intricate pattern of gullies and small ravines, separated by sharp spurs and buttresses. The gullies grow backwards into the adjoining upland, and the intervening ridges in turn are further cut up into smaller ribs and trenches (Fig. 7–1). Tracts of the al-most impassable country so developed are graphically described as *badlands* in North America, where they are widely scattered from Alberta to Arizona.

Curious structures known as *earth-pillars* develop locally from spurs left on the slopes of valleys carved in easily eroded rock con-taining boulders, or similar forms. A boulder or other resistant mass acts like an umbrella over the underlying less resistant materials protecting them from rain erosion, so that, where the slope is sheltered from strong winds, earth pillars of surprising height may be etched out before their protective caps topple off. The earth pillars eroded from volcanic tuff, 150 miles south-east of Ankara, Turkey, are celebrated for the dwellings and monasteries that have been excavated within them. Small examples of earth pillars occur in favourable situations in Scotland and other regions where boulder clay and easily eroded conglomerates are exposed to the weather (Fig. 7–2).

SOIL CREEP AND LANDSLIDES

Between the extremes of rain wash on gentle slopes and rock falls from precipices there are various kinds of mass movements of surface materials downslope, which result from the action in different combinations of water, frost, organisms, and gravity. All these processes co-operate with weathering in widening valleys.

Slow downward movement of soil on hill-sides, known as *soil creep*, is evidenced by tilted fences, piling up of soil against bulging

FIG. 7–1
Fretted erosion into turrets and spines of well-bedded and jointed strata at the head of Bryce Canyon, Utah. (*E. S. Shipp, United States Forest Service*)

FIG. 7–2
Earth pillar of soft conglomerate (Old Red Sandstone), on the valley side of the Allt Dearg, a tributary of the River Spey, above Fochabers, Morayshire. (*H.M. Geological Survey*)

FIG. 7–3
Soil creep, showing the over-
turning of the cleavage of
Cambrian slates, near St.
Davids, Pembrokeshire. (*W.
Jerome Harrison*)

walls, and the curving of tree trunks near the ground. Creep, a downhill migration, is the cumulative effect of innumerable tiny displacements of grains and particles in response to gravity. Rain and wind erosion, frost heaving, expansion and contraction whether due to temperature changes or to soaking and drying, the displacement of fine particles to the surface by burrowing animals, and the growth and decay of roots, all aid in loosening materials and downslope movement. Even the subsoil and the upper parts of the bedrock share in this movement. The upper ends of steeply dipping or cleaved beds are prised apart by frost and rootlets until they gradually curve over in the downhill direction (Fig. 7–3). This results in apparent dips which, exposed in cuttings and gullies, may depart considerably from those of the undisturbed formation.

When soil becomes water-logged, as happens particularly in colder climates and at high altitudes after the melting of snow, the downward creep passes into actual flow and is then described as *solifluction* (soil flow). *Mud flows* are similar phenomena which occur when materials like clay or shale become over-saturated with water and so dilated that they become "quick" (*i.e.* like a quicksand) and readily flow as a whole. They may transport debris, including large blocks of fallen rock. The danger of potential mud flows is il-lustrated by the flow, as sludge, of an oversaturated tip heap down the hillside at Aberfan in 1966, burying the infant school with great loss of life. Many of the so-called landslides along railway cuttings in the London Clay are mud flows of this type. The *bog bursts* of Ireland and similar regions of peat bogs are closely related to mud flows. Where peat is the infilling of a former shallow lake, water may percolate along or near the underlying rock surface during long-continued rain and find no exit. It then accumulates at some level within the peat bog or between it and the bedrock, and the bog swells up until something gives way. If it bursts externally, as occasionally happens, a deluge of muddy peat flows over the surrounding countryside.

The same group of processes operating in screes leads to similar results. Moreover, screes become bodily unstable as fragments fed from above gradually steepen the slopes. After a thorough soaking and lubrication by water from rain or melting snow, the weight is increased, while friction and the angle of repose (normally 25°–35°) are decreased. The scree thereupon begins to slide as a *rock avalanche* or *debris avalanche*. In regions of vigorous relief, like the Himalayas, rock avalanches sometimes occur on a gigantic scale and the valley below may be dammed across. A lake then forms on the upstream side and, bursting suddenly through the wall of debris, may cause a disastrous flood. In sub-arctic regions, where frost and thaw are especially active, *rock glaciers* spread outwards on suitable slopes.

It is a matter of common observation that steep grassy river banks are often scored at intervals with little *terracettes* or "sheep tracks" in the soil, particularly where the stream undercuts and steepens the banks. These features are due to small landslips which, as they are of frequent occurrence, contribute largely to the removal of mantle deposits. The

essential conditions are lack of support in front and a slip surface. Similar conditions favour *landslides* on a bigger scale, wherever sliding (Fig. 7–4) or slumping (Fig. 7–5) can occur on the sides of undercut slopes, precipices, and cliffs, or of road, railway, and canal cuttings, particularly where heavy massive rocks (*e.g.* plateau basalt) overlie weak and easily lubricated formations. Slumping takes place on a curved slip plane, and a backward tilting of the surface often results. Sliding occurs when bedding and cleavage planes, fault fractures, or joints dip towards a valley or other

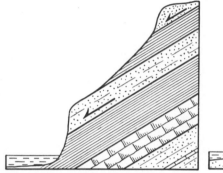

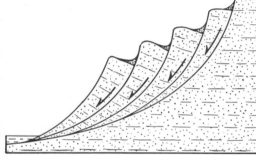

FIG. 7–4. (Far left) Diagram illustrating conditions favouring landslides on bedding planes after lubrication by rain.

FIG. 7–5 Diagram illustrating slumping on curved surfaces in unconsolidated or other weak formations; showing characteristic back-tilting at the surface.

FIG. 7–6 The "tools" of a river left stranded in dry weather. Valley cut in boulder clay, Anglezark Moor, east of Chorley, Lancashire. (*H.M. Geological Survey*)

depression at a dangerous angle, as near Glenarm on the Antrim coast road. The catastrophically heavy rainfall of August 1952 over Exmoor, chiefly remembered for the disaster it brought to the little town of Lynmouth (p. 105), also caused dozens of landslips into the Exe and neighbouring streams. The wet summer of 1960 provoked landslips and debris slides along the river banks of a wide region extending from Dartmoor and the New Forest to the Severn and the Trent.

EROSION AND TRANSPORT BY RIVERS

The work of river erosion is accomplished in four different ways, all of which actively cooperate.

(*a*) *Corrosion* is the solvent and chemical action of the water of the stream on the materials with which it comes into contact.

(*b*) *Hydraulic action* is the mechanical loosening and removal of materials by water alone. Flowing water can sweep away loose deposits and wash out particles from weakly resistant sediment. A river may not acquire much new material by sluicing its channel, but the coarser part of the load is likely to be dropped over and over again during transit (Fig. 7–6), and each time it has to be picked up afresh by the lifting force provided by turbulence before transport can proceed. Where the current is strong enough, as when a river is in spate, water may be driven under jointed slabs with sufficient force to hoist them up, turn them over, and so make them available for transport.

(*c*) *Corrasion* is the wearing away of the sides and floor with the aid of the boulders, pebbles, sand, and silt which are being transported. By scour and impact, with such tools, even the hardest bedrocks are excavated and smoothed. The drilling of *pot-holes* is one of the most potent methods of down-cutting. These develop in the depressions of rocky channels or from hollows where boulders and pebbles, acting like drilling tools, are rapidly swirled round by eddies (Fig. 7–7). Vertical holes are cut deeply into the rock as the water plunges in and keeps the drilling tools in action by its spiral motion. As the boulders wear away, and are swept out with the finer materials, new ones take their place and carry on the work. In front of a waterfall very large pot holes may develop in the floor of the

FIG. 7–7
Pot hole drilled in Tertiary basalt, Glenariff, Co. Antrim, Northern Ireland. (*R. Welch*)

"plunge pool." This leads to deepening of the channel, and at the same time a combination of hydraulic action and corrasion undermines the ledge of the fall. The eddying spray behind the fall itself is particularly effective in scouring out the less resistant formations that underlie the ledge (Fig. 7–14). Blocks of the ledge are then left unsupported and break off at intervals, thus causing a migration of the fall in an upstream direction, and leaving a gorge in front (Fig. 7–15).

(*d*) *Attrition* is the wear and tear suffered by the transported materials themselves, whereby they are broken down, smoothed, and rounded. The smaller fragments and the finer particles liberated as by-products are then more easily carried away.

The solid part of the load carried by a river includes the rock waste supplied to it by rain wash, surface creep, slump, and so on, and by tributaries and external agents such as glaciers and the wind, together with that acquired by its own erosive work, as described above. The debris is transported in various ways. The smaller particles are carried with the stream in suspension, the tendency to settle being counterbalanced by eddies. Larger particles, which settle at intervals and are then swirled up again, skip along in a series of jumps. Pebbles and boulders roll or slide along the bottom, according to their shapes. Very large blocks may move along on a layer of cobbles which act like ball bearings.

If the supply of debris exceeds the load that can be transported, or if the velocity of a river is checked, part of the material is left behind or deposited on the river bed, to be picked up later when the stream is running more vigorously. Each time, the largest ingredients of the load are the first to be dropped, and the finest are the first to be moved on again. In this way a river sorts out its burden, and from source to mouth the deposited materials gradually change in type from coarse to fine.

The transporting power of a stream rises very rapidly as the velocity increases. Experiments show that with debris of mixed shapes and sizes the load that can be carried by running water is proportional to something between the third and fourth power of the velocity. But for fragments of a given shape,

FIG. 7–8
The maelstrom of destruction in the bottleneck of Lynmouth. (*Syndication International*)

the largest size that can be moved is proportional to the sixth power of the velocity. Very large boulders which may remain stationary in the stream bed for long periods can thus be lifted and carried downstream by exceptionally swollen torrents. The almost incredible power of rivers in spate was tragically shown by the disaster that befell the North Devon seaside resort of Lynmouth in 1952. As a result of a downpour of 9 inches of rain in 24 hours on Exmoor, when much of the ground was already water-logged, the run-off became far greater than could be carried away through the existing channels. Part of the overflow from the West Lyn river concentrated itself into a new course, and tearing its way down the hillside, as a raging cataract, burst through the little town before rejoining its original channel. Roads, houses, and bridges were demolished; service pipes and cables were destroyed; 40,000 tons of boulders, uprooted trees and soil, and great masses of collapsed masonry were churned up together in a bottle-neck entanglement (Fig. 7–8). Lynmouth, however, adequately safeguarded, remained unscathed during the phenomenal floods of 1960.

In addition to their solid load, rivers transport a great deal of material in solution, most of which is contributed to them by surface and underground drainage waters. The proportions of dissolved and solid load vary enormously from place to place and from time to time. Taking all the chief rivers of the world over representative periods of years, it appears that on an average about 8,000 million tons of the products of rock waste are transferred to the sea each year, and that about 30 per cent of this total is carried in solution. The drainage areas are at present being worn down at an average rate of one foot in about 9,000 years, or 1 metre in 30,000 years, but the average rates for individual regions range from a foot in 400 years for the Irrawaddy basin to a foot in 47,000 years for the low-lying basins draining into Hudson Bay.

The long profile of a river, along its length from mouth to source, begins at sea level, or just below it if the profile is that of the river bed, and rises inland. The profile of a youthful river is likely to be more or less irregular, in conformity with the slopes and undulations of the initial surface and the nature of the rocks being eroded. Characteristic features of youth are lakes and swamps, waterfalls and rapids. However, all but the greatest of these irregularities, such as deep lakes, are destined to be smoothed out as the river matures.

In humid regions, starting on an initial surface with a general slope towards the sea, down-cutting of a river bed is dominant along its middle reaches. The effect is to steepen the gradient of the stretch leading down from the source, and to decrease the gradient from the middle reaches to the sea. Given ample time and no critical disturbances by earth movements or changes of climate, the profile is systematically modified until it approximates to a smooth curve, gently concave to the sky, practically flat at the mouth and steepening towards the source. When a river, or a particular stretch of a river, has such a profile it is said to be *graded* (Fig. 7–9).

Downward erosion of the valley floor does not cease when a river is graded, although it is negligible near the mouth and becomes slower and slower through the graded stretch as time goes on. Consequently the graded profile can be slowly flattened out. Base level, always being approached but never quite attained, is its only downward limit.

The level of the main river at the point where a tributary enters acts as a *local base level* for that tributary. In the uninterrupted development of a river system graded tributaries thus become so adjusted to the main stream that they join it tangentially, or nearly so. When tributaries fail to behave in this way the absence of adjustment is a clear indication that the cycle of erosion has been interrupted by changes of slope due, as a rule, to earth move-

FIG. 7–9
Diagram to show the relation between base level and an idealized graded profile. (*After R. S. Tarr and O. D. von Engeln*)

BASE LEVEL   GRADED PROFILE OF RIVER BED

GRADING OF RIVERS

Since a river which flows into the sea must have a gradient towards the sea, the deepening of a valley is necessarily limited by sea level. An imaginary extension of sea level under the land is called the *base level* of river erosion.

ments or to glaciation. The waterfalls from "hanging valleys" on the sides of deeply glaciated valleys (Fig. 9–20) are extreme examples of such lack of adjustment.

Various irregularities in a river channel may

postpone the general establishment of grade, although above and below these features individual reaches of the river may be temporarily graded to the local base levels controlling them. A lake, for example, acts as a local base level for the streams discharging into it. Lakes that occupy deep depressions have a very long life, but shallow ones are, geologically speaking, soon eliminated. A lake is a trap for sediments and so destined to be silted up by deltaic outgrowths from inflowing streams. At the same time the outflowing water erodes the outlet and lowers its level, so that the lake is partly drained and its area reduced (Fig. 7–10). Ultimately the lake is replaced by a broad lacustrine flat through which the river flows (Fig. 7–11). Down-cutting through the sediments and underlying rock floor then

proceeds until continuity of grade is established between the upper and lower reaches of the river. In the Lake District lakes can be seen in every stage of elimination, together with lacustrine flats in which young valleys are already being developed.

A resistant formation encountered by a river also retards the establishment of grade and acts as a temporary base level for the stream above until it is cut through by waterfalls and rapids. The latter persist so long as the outcrop of obstructive rock remains out of grade with the graded reaches in the softer rocks exposed above and below.

WATERFALLS

Where an outcrop of resistant rock is under-

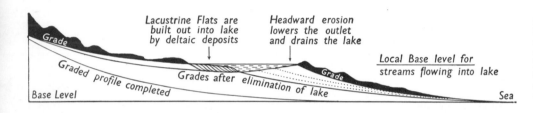

FIG. 7–10
Diagram to illustrate the elimination of a lake by sedimentation at the inlets and headwater erosion at the outlet. Successive positions of graded profiles before and after elimination are shown.

FIG. 7–11
Infilling of a lake by sedimentation. Head of Derwentwater viewed from the Wathendlath patch, English Lake District. (*G. P. Abraham Ltd, Keswick*)

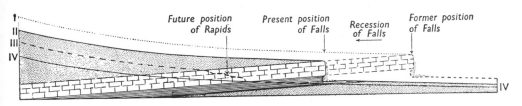

Future position of Rapids   Present position of Falls   Recession of Falls   Former position of Falls

FIG. 7–12
Successive stages in the recession and elimination of a waterfall:
I Profile of stream (drawn as graded) above an early position of the falls
II Profile above present falls
III Future profile after degeneration of the falls into rapids
IV Future profile (graded throughout) after elimination of falls and rapids

lain downstream by a weaker formation, the latter is relatively quickly worn down, and the resistant bed is undercut. At the junction, and subsequently above it, the river bed is steepened and the stream rushes down the slope as a *rapid*. If the face of the resistant rock becomes vertical, the stream plunges over the crest as a *waterfall*. The processes which bring about recession and gorge development have been described (pp. 103–4). Waterfalls eventually degenerate into rapids as the profile begins to approach grade (Fig. 7–12). A fall that descends in a series of leaps is sometimes referred to as a *cascade*. An exceptional volume of water is implied by the term *cataract*, which may be applied either to waterfalls or, more commonly, to steep rapids. Rapids are favoured throughout the wearing down of an obstructive formation if its dip is downstream or steeply upstream.

Where a bed of strong rock, horizontal or gently inclined upstream, overlies weaker beds the former is the "fall-maker", and

scouring of the latter leads to undermining and recession. At High Force in Teesdale the tough and well-jointed Whin Sill is the fall-maker. In the Yorkshire dales falls are commonly developed over ledges of carboniferous limestone underlain by shale. The *Niagara Falls* are the classic example of this type (Fig. 7–13). As shown in Fig. 7–14 the river plunges over a thick ledge of limestone. The American Falls (frontage, 1,060 feet; 323 m) are separated from the Canadian or Horseshoe Falls (frontage, 2,800 feet; 853 m) by Goat Island. The mean flow, before the diversion of much of the water to hydroelectric plants, was eighty-five times that of the Thames at Teddington. Most of the water passes over the Horseshoe Falls which, as their name implies, are receding much more rapidly than the American Falls. After the withdrawal of the last great ice sheet, and the uncovering of the pre-glacial Niagara escarpment about 12,000 years ago, the Niagara river descended from Lake Erie (572 feet; 174 m) to Lake Ontario (246 feet; 75 m) by way of a series of

FIG. 7–13
General view of the Niagara Falls looking southwards. The American Falls on the left are separated from the Canadian or Horseshoe Falls by Goat Island. (*Photographic Survey Corporation Ltd. Toronto*)

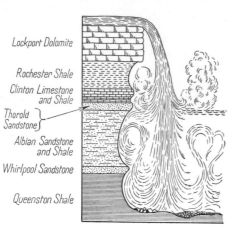

Lockport Dolomite

Rochester Shale

Clinton Limestone
and Shale

Thorold
Sandstone

Albian Sandstone
and Shale

Whirlpool Sandstone

Queenston Shale

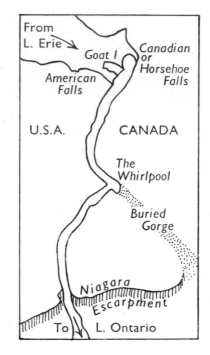

FIG. 7–14 (Far left)
Section across the Niagara
Falls showing the sequence
of hard and soft formations
and illustrating the mechanism
of recession by undercutting,
and the erosion of the river bed
in the "plunge pool" beneath
the falling column of turbulent
water.

FIG. 7–15
Sketch map of the Niagara
Falls and the seven-mile gorge
cut by headwater recession
since the Niagara River fell
over the Niagara Escarpment
about 9,000 years ago: looking
southwards as in Fig. 7–13.
The Whirlpool is scoured out of
glacial drift which now fills the
Buried Gorge of an earlier
"Niagara River".

rapids and one big vertical drop where the river fell over the escarpment. Here the falls began, and since then they have receded 7 miles (11 km), leaving a gorge of which the rim is about 200 feet (61 m) above the river and on average about 360 feet (110 m) above the river floor (Fig. 7–15). The rate of recession must have varied a good deal from time to time, but the measured rate for the Horseshoe Falls during the nineteenth century—about 4 feet (1·2 m) a year—is not far from the average of 3 feet a year (0·9m). Now, hydro-electric stations and the St Lawrence Seaway have greatly reduced the flow of water over the falls. Even so, the falls will recede until Lake Erie is reached and partly drained—an event too many thousands of years ahead to cause any present anxiety.

Uplifted areas of plateau basalts may provide the structural conditions for a long series of falls. The strong and compact internal parts of the flows make ideal ledges, which are undermined by the more rapid removal of the far less resistant vesicular or amygdaloidal margins. The many falls of Glenariff, where the river is vigorously descending step by step through Tertiary basalts of the Antrim plateau, provide outstandingly varied and exhilarating scenic attractions (Fig. 7–16).

MEANDERS AND VALLEY WIDENING

Valleys widened in homogeneous rocks characteristically have a V-shaped cross-profile which opens out more quickly in soft rocks than in hard, and this effect controls the form of the profile at all levels. Thus, in a valley carved through a series of alternating hard and soft beds the sides rise by slopes which are steep and precipitous where the edge of a hard band outcrops; terraced across the exposed tops of such a band; and of intermediate gradient where the rocks are less resistant. The Grand Canyon of the Colorado River, in Arizona, which during about 21 million years of complex history has become entrenched in a rising landscape, clearly illustrates this dependence of cross-profile on structure (Fig. 7–17).

Widening of valleys by the wearing back of the sides (slope retreat) is accomplished by a great variety of processes, most of which have already been described: these include rain wash and gullying; soil creep, slumping, and landslides; chemical weathering and leaching by ground waters; and the removal of loose material by wind. To these processes must be added the general co-operation of incoming tributaries, which widen the main valley where they enter it, and the work of the rivers them-

FIG. 7–16
"Tears of the Glen" waterfall, Glenariff, Co. Antrim, Northern Ireland. (*Northern Ireland Tourist Board*)

selves in extending their channels sideways and so widening the valley floors at the expense of the pre-existing valley sides. It is with this latter process that we are here most concerned.

Youthful streams are rarely straight for any distance, but tend to follow a winding course which, at one time, was thought to depend in the first instance on variations in the properties of the rocks encountered (Fig. 7–18). Work

with experimental streams in long tanks has revealed, however, that a stream will wind without the physical aids and restraints imposed by the different kinds of rocks over which it flows. An experimental stream which begins by flowing down a straight channel on a uniform slope of uniform sediment is always found to modify its channel by erosion and deposition so that it develops a series of

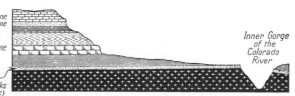

FIG. 7–17
Section across the Grand Canyon of the Colorado River at Grand Canyon Station, Arizona. Scale 1 inch = 1 mile (horizontal and vertical). (*After Darton*)

109

FIG. 7–18
Steep-sided youthful valley
with overlapping spurs, Cross-
dale Beck, Ennerdale, English
Lake District. (*H.M. Geological Survey*)

roughly symmetrical bends, like a sine curve (Fig. 7–19). This curious behaviour is, in fact, a direct consequence of the general principle that when one medium moves over another the plane of contact tends to assume a wave-like form. A light breeze blowing across a smooth sea ruffles the surface into ripples that quickly rise into waves as the wind increases. Wind blowing over loose sand builds up sand dunes with which the whole surface becomes rippled. The backwash of sea waves down the slope of a beach leaves a characteristic surface of ripple marks. Similarly water flowing over and against earth or rock serpentines, and the freely developing lateral curves are called *meanders* from their prevalence in the classic river Meander, the Menderes of today, in the south-west of Turkey.

When an experimental stream first flows down a gently sloping straight channel floored with sand, it oscillates up and down, and sideways. Along its floor, hollows and shoals develop, corresponding to the down and up oscillations. Moreover, the shoals are alternately built up a little to one side and a little to the other of the middle line: an indication of the sideways oscillations. This change in the floor affects the flow of the stream, which begins to swing from side to side. The main current winds round the outside of the shoals first on one side and then on the other and so on. Wherever the current impinges against the banks of the stream, lateral erosion occurs and bends are started. In this way the channel develops a serpentine form as seen in plan in Fig. 7–19. The distribution of shoals and hollows is now controlled by the swing of the current. As the curvature of a bend is increased by lateral erosion, the channel on the outside is deepened by vertical erosion, while on the inside it is shallowed by deposition (Figs. 7–20 and 7–21). In a model stream (Fig. 7–19) successive wave lengths, 2–2′, 3–3′, 4–4′, gradually lengthen and the bends themselves migrate downstream. This migration steadily continues, but the wave length gradually adjusts itself to a maximum of about 10 times the width of the channel.

The changes in a river channel and valley may be summarized in a general way as follows:

(*a*) The channel is deepened on the outer side of each bend, and particularly along the downstream part of the bend.

(*b*) The outer bank is worn back and undercut by lateral erosion, and the slopes above are locally steepened into river cliffs or "bluffs". At the same time banks of shingle or sand are built out on the inner side (Fig. 7–22).

(*c*) As the bends are thus widened by lateral erosion and deepened by downward erosion on the outside, and built out and shallowed on the inside, the river shifts its channel not only towards the outer bank but also downwards (Fig. 7–23). Eventually this oblique migration of the channel leaves gently rounded slip-off slopes on the inside of the growing curves; classic examples are those of the Rhine and of the Wye. In cross-profile the valley, as well as the channel floor, has become highly asymmetrical at every bend.

(*d*) Since each bend is increasingly enlarged in the downstream direction, it gradually migrates downstream in serpentine fashion.

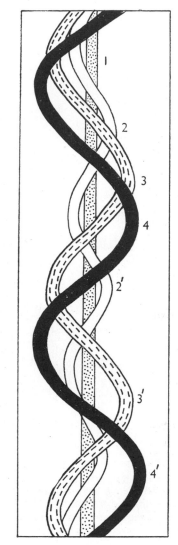

FIG. 7–19
Successive stages (1, 2, 3, 4) in the experimental development of incipient meanders in a model stream flowing in a bed of uniform sediment. The meanders migrate downstream and the wavelength (2 to 2′; 3 to 3′; 4 to 4′) increases until it is about ten times the width of the channel when full up to the brim.

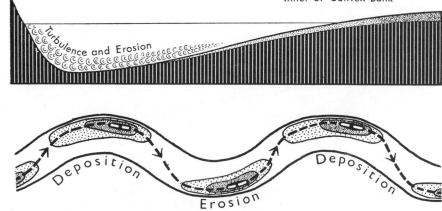

FIG. 7–20
Section across the bend of a river to show the asymmetrical profile due, on balance, to erosion on the outside and deposition on the inside. In floods, turbulence and erosion extend to the inner bank.

FIG. 7–21
Diagram illustrating erosion and deposition along a meandering stream. Depth of water is indicated by depth of shading. The broken line indicates the axis of flow under normal conditions. With rising water the axis widens into a belt that may extend to the convex banks and remove some of the alluvium previously deposited there.

FIG. 7–22
Alluvial deposits built out on the inside of a river bend, seen when the river is low. Glen Feshie, Inverness-shire. (*H.M. Geological Survey*)

Thus, the changes in a river channel are three-dimensional: downwards (vertical erosion); sideways (lateral erosion); and along (downstream migration of bends). At an early stage, when there are overlapping spurs, like those illustrated in Fig. 7–18, each spur is eroded and undercut every time it is reached by the outer part of a migrating bend. Eventually, as bend after bend migrates downstream, the spurs are all trimmed off. Similarly the slip-off slopes are all cut back, the valley is widened and a nearly flat trough-like valley floor is developed. The alluvial deposits extend in continuous stretches, with broad embayments bounded by bluffs or hills (Fig. 7–24).

The beginnings of a flood plain have been established (p. 114).

OX-BOW LAKES AND MEANDER BELTS

As the river continues to swing from side to side of its valley floor, it undercuts the bluffs wherever a bend impinges upon them, and so the widening of the valley floor proceeds, while the slopes above are slowly wasting away and receding. The channel is now mainly in river deposits, bedrock (if any) being exposed only in and below the bluffs. Each part of the material deposited on the growing flood plain is worked over in turn

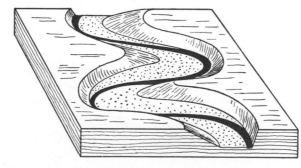

FIG. 7–23
Diagrammatic representation of widening and deepening of a valley floor by oblique erosion (lateral and vertical) on the outside of river bends, combined with downstream migration of the bends. The swinging stream eventually trims off the overlapping spurs and slip-off slopes.

FIG. 7–24
The meander belt of the River Glass, a flat-bottomed trough-like valley floor veneered with alluvium. Strath Glass, Inverness-shire. (*H.M. Geological Survey*)

during the downward sweep of the bends, fresh additions from above constantly making good the losses by erosion and transport. The bends, now free to develop in any direction, except where they encounter the valley side, are more quickly modified. Consequently many meanders continue to swell out into broad loops with gradually narrowing necks. If a flood occurs when only a narrow neck of land is left between adjoining loops, the momentum of the increased flow is likely to carry the stream across the neck and thus short-circuit its course. On the side of the "cut-off" a deserted channel is left, forming an *ox-bow* lake (Fig. 7–25), which soon degenerates into a swamp as it is silted up by later floods. By making artificial cut-offs the Mississippi River Commission has straightened long stretches of the river and so shortened transport distances, both by road and river, up to as much as several hundred miles.

The relics of many ox-bows, indicating the positions of abandoned meanders, may no longer be obvious topographic features on the ground. But their outlines can be clearly seen from the air (Fig. 7–26). This is because the soil and drainage of the former ox-bow lakes differ from that of ordinary river alluvium, and result in different vegetation. Ox-bow

FIG. 7–25
Successive stages in the development of meanders, showing the formation of an ox-bow lake by the "cut-off" of a loop.

FIG. 7—26
Meandering stream with numerous ox-bow lakes and many that have been infilled with sediment and more or less obscured by vegetation. NE. of Jesselton on the NW. coast of North Borneo now Sabah. (*Ministry of Defence* (*Air Force Department*), *Crown Copyright reserved*)

FIG. 7—27
Schematic section across the flood plain of a stream bordered by natural levees. Vertical scale greatly exaggerated.

lakes and their overgrown relics provide the most convincing evidence of the downstream migration of meanders.

The bordering slopes of the valley are cut back every time an individual meander impinges against them and so the valley floor continues to widen. After an immensely long period of time, with no important earth movements or climatic changes, the valley floor may have become several times as wide as the meander belt. This is because the meander belt has become "free", and the belt itself "meanders" to and fro across the widening flood plain, swinging down towards the sea in curves of much longer and more variable wave length than those of the actual stream. It should be noticed that while lowering of the channel floor is limited by base level, there is no such restriction on erosion of the banks: Widening can therefore continue long after significant lowering has ceased.

FLOOD PLAINS

As flood plains develop by the sweeping of meanders to and fro down the valley floor, and later perhaps by the swinging of the meander belt itself, the valley floor widens and the slip-off slopes become nearly flat. The flood plain may then have only a relatively thin veneer of mud and silt, generally with an underlying deposit of sand and gravel, covering a planed off surface of bedrock. This rock surface results from the slight erosion that occurs each time the bedrock is uncovered at the deepest part of a meander loop which has reached the bordering bluffs (Fig. 7—20).

Deposits left on the flood plain by flood water outside the actual channel are generally very thin, except adjacent to the river banks. Each time the river overflows its banks the current is checked at the margin of the

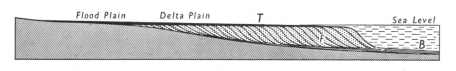

FIG. 7–28
Idealized section through the sediments of an arcuate delta. T, topset beds; F, foreset beds; B, bottomset beds.

channel, and the coarsest part of the load is dropped there. Thus, a low embankment or *levee* is built up on each side (Fig. 7–27). Beyond the levees the ground slopes down, and in consequence is liable to be marshy. During floods, levees may grow across the junctions of small tributaries. The latter are then obliged to follow a meandering course of their own, often for many miles, before they find a new entrance into the main river. Depressions occupied on the way become ponds which degenerate into swamps. The characteristic features of the flood plain of a meandering river include ox-bow lakes and marshes, levees, swamps and shallow lakes, and a complicated pattern of lateral streams.

Levees afford protection from ordinary floods, but the river then begins to silt up its confined channel with material that would otherwise have been spread as alluvium over the plain. Its level is raised, and the levees grow up with it, so that the danger from major floods becomes greater than before. To obtain increased protection artificial levees are often built, but these provide only temporary security, since they accentuate the tendency of the river floor to rise. In the flood plains of the Po in Italy and of the Hwang Ho and Yangtze Kiang in China the built-up levees are locally higher than the neighbouring house tops, and the rivers flow at a level well above that of the adjoining land. Such conditions are obviously extremely dangerous, as a severe flood may break through the levee and bring disaster to the agricultural lands over an enormous area.

Along the Mississippi and its tributaries the flood danger is a serious menace. Little more than a century ago floods were easily controlled by levees about four feet high. The levees have since had to be raised several times. By 1927 they were three or four times as high, but nevertheless a great flood then broke through and devastated about 20,000 square miles. Stronger levees up to 20 or 30 feet high have now been built, but it is clear that this method of flood control is far from satisfactory by itself. It can, however, be supplemented by reafforesting the upland regions (to reduce the rate of run-off), as is proposed for widespread areas in northern Italy since the disasterous flooding of Florence and the Po valley in 1966; by the straightening

and dredging of river channels; and by the allocation of certain areas as storage reservoirs for flood water. The destructive flooding of the Mississippi valley in 1951, and of the Po valley and Florence in 1966, resulted from exceptionally heavy rainfall: like the Lynmouth disaster (p. 105) of 1952, but over much greater areas.

Eventually, as a result of continued widening of flood plains, at the expense of intervening divides, adjacent flood plains may coalesce and form a type of old age surface that has been called a *panplain* (C. H. Crickmay).

DELTAS

When a river reaches the sea much of its load may be quickly deposited, partly because the current is checked and partly because the salt water coagulates the fine particles. The sediment thus settles more rapidly than in fresh water. Waves and currents, however, may be sufficiently strong to sweep away the material and so prevent the mouth from being silted up.

On the other hand, if tides and currents are weak, as in enclosed seas like the Mediterranean and the Black Sea, deposition takes place at the mouth of the river so that a broad, outward-sloping fan of sediment is gradually built up on the sea floor. The front of each part of the fan grows seawards, and the flood plain gradually extends seawards across its flat top (Fig. 7–28). Having blocked its only means of exit, the river breaks through, so making new channels which then proceed to obstruct themselves in the same way. Eventually a system of branching *distributaries* is formed. The resulting seaward-growing terrace of sediment, traversed by distributaries, is a *delta*.

The Delta of the Nile was the first to be so named, because its shape resembles the Greek letter Δ. It is the prototype of the *arcuate type* of deltas. It has an arc-like outer edge, modified by fringing sand spits shaped by marine currents (Fig. 7–29). After traversing a thousand miles of desert, the Nile has comparatively little water left when it reaches the apex of the delta. Much of the load is deposited before the water reaches the sea and frontal growth of the delta is correspondingly slow. Such continued accumulation of sediment is possible only because the region is subsiding. Subsidence must, indeed, have been in progress here for a very long time, since seismic exploration has revealed a thickness of at least 10,000 feet of poorly consolidated sediment. The Po delta extends more rapidly. Adria, now 14 miles inland, was a seaport 1,850 years ago, the average rate of advance thus indicated being about 1 mile in 120 years. Ostia, the seaport of ancient Rome, is now 4 miles from the mouth of the Tiber. The richly fertile delta of the Hwang Ho in North China has grown across what was originally a broad

bay of the Yellow Sea. A large island, now the Shantung peninsula, has been half surrounded. Since 1852 the main branch of the river has emptied to the north of Shantung, but before then if flowed across the southern section of the delta and reached the sea about 300 miles from its present mouth (Fig. 7–30). In that year and again in 1887 there were calamitous floods in which the loss of life from drowning and famine amounted to many hundreds of thousands.

Most deltas, like those mentioned above, are arcuate, and the composite 200-mile wide Mississippi delta plain, when considered as a

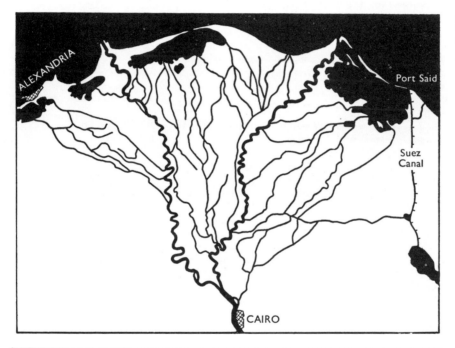

FIG. 7–29
The Nile Delta; classic example of the arcuate type.

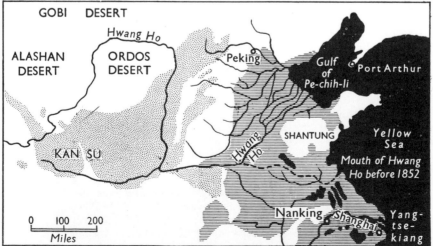

FIG. 7–30
Map of the Hwang Ho and its delta, showing the distribution of loess (dotted) and alluvium (horizontal shading) derived from loess. (*After G. B. Cressey*)

whole, conforms to this pattern. The Mississippi, however, reaches the sea via a peninsula-like extension from the delta plain, and extends its distributaries seawards, above the main delta, the surface of which is below sea-level, by way of channels, locally called "passes" which project into the Gulf of Mexico like outstretched fingers. This is the chief example of the *bird's-foot type* of delta (Fig. 7–31). The sediment brought down by the Mississippi is rich in fine mud and this is deposited mainly along the sides of the distributaries where levees are built up, whilst sand bars are built seawards from the mouths of the distributaries and so lengthen the bird's feet.

ALLUVIAL FANS AND CONES

Many youthful mountain ranges and plateaux descend steeply to the neighbouring lowlands:

commonly because they are bounded by eroded fault scarps. Where a heavily laden stream reaches the plain after flowing swiftly through a ravine or canyon, its velocity is checked by the abrupt change of gradient, it widens out, and drops much of its load of sediment. The deposited sediment spreads out as an *alluvial fan* and the obstructed stream, as in delta formation, may divide into an interlacing network of distributaries with shoals and islands of shingle and sand between. The river is then said to be *braided*.

In other circumstances, particularly in arid or semi-arid regions, most of the water sinks into the porous alluvium and the rest evaporates, so that the whole of the load is dropped. The sediment then piles up and builds an *alluvial cone* (Fig. 7–32). There are all gradations from wide fans, 10 to 100 miles (16 to 160 km) across, that are usually nearly flat (slopes less than 1°), through fans of

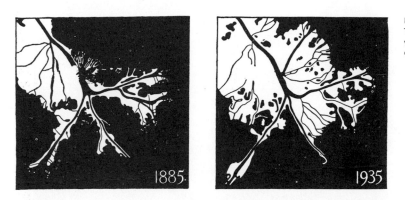

FIG. 7–31
The Mississippi Delta: fifty years' growth. Classic example of the bird's-foot type.

FIG. 7–32
Alluvial cones at the mouths of canyons in southern Utah. (*After C. E. Dutton, United States Geological Survey*)

moderate width and inclination (4° − 6°), to relatively small steep-sided cones (up to 15°) built of the coarser debris brought down by torrential streams. Where closely spaced streams discharge from a mountainous region across a *piedmont* (a mountain-foot lowland), their deposits may eventually coalesce to form a *piedmont alluvial plain*.

All these features are well displayed in western America: along the eastern base of Rockies, where the Front Range faces the Great Plains; along the eastern edge of the Sierra Nevada, where the eroded fault scarp slopes down to the Great Basin; and in many other similar situations on the flanks of the block mountains of the Great Basin. They are also developed on a large scale at the foot of the Himalayas and the Andes. Where there is a lake along or near the foot of the slope, an alluvial fan begun on the land passes into a delta which grows across the lake. Familiar examples which have divided what were originally single lakes into two are the fan deltas of Buttermere in the English Lake District, separating Buttermere from Crummock Water (Fig. 7–33), and of Interlaken in Switzerland, separating Lake Thun from Lake Brienz. A fan delta has spread into the sea at Lynmouth, where the East and West Lyn rivers rapidly descend from the plateau which they drain (Fig. 7–34).

FIG. 7–33
Buttermere and Crummock Water illustrating the division of a lake into two by the growth of a fan delta. (*G. P. Abraham Ltd. Keswick*)

FIG. 7–34
Lynton and Lynmouth, North Devon, showing the plateau drained and eroded by the East and West Lyn rivers, and the fan delta built into the Bristol Channel at their common outlet. (*Aerofilms Ltd*)

8
Development of River Systems and Associated Landforms

TRIBUTARIES AND DRAINAGE PATTERNS

A consequent stream is one whose original course is determined by the initial slopes of a new land surface. From a volcanic cone or an uplifted dome the first streams flow off radially. A long upwarp or geanticline provides a linear crest—the primary watershed or divide—with slopes on each side. In many cases the uplifted area consists of a coastal plain backed by an older land already drained by rivers. These continue down the new surface as *extended consequents*. If there is no "old land", the consequents begin some way below the crest, at each point where the drainage from above just suffices to initiate and maintain a stream. As the valley head widens and increased drainage is secured, each such stream is progressively lengthened

by headward erosion. If uplift continues, the consequent streams are correspondingly lengthened by seaward extension.

As the consequents dig themselves in, the valley sides furnish secondary slopes down which tributaries can flow. The tributaries lengthen by headward erosion, which picks out the least resistant parts of the rocks encountered, such as jointed or fractured belts, or beds of clay or shale. Subject to a general tendency to flow at right angles to the contours of the consequent valley, the pattern formed by tributaries and consequents thus depends largely on the nature and structure of the rocks which are being dissected. The latter may be homogeneous through a considerable depth, or they may consist of a stratified

FIG. 8—1
Aerial view of the dendritic drainage developed by insequent streams on massive granite. Tributaries of the Orange River near Aughrabies Falls, South Africa. (*South African Air Force*)

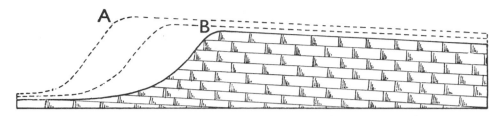

FIG. 8–2
Diagram illustrating the recession of a watershed from A to B as a result of the effect of unequal slopes on rates of erosion.

series of alternating strong and weak beds.

Where the rocks have no conspicuous grain and offer nearly uniform resistance to erosion, the headward growth of a tributary is governed primarily by the initial regional slope, with modifications controlled by chance irregularities of surface and structure. Because of these accidental controls such streams are said to be *insequent*. The regional slope, however, generally determines the prevalent direction followed by an insequent tributary; it commonly makes an acute angle with the upstream part of the consequent valley. As each insequent stream develops its own valley, it receives in turn a second generation of tributaries. The branching drainage pattern so established is tree-like in plan, and is described as *dendritic* (Fig. 8–1). If the rocks are well jointed, however, a more rectangular pattern is likely to result.

Where, as commonly happens, the rocks consist of belts of alternately weak and strong beds, dipping seawards, the consequent valley is narrow and steep-sided where it cuts through resistant beds (sandstones, limestones, lavas, or sills), and broad and open where it crosses outcrops of weak beds (clay or shale). A tributary beginning on weak rocks has a great initial advantage. Headward erosion guides it back along the weak bed, parallel to the strike. Such a tributary is called a *subsequent* stream. The rectangular drainage pattern formed by consequent streams parallel to the dip and subsequent streams parallel to the strike is described as *trellised* (Fig. 8–4). Later tributaries add further detail to the trellised pattern.

SHIFTING OF DIVIDES AND RIVER CAPTURE

The position of a divide remains permanent only if the rates of erosion are the same on each side, a state of affairs that is practically never achieved. It usually happens that the opposing slopes are unequally inclined, and that erosion is more effective on the steeper side. As a result the divide is gradually pushed back towards the side with the gentler slope (Fig. 8–2). Along primary divides this effect

is most rapidly produced by headward erosion of the consequent valley heads. Because some of the latter work back through the crest more vigorously than others, the divide becomes zigzag or sinuous, while the crest is notched and becomes increasingly varied in height. As deepening proceeds, the dissection of the ridge is steadily elaborated and the more resistant rocks between the valley heads stand out as peaks. Where the headward migration of one valley head encroaches on a valley head at the other side, the notch in the crest develops into a *col* or pass.

The new drainage area thus acquired by a headward growing consequent stream is generally of little importance. Migration of the secondary divides between neighbouring consequent valleys leads to far more revolutionary changes. One of the original consequent rivers may have a bigger drainage area than its neighbours: possibly because it occupies the largest hollow in what was an undulating initial surface, or possibly because it is an extension of an old river in the "old land" behind the uplifted coastal plain. In any case, the major river will deepen and widen its valley more quickly than the neighbouring consequents. If the lateral divides are worn back until they reach these minor streams, the latter and their drainage areas are absorbed by the larger river—a process technically described as *abstraction*.

Capture of drainage on a still bigger scale becomes possible when the major river acquires vigorous subsequent tributaries, each working along a feebly resistant formation and each wearing back the secondary divide at its head (Figs. 8–3 and 8–4). Endowed with a relatively low local base level, a deeply entrenched subsequent, *e.g.* S_1 in Fig. 8–4, cuts back towards a consequent C_2, which is still draining an area at a higher level. Eventually (Fig. 8–5) C_2 is intercepted, its headwaters are diverted into S_1, and its lower course is beheaded. This process is called *river capture*. The rectangular bend *e* at the point of diversion is known as the *elbow of capture*. The beheaded river, now deprived of much of its drainage, is described as a

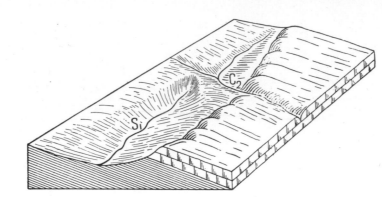

FIG. 8–3
Diagram showing impending river capture. The subsequent stream S_1 is cutting back at a relatively low level towards the consequent stream C_2.

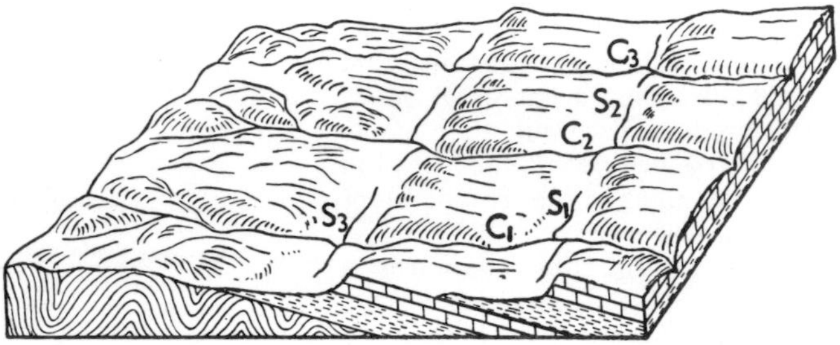

FIG. 8–4
Trellised drainage (consequent and subsequent streams), showing the dissection of a gently dipping series of hard and soft beds into escarpments and inner lowlands.

FIG. 8–5
Later development of the rivers of Fig. 8–4, illustrating river capture by the headward growth of the more vigorous subsequent streams: e, elbow of capture; Wg, wind gap.

misfit, since its diminished size is no longer appropriate to the valley through which it flows. Its new source is some way below the elbow of capture and the deserted notch, *Wg*, at the head of its valley becomes a *wind gap*. A subsequent stream S_2, which originally entered the captured stream near or above the elbow, now has its local base level lowered to that of S_1. It is thus enabled to deepen its valley and to extend backwards until it, in turn, reaches and beheads the next consequent, C_3. A major consequent river, with the aid of its subsequents, may in this way acquire a very large drainage area at the expense of its neighbours.

The rivers which flow into the estuary of the Humber illustrate the development of an actual river system by the process of capture outlined above. The uplift of the Pennines provided the slopes down which a number of consequent streams flowed into the North Sea. Of these only the Aire still maintains an uninterrupted course. The Wharfe, Calder, and Don were probably tributaries of the Aire from the start. The Nidd, Ure, and Swale, however, have each been captured in turn by the Ouse, a powerful subsequent stream which worked back northwards along the soft strata of the Trias (Fig. 8–6). On the eastern side of the Ouse it is difficult to trace the former courses of the beheaded streams, because of uplift of the Cleveland Hills and obliteration of the older valleys by glacial deposits. A more diagrammatic example is provided by the rivers of Northumberland. The three main streams, *a*, *b*, and *c*, of the North Tyne system clearly correspond to the Wansbeck, *a'*, a tributary of the Wansbeck, *b'*, and the Blyth, *c'*. The headwaters of the forerunners of these were captured by the North Tyne, a subsequent of the Tyne, as it worked back along the soft beds of the Scremerston Coal series.

122

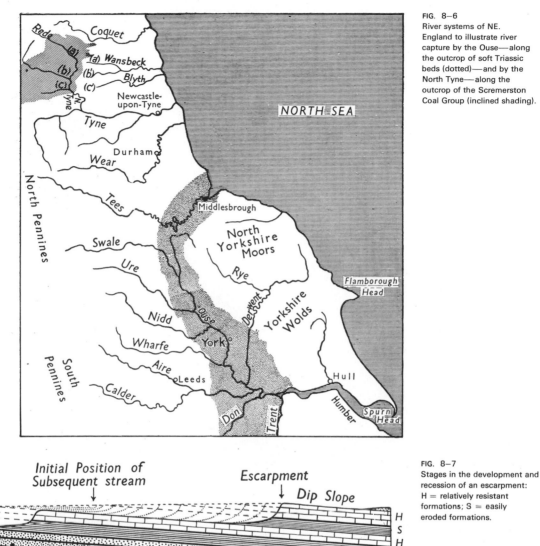

FIG. 8—6
River systems of NE. England to illustrate river capture by the Ouse—along the outcrop of soft Triassic beds (dotted)—and by the North Tyne—along the outcrop of the Scremerston Coal Group (inclined shading).

FIG. 8—7
Stages in the development and recession of an escarpment: H = relatively resistant formations; S = easily eroded formations.

Consequent streams flow northwards and southwards from the 'Weald dome and river capture, particularly by subsequent streams eroding along relatively soft beds of rock, has greatly modified the drainage (Fig. 4–9). The headwaters of the Medway, for example, once formed the headwaters of the Darent, from which they were captured by a subsequent stream flowing eastward to the Medway. Similarly the headwaters of the Wey once formed the headwaters of the Blackwater from which they were captured by a subsequent stream flowing eastward to the Wey. The river Arun provides an example of river capture by a consequent stream; by eroding backwards into the divide it captured the headwaters of the northward flowing Wey. As a result the source of the Arun now lies to the north of the crest of the Weald anticline.

ESCARPMENTS AND RELATED FEATURES

The valley of a subsequent stream is widened and deepened between divides formed by the bands of resistant rock on either side (Fig. 8–7). As the weak bed is gradually worn away, the upper surface of the underlying resistant bed is uncovered, and on this side the valley slope therefore approximates to the dip. On the other side the overlying resistant bed is attacked at its base and soon begins to steepen into the free face of an *escarpment*. Until it is restrained by approaching base level, the stream excavates its channel in the weak bed.

123

FIG. 8—8
Section across the Weald, (map, Fig. 4—9) approximately north and south through Brighton, with an indication (broken line) of the Pliocene erosion surface from which the present topography has been developed. Length of section 36 miles (58 Km). (*After S. W. Wooldridge and R. S. Morgan*)

FIG. 8—9
Hogback of Dakota Sandstone (Cretaceous) in the foothills east of the Front Range, Rocky Mts, Colorado. (*T. S. Lovering, United States Geological Survey*)

As a result of combined lateral and downward erosion being easier on one side, the stream shifts its channel obliquely in the direction of dip. The normal recession of the escarpment is thus intensified while a gentler slope is left on the other side of the valley. This is generally referred to as the *dip slope*. Small tributaries, known as *obsequent* streams, descend the escarpment, others, called *secondary consequents*, flow down the dip slope. Both sets of tributaries add detail to the trellis pattern of the drainage. As the main subsequent stream begins to meander, its valley becomes steadily wider and develops into an *interior lowland*.

Fig. 4—29 illustrates the succession of escarpments and interior lowlands between Gloucester and the London Basin. From the Lias clays and marls of the Severn valley the escarpment of the oolitic limestones of the Jurassic rises to the crest of the Cotswolds. The Oxford Clay is responsible for the interior lowland occupied by the Thames above and below Oxford. A minor escarpment, that of the Corallian limestone, is then followed by the interior lowland of the Kimmeridge Clay. Beyond this the Chiltern Hills represent the escarpment of the Chalk, the dip slopes of which lead down to the London basin (Fig. 6—5). The Chalk escarpment curves round to the eastern side of the Wash, and continues to the north as the Lincolnshire and Yorkshire Wolds. On the south side of the London basin the Chalk again emerges as the North Downs, with its well-known escarpment overlooking the Weald (Fig. 8—8). The scarp continues through Kent until it reaches the coast near Folkestone. Followed in the other direction it swings round the western border of the Weald, where it makes a less conspicuous feature, and continues on the far side as the South Downs; at Beachy Head (Fig. 3—14) it is again cut off by the sea. For illustrations of other escarpments see Figs. 3—12, 4—35, and 8—19.

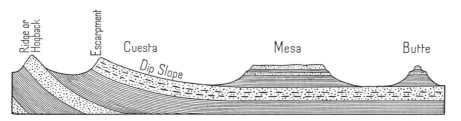

FIG. 8—10
Diagram to illustrate the
relation of various erosional
landforms to the structure
and dip of the strata from
which they have been eroded.

An escarpment and its dip slope together form a feature for which there is no English name. The Spanish term *cuesta* (pronounced *questa*) has therefore been internationally adopted. If the beds dip at a high angle, the dip slope becomes as steep as the escarpment and the feature corresponding to the cuesta is simply a ridge or *hogback* (Fig. 8—9). At the other extreme, in horizontal beds, the cuesta becomes a *mesa* (Spanish for table), that is, a tableland capped by a resistant bed and having steep sides all round (Figs. 8—10 and 10—16). By long-continued wearing back of the sides, a mesa dwindles into an isolated flat-topped hill. In America such a hill is called a *butte*, from its resemblance to the butt or bole of a tree, and the term has been widely adopted. In Western America buttes commonly occur where the beds dipping off the mountain flanks flatten out (Fig. 8—10). In South Africa, however, similar residual landforms, many of which are capped by isolated relics (outliers) of once continuous dolerite sills are called *kopjes*.

SUPERIMPOSED DRAINAGE

In many regions ancient folded rocks are now exposed which were formerly hidden beneath an unconformable cover of later sedimentary formations. The rivers initiated on the cover, with a drainage pattern appropriate to its

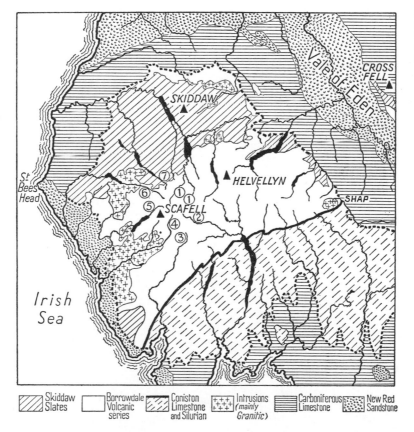

FIG. 8—11
Geological sketch-map of the
Lake District, showing the
radial pattern of the
superimposed drainage.

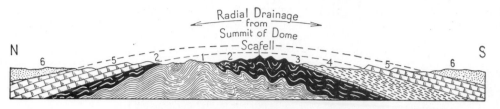

FIG. 8–12
Geological section across the
Lake District (igneous
intrusions omitted): 1.
Skiddaw Slates; 2. Borrowdale
Volcanic Series; 3. Coniston
Limestone; 4. Silurian strata;
5. Carboniferous Limestone;
6. New Red Sandstone.

structure, ultimately cut their valleys into the underlying rocks, maintaining their courses with little or no relation to the very different structures in which they then find themselves. As the cover is gradually removed by denudation, the old rocks are exposed over a steadily increasing area and the drainage pattern, an inheritance from the vanished cover, becomes *superimposed* on the old rocks.

The clearest example of superimposed drainage in Britain is afforded by the rivers and lakes of the Lake District. As illustrated in Figs. 8–11 and 8–12, the Lake District consists of an oval-shaped area of Lower Palaeozoic rocks (folded during the Caledonian orogenesis and having a general trend from ENE to WSW) enclosed in a frame of Carboniferous Limestone and New Red Sandstone, the beds of which everywhere dip outwards. The younger formations originally covered the older rocks. During Tertiary times the region was uplifted into a slightly elongated dome, with its axis curving towards the east from a culminating point which lay above the present summit of Scafell. The consequent streams that flowed radially down the slopes of the dome still persist, superimposed on the very different structure of the older rocks over which they now flow. The radial pattern of the valleys and mountainous ridges centred near Scafell is particularly striking. As numbered on Fig. 8–11, the valleys are (1) the headwaters of Borrowdale and Derwentwater; (2) Langdale and Windermere; (3) The Duddon; (4) Eskdale; (5) Wasdale and Wastwater; (6)

Ennerdale; and (7) Buttermere and Crummock. The lakes and many of the other scenic features of the Lake District have resulted from glaciation.

The Chalk originally covered most of the British Isles, and has been slowly eroded back to its present escarpment, which extends across England, from Yorkshire to Dorset. The underlying Jurassic strata have been worn away almost as extensively. At the time when the Cretaceous cover emerged from the sea to form land, rivers were initiated with a drainage pattern appropriate to the form of its surface. As the covering strata were removed the underlying rocks were gradually exposed over a steadily increasing area and, as uplift continued, the rivers maintained a close approximation to their original courses and became incised into the older, more resistant rocks, sometimes crossing the trend of their structures. The drainage pattern as we see it today has been superimposed on the older rocks.

THE CYCLE OF EROSION

It will now be abundantly clear that rivers, and indeed all landscape features, are continually changing. From the time when the sculpturing of a newly uplifted land area begins, the valleys and associated landforms pass through a series of well-characterized stages, referred to as youth, maturity, and old age, until, provided sudden interruptions due to earth movements do not intervene, the whole area is reduced to a plain (Fig. 8–13).

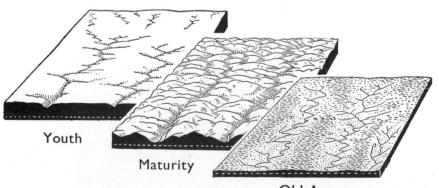

Youth

Maturity

Old Age

FIG. 8–13
Diagram illustrating the
three main stages in the
wearing down of an uplifted
land surface from youth,
through maturity to old age,
according to the Davisian
interpretation of the
"normal" cycle of erosion.

The sequence of changes involved in this evolution of landscape is known as the *cycle of erosion*.

There has been difference of opinion, however, as to the way in which areas of high relief are worn down until they become plains. The difference relates to the problem as to whether planation results from (*a*) flattening out of hillside slopes as they are worn back, so that they become progressively less steep; this is sometimes called the wearing-down process or; (*b*) wearing back of hillside slopes essentially parallel to themselves, sometimes called the wearing-back process (Fig. 8–14).

Davis, who introduced the concept of a cycle of erosion, more than sixty years ago, considered that as valleys are widened, the bordering slopes tend to become less steep during their retreat. Finally, during a lengthy old age, the region is worn down and reduced to an undulating plain. Relief is faint, apart perhaps from an occasional hill which owes its survival to the superior resistance of its rocks. Such residuals are sometimes called *monadnocks*, after Mt Monadnock in New Hampshire. The low-lying erosion surface which is the ultimate product of old age, Davis called a *peneplain* (L. *pene*, almost). This and the corresponding

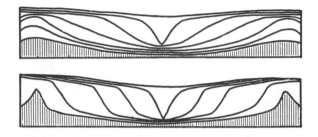

FIG. 8–14
Contrasted sequence of valley profiles from youth to old age: *above*, according to the wearing-down interpretation; *below*, according to the wearing-back interpretation.

FIG. 8–15
Ayers Rock, 200 miles (322 km) WSW. of Alice Springs in the middle of Australia, an inselberg 1·6 miles (2·6 km) long of nearly vertical Precambrian strata rising in impressive isolation 1,100 feet (335 m) above the surrounding pediplain. Mt Olga (left background) is 16 miles (26 km) to the west of Ayers Rock. (*Australian National Travel Association*)

127

term *peneplanation* have thus come to be firmly associated with two leading ideas: the decline and flattening-out of hillside slopes during their retreat, and the accompanying wearing-down of divides and residual hills into forms presenting a broad and gentle convexity towards the sky, but merging with equally gentle concavities into the surrounding plain.

The opposed view was introduced by Penck in 1924. He argued that most hillside slopes should not flatten out as they are worn back, once they have attained an angle that is stable for the type of rock or rock waste concerned.

Instead, he maintained, that each slope would be expected to retreat parallel to itself (Fig. 8–14). In 1930 Davis agreed that this was so for the rocky and stony slopes of arid and semi-arid regions, but not for humid regions like that of western Europe which he had previously been mainly considering.

Thus it came to be thought that two different cycles of erosion existed: (*a*) a supposedly normal cycle of erosion with gradually decreasing steepness of the hill-slopes, and (*b*) a cycle of arid erosion with parallel retreat of hillslopes. From studies

FIG. 8–16
A striking example of the inselberg type of landscape, north of Ribaue, Mozambique. (*Sketch by E. J. Wayland, 1911*)

FIG. 8–17
The Sugar Loaf, Rio de Janeiro, Brazil. An inselberg peak that now forms part of a celebrated coast of submergence. (*Brazilian Government Public Relations*)

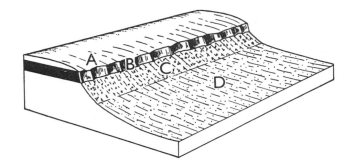

FIG. 8—18
Elements of hillside slopes.
(*After Alan Wood and Lester King*)

of landforms in arid regions, it is now well established that throughout the cycle of erosion the slopes retreat essentially parallel to themselves, so that a gently inclined surface, called a *pediment* is left in front of major slopes. As erosion proceeds, neighbouring pediments, encroaching from different directions, coalesce to form a *pediplain* (Fig. 8–15). As the escarpments retreat the pediplain at their foot increases in area, and because the slopes retreat parallel to themselves the residual hills are steepsided forms known as *inselbergs* (island mounts), Figs. 8–15 and 8–16. If, as originally supposed, there is a fundamental difference between the cycle of erosion in arid and humid regions, then inselbergs should be restricted to arid regions. It is now known, however, that inselbergs and pediments also occur in humid regions—for example, the Sugar Loaf, Rio de Janeiro, Brazil (Fig. 8–17). The primary conditions necessary for the formation of inselbergs are initial high relief and the presence of resistant crystalline rocks that have long been exposed to erosion. An inselberg, however, is not merely a core of rock which has been preserved by virtue of its structural soundness while weaker surrounding rock has fallen a prey to erosion. The surrounding rocks, now part of a pediment, are generally just as tough and massive as that of the inselberg that rises above them.

THE SLOPE PROBLEM

The difference of opinion between Davis and Penck served to focus attention on what has in recent years become known as the "slope problem". In practice this means trying to discover the conditions under which major slopes (*a*) tend to remain essentially parallel to themselves as they recede in consequence of surface wastage and erosion, or (*b*) become progressively less steep. Which combinations of the many interwoven processes favour

wearing-back and pedimentation, and which wearing-down and peneplanation?

A characteristic association of hillside slopes that constitute the sides of many valleys is illustrated in Figs. 8–18 and 8–19. This association forms the basis of an analysis of slope development presented by Alan Wood in 1942. In addition to the initial upland and the flood plain of broad valley floors, there are four possible intervening slope elements:

A. The *convex slope*, the part of the initial upland that tends to become convex by being rounded off at, and towards its edge with *b*.

B. The *free face*, a steep scarp face of bare rock representing the most actively eroded part of the hillside slope. As erosion proceeds the scarp face retreats parallel to itself—that is, it is worn back.

C. The *constant slope*, is that of the angle of rest of the scree debris which collects at the foot of the free face. As the scree grows in height the constant slope lengthens upwards at the expense of the lower part of the free face which it covers.

Because scree debris continues to be weathered, reduced in grain size, and washed downhill by rain, the scree slope ceases to be constant towards its lower edge and merges into:

D. The *waning slope* (pediment, valley-floor basement, or lower wash slope), which stretches to the valley floor or other local base level with a diminishing angle, so that it is more or less concave upwards.

According to local circumstances certain of these slope elements may be repeated, or they may be undeveloped or worn away. In the Grand Canyon of the Colorado river, (Figs. 2–11 and 7–17) elements B and C are repeated several times, because the layers of strong limestone or sandstone responsible for the scarps, B, are separated by less resistant beds of shale. The shale has been worn back to a slope that is at least as steep as the constant

FIG. 8–19
Escarpment of Carboniferous
Limestone, Eglwyseg
Mountain, north of Llangollen,
Denbighshire. Below the free
faces of the outcropping
limestone beds the constant
slope, determined by the
angle of rest of the screes,
is seen; this passes into
the concave slope that
leads down to the river.
(*H.M. Geological Survey*)

slope, so ensuring that all the debris liberated from the sides of the canyon ultimately reaches the river at the bottom. On the other hand, in an area of low and gentle relief, B is likely to be missing and C, if present at all, may be reduced to a short link between the summit convexity, A, and the concave waning slope, D. This type of smoothly undulating profile characterizes the more subdued landscapes of parts of the British Isles and New England. The pediment-with-inselberg landscape is a strongly contrasted type in which B and D are the dominant elements, the sharp angle between them resulting from the absence of scree and hence of slope C (Fig. 8–15). Where parallel down-cutting rivers have V-shaped valley sides that rise up to meet their neighbours in narrow ridges, the constant slope, C, is highly developed.

An investigation that yielded highly significant results was made by Schumm (1956) in the badlands of South Dakota. By measuring the angles of hillside slopes he found that (*a*) steep-sided hills eroded from the relatively impermeable strata of a scarp face (equivalent to B in Fig. 8–18) exhibited parallel slope retreat—that is, they illustrate the wearing-back process—and (*b*) low, rounded hills eroded from the underlying permeable strata illustrate the wearing-down process.

Immediately in front of the escarpment, residual hills sculptured from the relatively impermeable strata rise up with steep straight sides that form sharp angles at the summits. Schumm found there was no significant variation in the slope of the sides of these hills in a series ranging from the highest hills with the longest slopes to the lowest hills with the shortest slopes; the average lies between 44° and 45°. Evidently the slopes have remained parallel during denudation. Since these hills are formed of essentially impermeable strata erosion has been dominantly by rain-wash, accompanied by rill-wash.

In front of these hills, and at a lower level, low rolling hills have been eroded out of the underlying permeable strata. Here soil creep accompanied by small slumps and slides of wet mud account for most of the erosion. Schumm's measurements of the slopes of these hills show that during denudation there has been a decline in the slope angle from 33° for the longest slope to 8° for the shortest. These measurements indicate that the relatively gentle topography results from the wearing-down process.

Schumm's investigations suggest that parallel retreat (wearing-back) of approximately straight slopes is favoured where rain erosion is dominant, and that wearing-down is favoured by conditions appropriate to surface creep. In most areas, of course, both sets of processes are operative, and as Schumm tentatively concluded it is probable that "the areas in which creep dominates over rain wash, and *vice versa*, are end members of a continuous series ranging through all proportions of processes" according to the prevailing rock-types, vegetation, soils, and climate.

Despite the growing knowledge that erosion plains may result from pediplanation rather than from peneplanation, the term "pene-plain" is still widely used, particularly for older erosion plains that have been uplifted to become the initial surfaces of later, uncompleted cycles of erosion. It is not always easy to decipher the mode of origin of a surface that is now represented only by a few remnants, and to know whether it was formed as a peneplain, a pediplain, a panplain, or a plain of marine erosion. It would save much confusion if every such surface was simply called an *erosion plain* until adequate evidence has been collected to justify a more specific descriptive name.

On one point at least there is now general agreement: the Davisian scheme can no longer be properly described as "normal". If we consider how the climates of particular latitudes have changed during the last 25,000 years or so (Fig. 8–20), we find that regions like New England and the British Isles passed through great fluctuations of climate. Most of their landscapes are products, not of the temperate conditions regarded as "normal", but of repeated successions of glacial, permafrost, and temperate-humid conditions. On the other hand, the regions now characterized by steppes and savannahs have had little, if any, change. The pediments and pediplains characteristic of these regions have, therefore, been formed by the processes that are still operating. These processes and their results

can be and are being observed, and consequently the development of the pediment-inselberg type of landscape is becoming reasonably well understood. It is this type of landscape, which not so long ago was a profound mystery, that now provides us with an acceptable standard of reference.

From this standard there are two main deviations: (*a*) towards permafrost and glacial conditions; and (*b*) towards desert conditions, in which wind erosion plays a leading part. Our present landscapes of the temperate zones are composite products of all the varied processes involved in the first of these deviations. This means that the processes we now see modifying these landscapes are generally *not* those by which their major features were formed. Glaciated landscapes are easily recognized and are still well preserved in many parts of the temperate zone. And it is just because so many of us are familiar with landscapes of mixed origin that opinions diverge as to what purely temperate landscapes would look like.

Present-day landscapes have also been strongly affected by the many changes of level that have occurred since the beginning of the Pleistocene. On balance these changes have been responsible for land emergence on a widespread scale in many parts of the world. In the south-east of England, for example, the land of today stands about 600 feet higher, relative to sea level, than it did a million years ago. Consequently a great number of rivers are either still in the stage of youth or have been rejuvenated so that their capacity for erosion and transport is still great.

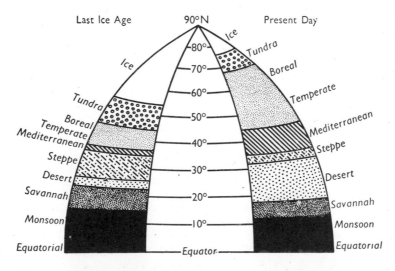

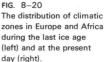
FIG. 8–20
The distribution of climatic zones in Europe and Africa during the last ice age (left) and at the present day (right).

THE ISOSTATIC RESPONSE
TO DENUDATION

The reduction of a region to an erosion plain involves the removal of an immense load of material, the mass of which is proportional to the height of the initial surface. While the crust was being thus unloaded by denudation, slow isostatic uplift must have been continuously in progress, thereby giving the rivers more work to do and delaying its completion. This effect has so far been tacitly ignored for the sake of simplicity of treatment, but it should not be overlooked.

Let us suppose that a thickness of 1,000 feet of rock having an average density of 2·6 has been removed from a region while isostatic equilibrium is maintained and no independent earth movement occurs. The mass lost is proportional to $2·6 \times 1,000$, and this must be made good by the inflow at depth of a thickness h of material with a density of about 3·4. The condition for the maintenance of isostasy is that $3·4h = 2,600$ feet; whence $h = 765$ feet. This influx of sima raises the plane AB (Fig. 8–21a) to A'B', and the new surface is only 235 feet below the original level of the denuded block of country. For the reduction to base level of a plateau which originally had an elevation of 1,000 feet, the thickness of rock to be removed is not 1,000 feet but about four times as much.

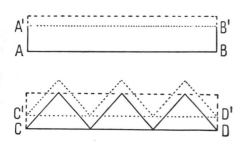

Such uplift must be considered a normal accompaniment of a cycle of erosion. It involves the curious effect that during late youth and early maturity the summits of peaks and divides become elevated above the initial surface. This is illustrated by Fig. 8–21b. When the cross-sectional areas of valleys and divides are equal, half the mass of the denuded block has been removed. The plane CD will by then have been raised to C'D', i.e. by 765/2 feet, assuming the summits to be 1,000 feet above the valley floors.

The great peaks of the Himalayas probably owe part of their exceptional elevation to the effect of isostatic uplift. Instead of a 1,000-foot block, carved into hills and valleys, we have here a 16,000-foot block, and the corresponding isostatic uplift would therefore be more than 6,000 feet. This little exercise, however, indicates that some other process must be at work in the depth to account for the exceptional height of Everest and the Karakoram giants.

INTERRUPTIONS IN THE CYCLE OF EROSION

At any stage in an uncompleted cycle, the normal sequence of changes may be slowed down by the effects of isostasy or by those due to a slow lowering of sea level. More serious interruptions may be due to earth movements of uplift or subsidence, with changes of slope due to tilting, and commonly with production of fault scarps; to volcanic action; or to changes of climate leading to glaciation, increased rainfall, or aridity. The distinctive landscape features developed under glacial and desert conditions are described in later chapters. Meanwhile, however, it must be remembered that glaciation involves (a) abstraction of water from the sea to form ice sheets and its subsequent restoration when the ice melts away, with corresponding changes in sea level and consequently in base level; and (b) isostatic depression due to the loading of an area by an ice sheet, followed by uplift when the ice sheet retreats and disappears.

Volcanic activity may introduce local accidents, such as the obstruction of a valley by a lava flow. Youthful features are then temporarily restored while the river is regrading its course through the obstacle. On a larger scale whole landscapes may be buried beneath a thick cover of plateau basalts, in which case a new cycle then begins on the volcanic surface.

If a region is depressed by earth movements, its surface is brought nearer to base level, the work to be done by erosion is diminished, and the stages of the cycle then in progress are passed through more quickly. When coastal regions subside—unless sedimentation keeps pace, as in subsiding deltas—the sea occupies the lower reaches of valleys and estuaries are formed. Tributaries which entered the valley before it was drowned now flow directly into the tidal waters of the estuary and become *dismembered streams*. Rivers like the Thames and Humber are sufficiently active—with

FIG. 8–21 (Far left) Isostatic response to denudation: (a) uplift of a plateau; (b) uplift of mountain peaks.

FIG. 8–22
Typical scenery of the
Norfolk Broads, near
Wroxham, 4 miles NE. of
Norwich. River Bure (looking
east) with Salhouse
Broad on the right (south)
and part of Hoveton Great
Broad on the left (north).
(Aerofilms Ltd)

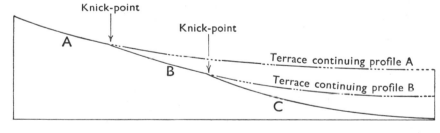

FIG. 8–23
A long profile of graded
reaches, A, B, and C,
with knick-points at their
intersections. Profiles A
and B may be indicated by
terraces preserved on the
valley sides.

some human assistance—to keep their channels open. More sluggish rivers however, may be unable to prevent the growth of obstructive bars and spits across their estuaries, and the latter then become silted up and overgrown with peat-making vegetation.

Until recently, the Broads of East Anglia (Fig. 8–22) were thought to be natural relics of the formerly widespread estuary of the rivers Bure, Yare, and Waveney. They are indeed a result of almost continuous submergence since 700 A.D., but they are the flooded sites of excavations dug in peat beside the rivers to depths of 10 feet or more. For nearly 400 years, from 900 A.D. onwards, a peat industry flourished in the area, until it declined as a result of flooding from the sea and the rivers. The flooded pits left by the peat cutters could not be drained, and by 1350 it had become more profitable to use them as fisheries. Today, they form the Broads.

Geologically, the Broads may be said to owe the possibility of their existence to a local subsidence of the land relative to sea level—that is, to the rise of base level. If, on the contrary, base level is lowered—that is, the land is elevated relative to sea level—then the work to be done by erosion is increased and a river is endowed with renewed energy to begin the task of regrading its profile to the new base level. The river is *rejuvenated*. The change begins with the restoration of youthful features where the gradient is steepened, and gradually works upstream. During the process of regrading there is a more or less marked change of slope at the place of intersection (the *knick-point*) of the newly graded profile with the older one (Fig. 8–23). The knick-point is particularly conspicuous when the uplifted region is bounded by a growing fault scarp, or in any other circumstances favourable to the development of rapids or a waterfall. The newly deepened part of the valley may be excavated as a gorge or narrow V in the wide V- or trough-shaped floor of the pre-existing valley. Consequently the cross-profile also shows a steepening of slope below the point where the earlier valley form is intersected by the new. The valley sides tend to become convex as a result of an increased rate of down-cutting.

The remaining sections of this chapter are devoted to features of special significance, such as river terraces, canyons, and entrenched meanders, developed in response to changes of base-level which have been relatively rapid compared with the slow isostatic uplifts induced by erosion.

RIVER TERRACES

When a river that has already established a flood plain is rejuvenated, it cuts through its own deposits into the underlying rocks. The sides of the original alluvial plain are then left as flat terraces above the new level of the river. In the course of time the new valley is widened and a second flood plain forms within the first one, of which only local remnants may survive. By subsequent uplift and rejuvenation a second pair of terraces may then be left on the valley side. The sides of many of the valleys of Britain (Fig. 8–24) and Western Europe—and indeed in many other parts of the world—are bordered by a series of such river terraces, each corresponding to a phase of rejuvenation and valley deepening followed by one of rising base level and valley widening. A typical terrace is a platform of bedrock thickly veneered with a sheet of river gravel and sand passing upwards into finer alluvium. As indicated in Fig. 8–23, such terraces slope gently seaward and so provide a means of reconstructing earlier profiles and of estimating the sea levels towards which they were graded.

Since the early Pleistocene there have been at least a dozen well-marked changes of level in the London Basin, recorded by terraces and also by buried channels which can be discovered only by boring and excavations. Fig. 8–25, shows the three terraces

FIG. 8–24
Alluvial terraces of the River Findhorn, looking north from Daless, Nairn, Scotland, cut through glacial deposits and marking successive stages in the erosion of the valley. (*H.M. Geological Survey*)

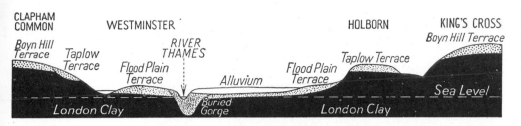

FIG. 8—25
Section across London to show
the paired terraces and one
of the buried "gorges" of
the Thames valley. (After
H.M. Geological Survey)

of the Thames valley that can most easily be recognized in and near London:

(a) The *Boyn Hill Terrace*, named after a locality near Maidenhead, reaches a height of about 200 feet, but at Swanscombe (near Gravesend, 50 miles nearer the sea) it is much lower and corresponds to a sea level of about 100 feet. At Swanscombe it is particularly well exposed on a platform of Chalk. The sequence of gravel and loamy clay corresponds to a long history of a warm and genial climate followed by cold and the cutting of a deep channel, after which more temperate conditions were again restored. The gravels, mostly composed of flint, contain the fossil remains of extinct species of elephant, hippopotamus, and rhinoceros. Palaeolithic flint implements are also found.

(b) The step down to the *Taplow Terrace*, which would originally have been a fairly steep bluff, is generally hidden by downwash from the terrace above. This is illustrated by Clapham Common (Fig. 8–25), and the slopes in its vicinity. The type locality, Taplow, is farther upstream, near Maidenhead. The most familiar example of this terrace is Hyde Park and Kensington Gardens. Bones and skulls of lions and bears have been found in the lower gravels, but nearer the surface these are absent and remains of the hairy mammoth appear, indicating the oncoming of much colder conditions.

(c) The step down to the *Flood Plain Terrace* has also become a gentle slope in most built-up localities; for example, South Kensington station and the museums are on the flood plain, while most of the Imperial College buildings and the Albert Hall are on the slope leading up to the Taplow Terrace of Kensington Gardens. In the other direction the gradual descent towards the Thames takes us through Chelsea, mostly built on the gravel and alluvium of modern times. The earlier deposits of each part of this composite Flood Plain Terrace contain occasional fossils, all indicative of a frigid climate. In the oldest of these, remains of the mammoth have been found

accompanied by reindeer and elk. In the Lea valley there is a celebrated "Arctic-Plant Bed". Excavation of the London docks has revealed the presence of several beds of peat, those in the later deposits containing relics of oak and beech. The latest of these fossil forests is followed by the first signs of the Bronze Age, which began about 4,000 years ago.

ENTRENCHED MEANDERS

If, at the time of rejuvenation, a stream was meandering on a valley floor underlain by resistant bedrock, with no more than a thin cover of easily eroded mantle deposits, the deepening channel is soon etched into the underlying rocks, while the original winding course is still preserved. In this way *incised* or *entrenched* meanders are produced. The "hair-pin gorge" of the Wear at Durham is a familiar British example (Fig. 8–26). A well-protected site within the loop was selected for the cathedral, which is thus enclosed by the gorge on three sides. The fourth and easily vulnerable side was safeguarded by building a castle which is now the home of the senior college of Durham University.

The change of form of entrenched meanders, and the wearing back of the confining walls are relatively slow processes controlled by lateral undercutting of the river banks. Localized undercutting on both sides of the narrow neck of a constricted loop sometimes leads to the formation of a natural bridge. On each side of the constriction a cave is excavated, especially if the rocks at river level are weaker than those above. Eventually the two caves meet, and the stream then flows through the perforation. The stronger rocks of the roof remain for a time as an arch spanning the stream, and the loop-shaped gorge at the side is abandoned. In Utah, where recent uplift has made possible the development of many deeply entrenched meanders, there are several examples of such arches. The most impressive of these is Rainbow Bridge (Figs. 8–27 and 8–28), a

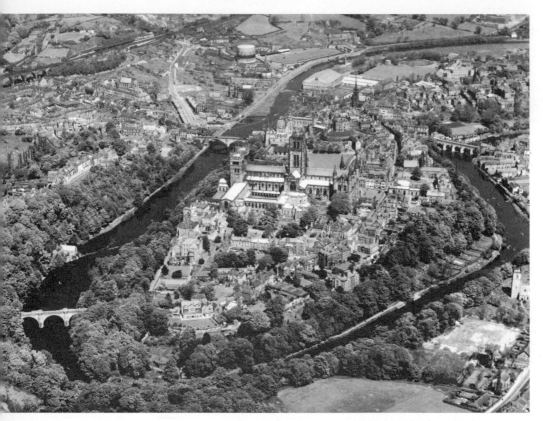

FIG. 8–26
The entrenched meander of
the River Wear at Durham
(*Aerofilms Ltd*), with
explanatory map and section.

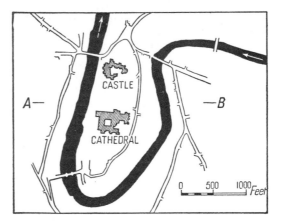

graceful arch of sandstone which rises 309
feet over Bridge Creek in a span of 278 feet.

ANTECEDENT DRAINAGE

During the uplift of a great mountain range
it may happen that a river which was already
flowing across the site of the future mountains
continues to deepen its valley while the uplift is in progress, so that it becomes entrenched
in the rising landscape. A river which thus
succeeds in maintaining the slope of its channel
from a source behind the mountains to the
plains in front is called an *antecedent* river,
to express the fact that the river was in
existence before the mountains which have
risen across its course.

By far the most remarkable examples of
antecedent rivers are those which cross the
Himalayas. The watershed is not along or
near the highest peaks, as might have been
expected, but well to the north in Tibet.
From their upper courses on the plateau the
Indus, Bramaputra, and some of the headwaters of the Ganges traverse the ranges by
way of deep gorges cut in the bottom of steep
V-shaped valleys. As the Indus passes through

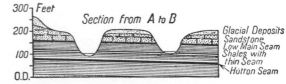

FIG. 8—27
Rainbow Bridge, Bridge
Creek, Utah. (*Ewing
Galloway*)

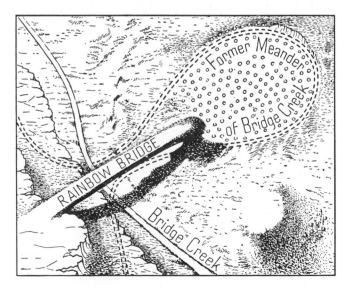

FIG. 8—28
Diagram illustrating the mode
of origin of Rainbow Bridge.

Gilgit in Kashmir, the river itself is only 3,000 feet above its delta, but the precipitous walls by which it is confined rise to heights of nearly 20,000 feet. Like a gigantic saw the river has cut through 17,000 feet of rock, keeping pace with a like amount of uplift.

The Grand Canyon of the Colorado river, one of the world's most owe-inspiring scenic wonders is also an antecedent river. It deepened its valley while uplift was in progress, and so became entrenched in the rising landscape. Various upwarps occurred across the course of the river, including one which was formed early in the Pliocene near the site of the present Lake Mead. Here the river failed to keep pace with the rate of uparching of the ground beneath it, and in consequence its waters were ponded back, as they are today by the Hoover Dam. This Pliocene lake deepened until it could spill over the lowest point of the rim,

the old canyon floor. In due course the lake was eliminated by sedimentation from the inlet and headwater erosion from the outlet.

UPLIFTED EROSION PLAINS

Erosion plains representing the practically completed cycles of former periods, but since uplifted to form the initial surfaces of later or present-day cycles, can be detected in many landscapes. In the Grampian Highlands an old erosion plain, now dissected into a landscape of late youth or early maturity (though modified by glaciation), is easily recognized by the even skyline corresponding to a widespread uniformity of summit levels at about 2,000 feet (Fig. 8–29). The plane through these summits, the "summit plane", is commonly referred to as an ancient peneplain: while the occasional peaks that rise

FIG. 8–29
The sky-line of the Grampian Highlands of Scotland, looking south from Ben Nevis. An example of summit levels representing an uplifted erosion plain which has been deeply dissected by rivers and former glaciers. (*H.M. Geological Survey*)

FIG. 8–30
Projected section through Wales to show the summit levels representing the uplifted erosion plain known as the "2,000-foot High Plateau". Length 175 miles (282 km). (*After E. H. Brown*)

to higher altitudes have been interpreted as the relics of the monadnocks that diversified that surface. As indicated on p. 131, it would be better to replace this nomenclature by terms free from hypothetical implications. Whatever kind of erosional origin the Grampian summit plane may have had, we can at least be certain that it was produced later than the time of intrusion of the Tertiary dykes, since some of these have been truncated by it. Our British landscapes are largely the products of erosion stimulated by a series of Tertiary earth movements, accompanied by independent changes of sea level. Such changes of sea level whether due to growth or melting of ice sheets, to displacement of sea water by deposition of sediments, or changes in the volume of the ocean basins, are said to be *eustatic*. The factors concerned are so numerous that their individual influence is not easily recognized in the "old lands", such as Wales, the Lake District, and the Highlands, which have lost whatever covering rocks they may once have had. It is notable, however, that in all these areas, and also in the Southern Uplands of Scotland and in various parts of Ireland, a summit plane roughly corresponding to the 2,000-foot level can be detected, as well as others leading down like a staircase to the "600-foot" marine platform that appears to have heralded the beginning of the Pleistocene in so many places (Fig. 8–30).

9
Glaciers and Glaciation

SNOW FIELDS AND THE MAINTENANCE OF GLACIERS

Glaciers are masses of ice which, under the influence of gravity, flow out from the snow fields where they originate. Permanent snow fields occur in every continent except Australia. The level up to which the snow melts in summer—that is, the lower edge of a permanent snow field (if present)—is called the *snow line*. Its height varies with latitude from sea level in the polar regions to 2,000 feet (600 m) in S. Greenland and S. Chile, 5,000 feet (1,500 m) in S. Norway and S. Alaska, 9,000 feet (2,700 m) in the Alps, 14,500–19,000 feet (4,400–5,700 m) in the Himalayas, and 17,000–18,000 feet (5,000–5,500 m) on the high equatorial peaks of Africa and the Andes. It is of interest to notice that the higher summits of the Scottish Highlands—for example, Ben Nevis—just fail to reach the level of the snow line as it would be in Scotland.

Low temperature alone is not sufficient to ensure the growth of a snow field. Although northern Siberia includes one of the coldest regions of the globe, it is kept free from perpetual snow because the scanty winter falls are quickly dissipated in the spring. Snow fields are formed and maintained where the winter snowfall is so heavy that summer melting and evaporation fail to remove it all. Snow may also be swept away by the wind, or lost from steep slopes by avalanching. The most favourable situations are therefore gentle slopes and hollows shaded from the sun and sheltered from the wind. A balance of the snowfall is then left over to accumulate from year to year, and the snow field grows in depth and surface area until pressure on the ice which is formed in depth is sufficient to start its outward flow as a glacier.

As the loose feathery snow that first gathers in the collecting grounds is buried by later falls it gradually passes into a closely packed form—the *névé*—retaining a white colour because of the presence of entangled air. As the snow crystals are buried and compacted, the air between them is squeezed out, water from melting snow seeps in and freezes, and so the deeper layers are transformed into ice. Minute bubbles of air still remain and as the bubbles become smaller, fewer, and more dispersed, the colour of the ice changes from the usual opaque white to the clear blue that is commonly restricted to particular bands. Glacial ice in bulk is a granular aggregate of interlocking grains, each grain being an individual crystal of ice. Between the grains there remains an extremely thin *intergranular film* consisting of an aqueous solution containing chlorides and other salts, mainly of sodium. The presence of these ions lowers the freezing point and so maintains the film in a liquid state. The same phenomenon is put to practical use when salt is sprinkled over an icy pavement to "melt" the ice. In a glacier the intergranular film plays an important role in regulating the flow of the ice.

Glaciers originating in and around the heads of valleys creep slowly downwards as tongue-like streams of ice, the material and pressure responsible for the flow being maintained by the yearly replenishment of the névé fields above. Ultimately the glaciers dwindle away by melting and evaporation, their fronts or *snouts* reaching a position—which may be thousands of feet below the snow line—where the forward movement of the ice is just balanced by the wastage. In response to seasons of heavy snowfall whereby the supply is increased, or of low temperature whereby the wastage is reduced, the glacier extends farther down the valley, and the snout then becomes steep. Conversely, in response to a falling off in the rate of supply or to an increased rate of wastage the snout tapers (Fig. 9–1) and recedes up the valley. The glacier may be said to retreat or recede, but this is only a manner of speaking. It is not the ice that moves backwards, but the position of the terminus or snout.

The capacity of powerful valley glaciers to extend far below the snow line before they melt away is due not only to the immense supplies of ice which are drained from the upland gathering grounds but also to the fact that the area exposed to wastage is small relative to the great volume of ice. Because a glacier moves extremely slowly, it occupies its valley to a very great depth. On an average slope, with gravity as the only motive force, water can flow about 100,000 times as fast as ice. To drain a given area the cross-section of a glacier has therefore to be enormously greater than that of the corresponding river, and in

FIG. 9—1
The Rhone Glacier, showing
the area of accumulation in
the high snow fields, a cirque
or corrie at the valley head,
and the zone of wastage
(*ablation*) terminating in
the snout. (*Aerofilms Ltd*)

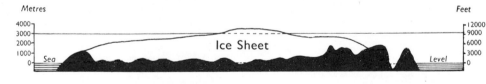

FIG. 9—2
Profile across central
Greenland from Disco Bay
on the west to Franz Josef
Land on the east. Rock
basement black. (*After P. E.
Victor, Laugh Koch 1949—54
Expedition*)

consequence the streams that suffice to carry off the summer melt water from the snout of a glacier always appear small and insignificant (Fig. 9–1).

When glaciers overflow the land and terminate in sea water sufficiently deep to allow the ice to float, huge masses break away from the front and become *icebergs*. Theoretically about nine tenths of an iceberg would be submerged if it were made of pure ice. The actual proportion, however, is subject to variation according to the proportion of entangled air and the load of rock debris present in the ice. Some of the vast tabular icebergs liberated from the front of the Antarctic ice (Fig. 9–3) float with as much as one sixth of their total height above the sea.

TYPES OF GLACIERS

Glaciers fall naturally into three main classes:

(*a*) *Ice sheets* and *ice caps* that overspread continental or plateau regions of supply, where the snow line is low, creeping with a slow massive movement towards the margins.

(*b*) *Mountain* or *valley glaciers* occupying the pre-existing valleys of mountain ranges that rise above the snow line.

(*c*) *Piedmont glaciers*, consisting of sheets of ice formed by the coalescence of several valley glaciers which have spread out below the snow line—like lakes of ice—over a lowland area of wastage.

Many gradational and subsidiary types also occur, and some of these are referred to below.

Greenland and Antarctica provide the only examples of *continental ice sheets* that still exist. There is, however, overwhelming evidence that during the Pleistocene immense ice sheets of similar character covered half of

FIG. 9–3
Tabular iceberg from the Ross Barrier, off Beaufort Island, at the entrance to the Ross Sea, Antarctica; the visible part above sea level is 120 feet high (37 m). (*New Zealand Geological Survey*)

Fig. 9–4
Axel Heiberg, Canadian Arctic, looking eastwards. The hanging glaciers on the far side of the valley drain the Schei ice-field. The protruding peaks and ridges are over 7,000 feet (2,134m) above sea level. The ice tongues coming from the right drain the Krueger ice field. (*National Air Photo Library, Department of Energy, Mines and Resources, Canada*)

North America and most of North-Western Europe (Fig. 9–11). The present Greenland ice sheet, about half a million square miles in extent, is largely enclosed within a mountainous rim. Near the middle of the sheet the ice has been shown by seismic methods to be over 10,000 feet (over 3,000 m) thick. The immense weight has isostatically depressed the rock floor, which now has a saucer-like surface, parts of which are below sea level (Fig. 9–2). Towards the edge, the higher peaks and ridges of the mountains project through the ice as *nunataks*. The ice itself overflows through passes in the mountain zone and terminates in the sea or in the valleys leading down to the green coastal belt.

The ice sheet of Antarctica, more than seven times as extensive as that of Greenland, forms a great plateau rising to over 14,000 feet (over 4,250 m). Except in a few localities of fringing mountains, where there are marginal glaciers and a coastal strip, the ice sheet overruns the coast and spreads over the sea as vast masses of more or less floating ice. The best known of these is the Ross Ice Shelf, which reaches a thickness of over 1,300 feet (about 400 m). The shelf terminates in sheer cliffs of floating ice rising 100–160 feet (30–50 m) above the Ross sea and known as the Great Ross Barrier. The shelf ice is worn away by submarine thawing, marine erosion, and the breaking off of gigantic icebergs (Fig. 9–3).

Smaller ice sheets, distinguished as *plateau glaciers* or *ice caps*, cover large areas in Iceland, Spitzbergen, and the Arctic islands of northern Canada (Fig. 9–4); areas from which they emerge through marginal depressions as blunt lobes or large valley glaciers. The tips of the underlying mountains project from certain less continuous caps of highland ice. Where the supply of ice is rather less, these pass into a network of connected glacier systems, the ice of each valley system overflowing the cols into neighbouring valleys and smothering all the lower divides. Such gradational types, well represented in Spitsbergen, lead to the more familiar valley glaciers.

Trunk glaciers, and the tributary valley glaciers feeding into them, occupy the upper parts or the whole of the valley system of a

FIG. 9–5
The eastern part of the Malaspina Glacier, Alaska, looking NW towards Mt St Elias (18,008 feet: 5,489 m); the high peak on the right is Mt Augusta (14,070 feet: 4,289m). The fold structures result from differences in the rate of flow of debris-laden ice fed into a shallow basin by the Seward and other mountain glaciers. (*Bradford Washburn*)

143

single drainage area (Fig. 9–9). Smaller valley glaciers tend to be confined to single valleys. Valley glaciers characteristically originate in deep armchair-shaped hollows called *cirques* or *corries*, situated at the valley heads (Figs. 9–1 and 9–16). Small isolated glaciers occupying cirques or hanging valleys that are now perched high on the side of a deeper valley are referred to as *cirque* or *corrie glaciers*, or as *hanging glaciers* (Fig. 9–4).

Where a glacier passes from a restricted channel to a more open lowland, it fans out into an *expanded foot*, and where several neighbouring glaciers so emerge a *piedmont glacier* results. The outstanding example of the latter type is the great Malaspina Glacier of Alaska (Fig. 9–5). Maintained by the confluence of the glaciers from the St Elias Range along the Canadian frontier, it has an area of about 850 square miles (2,200 km²), and locally reaches the sea. As a result of surface melting, much of the marginal ice is covered with morainic debris and soil which here and there support dense forests of pine.

THE MOVEMENT OF GLACIERS

Were it not for the fact that ice in bulk behaves as a rheid and flows under its own weight, the world would now present a very different appearance. Practically all the water of the oceans would be locked up in gigantic circumpolar ice fields of enormous thickness. The lands of the tropical belts would be deserts of sand and rock, and the ocean floors vast plains of salt. Life would survive only around the margins of the ice fields and in rare oases fed by juvenile water.

The most rapidly moving glaciers are those of Greenland, some of which advance as much as 60 feet a day in the summer. In general, however, a few feet a day is a more characteristic rate. The Beardmore Glacier of Antarctica, the greatest in the world, moves at less than 3 feet a day, while the rate of outward flow of the great ice sheet itself is probably no more than a few feet a year.

By observing the changes in position of lines of stakes driven into the ice it is found that the middle of a glacier moves more rapidly than the sides, and that there is a similar decrease in velocity near the floor. The rate of flow increases with the steepness of the slope, with the thickness and temperature of the ice, and with constriction of the valley sides. Movement is retarded by the presence in the ice of a heavy load of debris and by friction against the rocky channel. These facts suggest that the flowage of glaciers is controlled mainly by stress differences and temperature.

It is well known that increase of pressure lowers the melting point of ice, and thus stimulates its transformation to water. More important, however, is the fact that stress differences are very much more effective in liberating molecules of water from rigid grains of ice. The mechanism of skating provides a clue to the problem of glacier flow. A skater really glides in a narrow groove of water formed momentarily under the intense stress applied to the ice by the thin blades of his skates. As he passes, the water immediately freezes again.

In a glacier or ice sheet, the shear stresses due to weight increase with depth and tend to squeeze the ice in the direction of least resistance. Lowering of the melting point at the base, where pressure and stress are greatest, and the rise of temperature that accompanies friction and erosion may partially offset the braking effect of frictional resistance. By means of tests carried out in deep bore-holes it has been shown that part of the motion of cirque and valley glaciers results from slipping and sliding, especially where there is a well-smoothed floor. But movement is mainly achieved by distortion of the ice.

The intergranular film of unfrozen saline water, already mentioned on p. 140, facilitates minute movements of the grains of ice amongst themselves. Wherever the interlocking crystals are subject to stresses that vary from point to point, mobile molecules of water are temporarily liberated at points where the strain is most severe. The temporary excess of water diffuses through the intergranular film into places where the stress is lower, and there an equivalent trace of water crystallizes on to the adjacent grains. In this way an average granule of ice may advance about 0·0001 of its own diameter in the course of a day. The migration is cumulative from points of high pressure and stress to points where these are lower. In the case of valley glaciers this commonly means that the direction of flow approximates to that of the downward slope of the valley. But flow does not necessarily come to an end if the floor happens to slope upwards. The Malaspina Glacier completes its journey to the sea over a rising floor. For this to be possible the upper surface of the ice must have a downward slope, as indeed it has across the apparently stagnant expanse of the Malaspina.

Movement in the same general direction—from high stress to low—also takes place by mechanical slipping along planes of fracture or dislocation in the individual grains of ice within a glacier. Recent studies with the electron microscope show that in stressed crystals of ice the dislocations (imperfections in the lattice structure) commonly migrate to the edges, in much the same way as the ruck in a carpet can be swept out. Thus every part of a grain of ice is provided in turn with an internal plane on which slipping can occur, and this process goes on repeatedly so long as there is sufficient stress to generate dislocations, and an intergranular film to accommodate the change of position implied by each minute slip. In all these ways each grain changes its shape and position under the influence of stress differences, waxing on one side, and waning on the other, so that the whole behaves as a rheid and flows continuously forward.

CREVASSES

A glacier generally has an upper crust, sometimes as much as 200 feet thick but usually much less, which readily cracks and so behaves like an elastic solid rather than a rheid. This more or less passive and brittle crust is carried along by the flowage of the deeper parts and the strains so induced within it are applied too rapidly for the process of flow described above to come into effective opera-

tion. If the ice becomes overstrained and gives way by stretching, as it commonly does, it breaks into the gaping fissures known as *crevasses*. On the other hand, where the ice passes through a constriction in a valley it thickens, and the crust is thrown into wave-like *pressure ridges*.

Stretching of ice, witnessed by the formation of crevasses, takes place when a glacier passes round a bend or over a convex slope in its floor, or spreads into an open valley or plain. *Marginal crevasses* result from differential drag against the valley sides. They develop,

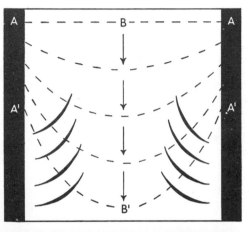

FIG. 9–6
Diagram to illustrate the development of marginal crevasses, arranged *en échelon*, as a result of the differential flow of glacier ice.

FIG. 9–7
The Rhône Glacier, showing crevasses. Viewed from the ridges above the Belvedere Hotel, near Gletsh, Switzerland. (*F. N. Ashcroft*)

145

as shown in Fig. 9–6, pointing or curving upstream from the sides of a glacier. The middle part of a glacier travels more rapidly than the sides (p. 144), where the ice is thinner and has to overcome the frictional resistance of the walls. Thus any line *ABA* is extended into a gradually lengthening catenary, such as *A′B′A′*. If the rate of extension is relatively slow, the moving ice can continue to adapt itself to the differential flow without cracking. But if the extension takes place more quickly, as is commonly the case, the ice will sooner or later crack. If *A′B′* were a straight line the crack would be at right angles to it, but since *A′B′* is curved the cracks and the resulting crevasses also tend to be curved. This curvature can be clearly seen in Fig. 9–7.

Transverse crevasses develop across a glacier wherever the floor is markedly convex (Fig. 9–8a). *Longitudinal crevasses*, roughly parallel to the direction of flow, form when ice spreads out laterally.

A special type of crevasse, which may be very wide and deep, is the *bergschrund*. This opens in summer near the top of the névé field of a cirque, where the head of a glacier is pulled away from the precipitous walls or from the ice adhering to them (Fig. 9–8a). Frequently several such fissures form instead of an especially large one (Fig. 9–8b).

Since crevasses are a by-product of flow they are not permanent features; some are closing up while others are opening. This adds to their danger; but the treacherous surface becomes most perilous to cross after a snowstorm, when the crevasses are likely to be hidden by snow bridges.

MORAINES

Rock fragments liberated from the steep slopes above a glacier, mainly by frost shattering, tumble down on the ice and are carried away. Thus the sides of a glacier become edged with long ribbons of debris described as marginal or *lateral moraines*. When two glaciers from adjacent valleys coalesce, adjoining lateral moraines unite and form a *medial moraine* on the surface of the united glacier. A trunk glacier fed by many tributaries may thus come to be ridged with a series of medial moraines composed of materials from different parts of the area of supply (Fig. 9–9).

Sooner or later part of the debris is engulfed by or washed into crevasses. Material that is enclosed within the ice is referred to as *englacial moraine*. A certain proportion reaches the sole of the glacier, and there, together with the material plucked or scraped from the rocky floor, it constitutes *subglacial moraine*.

If the lower part of the ice becomes so heavily charged with debris that it cannot transport it all, the excess is deposited as *ground moraine*, which is then over-ridden by the more active ice above. All the varied debris, ranging from angular blocks and boulders to the finest ground rock flour, that finally arrives at the terminus of the glacier is dumped down haphazardly when the ice melts. If the ice front remains stationary for several years an arcuate ridge is built up, called a *terminal* or *recessional moraine*. If, however, the snout is retreating, summer after summer, no piling up of a ridge is possible. The load liberated from the receding front then forms an irregular sheet which rests on the ground moraine already deposited.

Thin isolated slabs of rock or patches of debris on the surface of a glacier may be sufficiently heated by the sun to melt the underlying ice. Larger blocks, however, act as

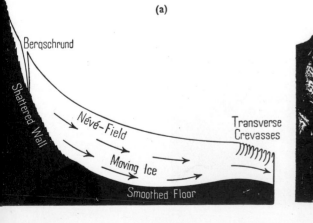

(a)

(b)

Bergschrund

Shattered Wall

Névé-Field

Moving Ice

Smoothed Floor

Transverse Crevasses

FIG. 9–8
(*a*) Schematic section through a cirque occupied by the head of a glacier, showing the bergschrund near the top and transverse crevasses above the threshold. (*b*) Bergschrund crevasses in an ice-filled cirque at the head of a glacier. (*Drawn from an aerial photograph of the Gelmerhorner, Switzerland*)

FIG. 9—9
Barnard Glacier, Alaska,
showing lateral moraines and
their coalescence into a
multiple series of medial
moraines. The high peak
on the skyline is Mt
Natazhat (13,480 feet:
4,109 m) on the Alaska-Yukon
boundary, 25 miles (40 km)
away. (*Bradford Washburn*)

a protection from the sun's rays, and as the surrounding ice melts away they are left as *glacier tables* perched on a column of ice. Even morainic ridges may stand out for a time on thick walls of ice.

In sunny weather small pools and rills diversify the surface, gathering into streams which mostly fall into crevasses. By a combination of melting and pot-hole action (aided by sand and boulders) deep cauldrons called *glacier mills* or *moulins* are worn through the fissured ice, and the water may escape to the snout through a tunnel. There, with melt water draining down the tapering end, it begins to flow down the valley as a milky stream laden with fine particles (Fig. 9–1).

GLACIAL EROSION

As we have seen, a glacier soon acquires a load of morainic material. Moreover, loose debris on the floor and sides is quickly dislodged and engulfed by actively advancing ice. Blocks from protuberances of jointed bedrocks are firmly grasped by the ice and withdrawn from the down-stream and unsupported side by a quarrying process referred to as *plucking*. The ice works its way into joints, bedding planes, and other fractures and closes round projecting masses with a firm grip, so that block after block is torn out of position

and carried away. The ragged surface left behind is readily susceptible to further plucking, and the process continues until the obstruction is removed or the glacier wanes.

Thus, even pure ice, which by itself would be a very ineffective tool for eroding massive rocks, is sooner or later transformed into a gigantic flexible file with embedded fragments of rock for teeth. *Abrasion* is the scraping and scratching of rock surfaces by debris frozen into the sole of a glacier or ice sheet. The larger fragments cut into and groove the floor and sides (Fig. 9–10), and are themselves worn flat and striated. The finer materials act like sandpaper, smoothing and polishing the rock surfaces and producing more powdered rock, or *rock flour*, in the process.

The rate of glacial erosion is extremely variable. Theoretically, the maximum rate of abrasion is approximately proportional to the cube of the velocity of the ice against its channel. Thus a powerful glacier in Northern Greenland may be 30,000 times more effective than the sluggish glaciers of the Alps. A continental ice sheet moves so slowly that it may do little more than remove the soil and smooth-off the minor irregularities of the buried landscape. In such a case the broader features of the pre-glacial relief are, on the whole, protected from denudation, though the surface is modified in detail into a character-

FIG. 9–10
Snout of the Woodworth Glacier, Tasnuna Valley, Alaska, which by its retreat has revealed a heavily grooved rock surface, crossed by a conspicuous esker. (*Bradford Washburn*)

istically hummocky form of knobs and hollows which reflect the varying resistances offered by the rocks to abrasion. But when the outflowing ice, or a valley glacier in a mountain district, is concentrated in a steeply descending valley, the erosive power reaches its maximum, and the pre-glacial relief is strongly accentuated. Beyond the region of steep gradients and rapid movement the rate of erosion gradually falls off and gives place to deposition as the ice becomes overloaded and reaches the zone of wastage. The three realms of accumulation, movement, and wastage are clearly seen in Fig. 9–1.

The geological work accomplished by ice, including erosion and deposition and the resulting effects of these processes on the surface, is collectively known as *glaciation*. The sculpturing of the surface beneath existing glaciers can be studied directly only in a limited way, by exploring ice caves and descending crevasses. Much more can be learned by taking advantage of the fact that most of the familiar glaciers of today—quite apart from the revealing recessions that have occurred during the last hundred years—are but the shrunken descendants of immense ice

caps that covered mountainous regions, or of even greater continental ice sheets that spread over most of North-Western Europe and half of North America during Pleistocene times (Fig. 9–11). Moreover, glaciation to this extent happened not once but repeatedly.

One of the earliest observers to suspect that glaciation was formerly far more extensive was de Saussure, the first scientific explorer of the Alps. In 1760 he noticed that miles below the snouts of the Alpine glaciers the rock surfaces were scratched and smoothed—in striking contrast with the frost-splintered peaks above—and strewn with morainic material exactly like that still being carried and deposited by the ice. He rightly concluded that the glaciers had formerly extended many miles beyond their then limits. But the "glacial theory" met with scant approval until after 1840, when the great naturalist Louis Agassiz awakened more general interest in the subject by the publication of his classic studies on the glaciation of the Alps. In later years Agassiz recognized that the similarly striated rock surfaces and morainic deposits of Scotland were also due to the former passage of ice. With a wealth of

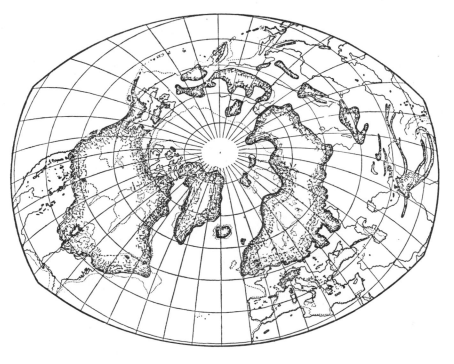

FIG. 9–11
Map showing the maximum
extent of the Pleistocene
ice sheets and ice caps in
the Northern Hemisphere.
(*After E. Antevs and R. F.
Flint*)

irresistible evidence he convinced the scientific world that such features could be accounted for in no other way. It is now familiar knowledge that the landscapes of vast areas of Europe and North America bear the unmistakable hall-marks of glaciation. Thus it happens that in many countries the characteristic effects of ice erosion and deposition, modified but little by subsequent weathering and river action, can be seen and studied close at hand.

Among the evidences of erosion by continental and valley glaciers, striated surfaces (Fig. 9–10) and ice-moulded hummocks of the more resistant bedrocks (Fig. 9–12) are of widespread occurrence. The residual hummocks vary widely in size, and have a characteristically streamlined form which is related to the direction of ice movement. The side up which the ice advanced rises as a smoothly abraded slope, while the lee side falls more steeply, sometimes as an abraded slope, but often by a step-like series of crags and ledges obviously due to the plucking out of joint blocks (Fig. 9–13). Seen from a distance the more isolated examples resemble sheep lying down, or wigs placed "face" downwards. They are, therefore, described as *roches moutonnées*, a term first used by de Saussure in 1804 in reference to the sheepskin wigs, styled *moutonnées*, which were then in vogue.

Highly resistant obstructions on a large scale, such as old volcanic plugs that lay in the path of the ice, are responsible for an erosional feature known as *crag and tail* (Fig. 9–14). The *crag* boldly faces the direction from which the ice came, while the *tail* (bedrock with or without a covering of boulder clay) is a gentle slope on the sheltered side, where the softer sediments were protected by the obstruction from the full rigour of ice erosion. A classic example is provided by the Castle Rock of Edinburgh, from the eastern side of which the High Street follows the sloping crest of the tail. The massive basalt plug diverted the ice flow, and deep channels, now occupied by Princes Street Gardens and the Grassmarket, were excavated in the sediments on each side of the crag and tail feature. Slieve Gullion, in Northern Ireland (Figs. 4–43 and 9–15), provides another example of crag and tail where glacial debris has been concentrated on the sheltered side upon a tail of igneous bedrock.

In mountainous and upland coastal regions with well-developed valley systems, the topographic modifications superimposed on the landscape by glacial erosion include U-shaped valleys with truncated spurs and hanging tributary valleys; corries or cirques surmounted by sharp-edged ridges and pyramidal peaks; and rock basins and fjords. Waterfalls descending the precipitous valley sides, and lakes occupying the overdeepened hollows of the valley floors, add variety to an assemblage of features that can be easily distinguished from the landscapes of unglaciated regions.

CIRQUES (CORRIES) AND ASSOCIATED FEATURES

It has been observed that chance hollows occupied by persistent snowbanks are steadily cut back and deepened by (*a*) disintegration of the marginal and underlying rocks by frost and thaw, and (*b*) removal of the shattered debris by falling, avalanching, solifluction, and transport by melt water. By this process of snow-patch erosion or *nivation* the slopes above are undercut and the surrounding walls are kept steep as they recede (Fig. 9–16). The

FIG. 9–12
Ice-sculptured surface of *roche moutonnée* type. East of Sanna Bay, Ardnamurchan, Scotland. (*H.M. Geological Survey*)

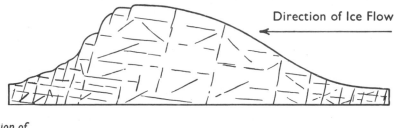

Direction of Ice Flow

FIG. 9–13
Section through a typical *roche moutonnée*, showing the effects of ice abrasion where the rock is sparsely jointed, and of plucking where jointing is well developed.

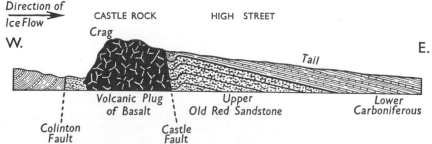

Direction of Ice Flow

CASTLE ROCK   HIGH STREET

Crag

W.   E.

Tail

Volcanic Plug of Basalt

Upper Old Red Sandstone

Lower Carboniferous

Colinton Fault

Castle Fault

FIG. 9–14
Crag and Tail, Edinburgh. The Castle Rock, a volcanic plug, probably represents an early outbreak of the Arthur's Seat volcano. See Fig. 4–35.

FIG. 9—15
Crag and Tail. Slieve Gullion, the relic of a Tertiary volcano, forms the Crag with its "Tail", on the right, extending southwards like a sloping railway embankment: viewed from near Forkhill, Co. Armagh, Northern Ireland. (*Doris L. Holmes*)

FIG. 9—16
Cirques developed by "snow rotting" on the cliffs of Spitsbergen. (*Sketch by F. Nansen*)

larger hollows grow more rapidly than the smaller ones, especially near and above the snow line, until the mountain slopes and valley sides are festooned with deep snow fields, the largest of all being at the valley heads. Eventually these nourish small glaciers which carry away the debris and begin more active excavation of the floor. Headward erosion of the walls continues, not only by frost sapping at the exposed edges of the snow field, but also by a process of subglacial disintegration which comes into play whenever the bergschrund allows surface water to reach the rocks behind or beneath the ice. Draining into cracks and joints, the water freezes and breaks up the rocks until they are gripped by the ice, and carried away as ground moraine. Thus by the co-operation of several processes great amphitheatres are eventually hollowed out. These are known as *cirques* in the Alps, *corries* in Scotland, and *cwms* in Wales (Figs. 9–1 and 9–16).

During the stage of most intense glaciation the floor and sides of a growing cirque are subjected to vigorous abrasion in consequence of the great thickness and high pressure of the ice and snow above it. A shallow rock basin may then be excavated by the outflowing ice,

to become the site of a mountain tarn or lake after the ice has disappeared (Fig. 9–17). Such lakes may also be held back by arcuate ridges of morainic material left stranded by the waning ice during its final recession.

Two adjoining cirques may approach and intersect until only a sharp-edged dividing wall remains between them. The resulting precipitous ridge is known as an *arête*. When the ice has gone the steep rocky slopes fall a ready prey to frost action, and soon become aproned with screes. Many an upland region has been eaten into by cirque erosion from several sides at once, and so reduced to a series of arêtes radiating like a starfish from a central summit. Snowdon and Helvellyn are good examples. At a later stage the arêtes themselves are worn back, and the central mass, where the heads of three or more cirques come together, remains isolated as a conspicuous pyramidal peak. In this way the *horns* of the Alps have been formed, the world-famous Matterhorn being the type example of its class (Fig. 9–18).

MODIFICATIONS OF VALLEYS BY GLACIAL EROSION

By the passage of a vigorous glacier through a

FIG. 9—17
Snowdon (3,560 feet:
1,085 m) and Glaslyn, a tarn
occupying an ice-eroded
rock basin, viewed from
the long arête of Crib Goch,
North Wales. (*G. P. Abraham
Ltd, Keswick*)

FIG. 9—18
The Matterhorn (14,704 ft:
4,482 m), highest peak of
the Pennine Alps, along
the Swiss-Italian frontier.
(*G. P. Abraham Ltd, Keswick*)

FIG. 9–19
Typical U-shaped valley. Glen Rosa, Island of Arran, Scotland. (*H.M. Geological Survey*)

pre-existing river valley the mantle of rock waste is removed, the overlapping spurs are trimmed off and ground into facets, and the floor is worn down. The valley is thus widened and deepened, and is eventually remodelled into a U-shaped trough with a broad floor and steep sides and a notable freedom from bends of small radius (Fig. 9–19). Flat floors are not uncommon, however, where the bottom of the trough has been levelled up by subsequent deposition of alluvium (Fig. 9–22). Whole valley systems have been completely overwhelmed by ice sheets, but in less severely glaciated regions, where valleys have not been entirely filled by ice, the upper slopes may remain as high-level benches which meet the ice-steepened walls in a prominent shoulder. The cross profile is like a U sunk in a V.

Tributary valleys have their lower ends cut clean away as the spurs between them are

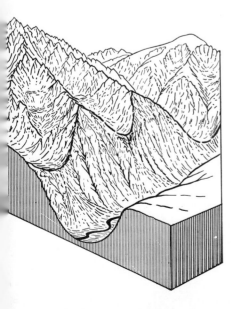

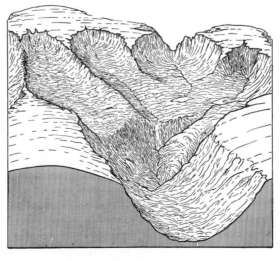

FIG. 9–20
Block diagram illustrating some of the characteristic landscape features of glaciated valleys and mountains: U-shaped valley; truncated spurs; hanging tributary valleys; cirques, arêtes, and horns. The bench across the lower right-hand corner is depicted as unglaciated. (*Modified after W. M. Davis*)

FIG. 9–21
Block diagram to illustrate the "trough-end" at the head of a valley glaciated by tributary glaciers from several confluent cirques. The hill summits are depicted as unglaciated. (*Modified after W. M. Davis*)

153

ground back and truncated (Fig. 9–20). The floor of a trunk glacier, moreover, is deepened more effectively than those of lateral feeders (Figs. 9–20 and 9–21). Thus, after a period of prolonged glaciation the side valleys are left hanging high above the flanks of the main trough. The streams from such *hanging valleys* plunge over their discordant lips in cascades or waterfalls, some of which are amongst the highest in the world. Yosemite Valley in the Sierra Nevada of California is renowned for its impressive examples of these and other spectacular features due to glacial erosion. A remarkably similar glacial trough—the finest of its kind in Europe—is the Lauter-brunnen valley, with its celebrated Falls, between Interlaken and the Jungfrau. Fig. 9–22 illustrates a British example.

Glacially excavated floors are deepened very unevenly, the depth at each point depending on the thickness and velocity of the ice and the nature and structure of the bedrocks. Poorly consolidated strata are scoured out more rapidly than resistant rocks, and tracts of well-jointed rocks are selectively quarried away by plucking. Thus, where the ice encounters a sequence of rocks of varied resistance the floor is excavated into a series of steps, often with abrupt descents from one tread to the next, so that the long profile of a heavily glaciated valley may resemble a giant stairway (Fig. 9–23). Sometimes a step is hollowed out into a basin behind a barrier of resistant rock. Such rock basins are later filled by lakes, or by tracts of alluvium representing

the sites of shallow lakes that have since been silted up. Examples of lakes occupying such "over-deepened" basins and troughs are recorded in the table below. Morainic deposits on the bedrock barrier add slightly to the depth of water in some of these lakes.

Fjords are greatly overdeepened glacial troughs that reach the coast below sea level, so that, instead of forming elongated lake basins, they have become long arms of the sea stretching inland between steep rocky walls (Fig. 9–24). The terminal rock barrier (with or without a cover of moraine) occurs near the seaward entrance, and is wholly or partly submerged. This is the *threshold* of the fjord. Along the west coast of Scotland there are all gradations from the submerged thresholds of the sea lochs (fjords) to the more or less exposed barriers that separate freshwater lochs from the sea. The terminal rim of Loch Morar is close to the sea and rises only 30 feet or so above it. The threshold of Loch Etive is lower and is uncovered only at low tide. Twenty-three of the remaining sea lochs have thresholds near their entrances which, at the present sea level, are permanently submerged.

Fjords have been developed during the intense glaciation of dissected coastal plateaux and mountains of appropriate structure in countries such as Scotland, Norway, Greenland, Labrador, British Columbia, Alaska, Patagonia, and New Zealand. In plan (Fig. 9–25) they everywhere have a characteristic rectilinear pattern which is clearly determined by the distribution of belts of structural weak-

LAKES	MAXIMUM DEPTH (IN FEET)	HEIGHT OF SURFACE ABOVE SEA LEVEL	MAXIMUM DEPTH OF FLOOR BELOW SEA LEVEL
ENGLISH LAKE DISTRICT			
Windermere	219	128	91
Wastwater	258	200	58
SCOTLAND			
Loch Coruisk	125	25	100
Loch Lomond	653	20	633
Loch Ness	771	53	718
Loch Morar	1,017	30	987
SWISS-ITALIAN ALPS			
Lake Maggiore	1,220	636	584
Lake Como	1,345	650	695
NORTH AMERICA			
Lake Michigan	984	580	404
Lake Superior	1,302	602	700
Great Slave Lake	2,014	492	1,522

FIG. 9–22
Waterfall descending from the hanging valley of Allt Coire Mhail, Glen Nevis, Inverness-shire. (*H.M. Geological Survey*)

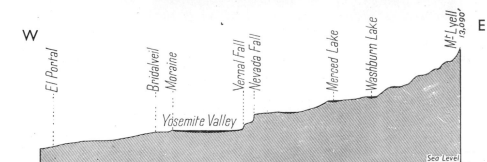

W   E

El Portal   Bridalveil   Moraine   Vernal Fall   Nevada Fall   Merced Lake   Washburn Lake   Mt. Lyell 13,090'

Yosemite Valley

Sea Level

FIG. 9–23
Longitudinal profile along the Yosemite Valley, about 150 miles east of San Francisco. A typical "glacial stairway" developed by selective ice erosion. The length of the section is 36 miles (58 km).

FIG. 9–24
Naeröyfjord, on the south side of Sognefjord, Norway. (*Mittet Foto, Norway*)

ness. The latter may be synclines of relatively weak sediments or schists enclosed by massive crystalline rocks (as in the Sogne and Hardanger Fjords of Norway), but more commonly they are fractured belts with closely spaced joints locally accompanied by faults and dykes. The pre-glacial rivers carved their valleys along these lines of least resistance. The valleys in turn confined the ice and guided its flow, and because the structure facilitated plucking, the valley floors were steadily deepened, often to an extraordinary degree. In

155

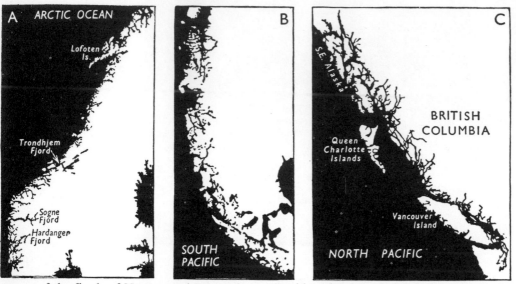

FIG. 9—25
Three examples of fjord coasts: (A) Norway (B) Southern Chile (C) SE. Alaska and British Columbia

some of the fjords of Norway and Patagonia the sea is over 4,000 feet (1,200 m) deep. Neighbouring fjords, however, vary enormously in depth, in accordance with the varying resistance of the excavated rocks. The distribution of fjords is thus conditioned by (*a*) appropriate tectonic structures in upland regions near the sea, (*b*) pre-existing valleys which followed these structures, and (*c*) heavy glaciation by seaward-moving ice of sufficient thickness and surface slope to ensure that the main valleys were overdeepened up to or beyond the present coast.

GLACIAL DEPOSITS

As glaciers and ice sheets reach the zone of wastage beyond the region of active erosion they become overloaded and begin to drop their burden of debris. During the subsequent disappearance of the ice, in response to an amelioration of climate, the zone of deposition retreats with the receding ice front until the whole of the load has been deposited. The *glacial* deposits thus left stranded on the landscape and the *glaciofluvial* sands and gravels transported and deposited by the associated melt waters have long been grouped together under the general term *drift*. At one time the vast spreads of drift that indicate the former extent of the ice across Europe and North America were thought to be flood deposits, and many attempts were made to assign them to the deluge of Noah. Eventually, however, it was recognized that the commonest type of drift, the haphazard assemblage of material known as *boulder clay* or *till*, could not possibly have been deposited by water.

Boulder clay has obviously been dumped down in a completely unsorted and unstratified condition. Its constituents range from the finest rock flour to stones of all sizes up to boulders that are occasionally of immense bulk. It usually consists of a varied assortment of stones embedded in a tenacious matrix of sand, clay, and rock flour. Most of the stones, like those of screes, are irregular fragments showing little or no sign of wear or tear, but a few can generally be found which have been rubbed down and scratched and grooved, clearly by scraping along the rocky floor over which they were dragged by the ice.

A characteristic feature of glaciated regions is the occurrence of scattered boulders of rocks that are foreign to the place where they have been dropped. These ice-transported blocks, carried far from their parent outcrops, are called *erratics*. The largest ones commonly rest on abraded surfaces where the normal drift is thinly scattered or confined to hollows. Some have been stranded in exposed and precarious positions. Such *perched blocks* are striking monuments to the former passage of ice, and as such they were amongst the first evidences of glaciation to be recognized. In 1815 Playfair pointed out that "a glacier . . . which conveys the rocks on its surface . . . is the only agent we now see capable of transporting them to such a distance." The long trails of erratic blocks of easily recognized rocks afford an unfailing guide to the direction of movement of the ice that carried them. Boulders of the well-known Shap granite, for example, can be traced from their original home in Westmorland across the Pennines by way of the Stainmore Pass into the

Vale of York. Ailsa Craig in the Firth of Clyde is an upstanding mass of finely speckled granitic rock which can be identified with certainty. Erratics of this rock, as isolated blocks and as stones embedded in boulder clay, are found in Antrim, Galloway, and the Isle of Man, and on both sides of the Irish Sea as far as Wicklow and South Wales, and show that Ailsa Craig lay in the track of a great southward-travelling glacier. Familiar Norwegian rocks from the Oslo district, such as rhomb-porphyry and larvikite (a shimmering blue syenite much used for shop fronts) occur as erratics along the Durham and Yorkshire coasts, and prove that the Scandinavian ice sheet crossed the North Sea and at times overran the British shores. At other times these rocks reached northern Germany, showing that the directions of ice dispersal were not always the same.

At or near the maximum extension of a glacier or ice sheet the front may have remained stationary or nearly so (forward movement being just balanced by wastage) sufficiently long for a ridge-like *terminal moraine* to be heaped up. Similar, but later, terminal moraines, distinguished as *recessional moraines*, mark the sites of halting stages during the shrinkage of the ice, and indicate that forward flow was maintained so that a

steady supply of debris was brought up to the ice front. In certain lowland regions the ice appears to have fanned out and become stagnant. Such "dead" ice simply melts away from the top and sides, and also from the edges of crevasses, and liberates its debris without forming terminal moraines.

The terminal and chief recessional moraines formed at successive stands of the European ice sheet are shown in Fig. 9–26. Similar features, traversing the country in broad loops to the south of the Great Lakes, mark the various pauses in the recession of the North American ice. The terminal moraines left by mountain glaciers cross their valleys as crescent-shaped embankments (concave upstream) which in some cases continue along the valley sides as less conspicuous lateral moraines (Fig. 9–27). Many of the lakes of glaciated valleys are partly held up by morainic dams, like Lake Garda at the foot of the Italian Alps (Fig. 9–27). Most of the larger lakes of the Lake District and many of the Scottish lochs have morainic dams. Examples can also be found where lakes, held up by recessional moraines, have now disappeared. In South Wales, for example, the river Neath has a glaciated valley with tributaries entering from hanging valleys in its upper course. At Aberdulais a recessional

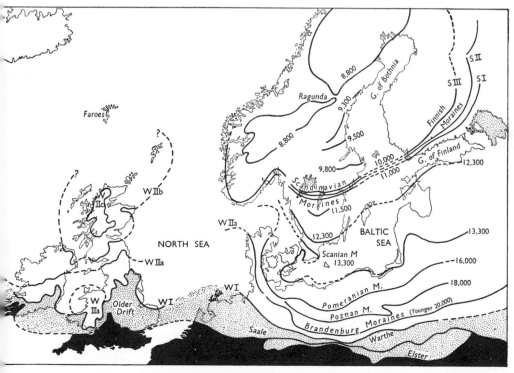

FIG. 9–26
Map illustrating the extent of Pleistocene glaciations over NW. Europe and the chief moraines and drift borders marking stages in the recession of the last great ice sheet. The dates are expressed in years before the present.

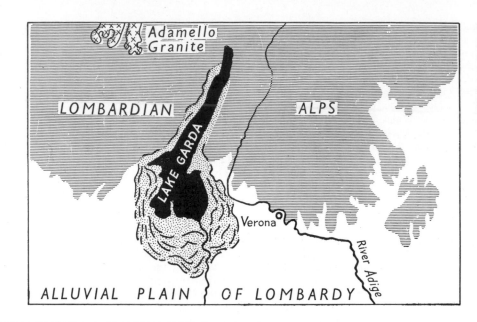

FIG. 9–27
Lake Garda at the foot of
the Italian Alps, with its
bordering lateral and terminal
moraines. The lake owes
490 feet (149 m) of its
depth to the thickness of
the morainic barrier. Below
that level, down to a maximum
depth of 1,135 feet (346 m),
the lake occupies an ice-
excavated rock basin.

FIG. 9–28
"Basket of eggs" topography.
A typical landscape of
drumlins which have been
moulded into streamlined
forms by the passage of ice
moving from right to left.

moraine dammed back the river in early post-glacial times and so formed a lake that disappeared long ago. Fan deltas, formed where hanging tributary valleys entered the lake, still remain as evidence; one of these now truncated by the river Neath, can be seen at Resolven. The flat tops of these fan deltas indicate that they mark the margin of a former lake.

In the tracts between the morainic embankments, the spreads of boulder clay naturally vary widely in character and thickness from place to place. In certain regions where the boulder clay is thickly plastered over a floor of low relief it has been moulded by the ice into swarms of whale-backed mounds called *drumlins* (Gaelic, *druim*, a mound). Being distributed more or less *en échelon* the mounds give rise to what has been aptly described as "basket of eggs" topography (Fig. 9–28). In the intervening depressions drainage is poor and confused, and is responsible for such features as ponds, marshes, and water-logged meadows. One of the most densely packed drumlin belts stretches across northern Ireland from Co. Down to Donegal Bay, and con-

tains tens of thousands of these stream-lined mounds (Fig. 9–29).

Drumlins are commonly a quarter to half a mile long, but there is every gradation from low swells to enormous examples a mile or two in length and 100 to 200 feet high. Most of them are elongated in the direction of ice movement, and the end facing upstream is relatively broad and blunt compared with the end or "tail" tapering downstream (Figs. 9–28 and 9–30). This is a typical streamlined form; implying that the surface between the moving ice and the sub-glacial drift was moulded by both erosion and deposition towards the form offering the least resistance to the advancing ice. A blunt-nosed fish or a whale swims with the blunt end in front; that is to say (remembering the relativity of motion) it faces the direction of flow of the water streaming past it, and so avoids creating energy-consuming eddies. In the same way drumlins and crag-and-tail features present their blunt ends *towards* the advancing ice flow. Roches moutonnées are an exception to this rule because they are only partially streamlined, the end past which the ice was flowing being steep and irregular because it resulted from the plucking-out of blocks of strong but well-jointed rock.

The regional distribution of drumlins (Fig. 9–31) indicates that they developed under deep ice at a distance of many miles from the front towards which the ice was advancing. Consequently, it is impossible to see drumlins in course of formation, and their origin can be deduced only by analogy with related phenomena produced when one medium is flowing over another. Wind blowing over sand produces sand dunes. Water flowing over beach sand or river sand produces sandbanks. In both cases material is continually eroded from one side of the structure and deposited on the other, so that the structure as a whole migrates slowly in the direction of flow. It seems probable that drumlins are formed in an essentially similar way, the high viscosity and slow rate of flow of ice being compensated by an abundance of time.

GLACIOFLUVIAL DEPOSITS

The drainage from the long front of an ice sheet escapes by way of an immense number of more or less temporary and constantly shifting

FIG. 9–29
Map of part of a drumlin tract in Co. Down, Northern Ireland. (After J. K. Charlesworth)

FIG. 9–30
Typical drumlin country around Wigtown in the SW. of Scotland. (H.M. Geological Survey)

streams. These carry off a great deal of sediment and, as the velocity is checked, low alluvial fans or deltas are deposited, according as the ice terminates on land or in standing water. On land the fans spread out and coalesce into gently sloping *outwash plains* (Fig. 9–31) of irregularly stratified drift, ranging from coarse gravels near the source to sand further out, and finally to clay. Valley floors are choked with similar deposits; mainly coarse, however, because the finer materials are rapidly washed downstream.

Where the supply of debris is abundant, outwash plains may extend for many miles beyond the terminal moraines of ice sheets.

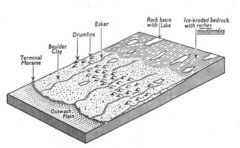

FIG. 9–31
The characteristic assemblage of features seen on a recently glaciated area of low relief.

Vast areas of the North American prairies have been smoothly veneered with sediment in this way. Between successive moraines the outwash drifts rest on previously deposited boulder clay. Masses of stagnant ice, left stranded between deep crevasses as the main front melted back, are often surrounded and even buried by drift, and as they melt away they leave the surface pitted with depressions known as *kettle holes*, many of which still contain lakes or ponds (Fig. 9–32).

Such drift-covered regions are further diversified by mounds (*kames*), long winding ridges (*eskers*, Figs. 9–10 and 9–33), and relatively short and straight ridges (*crevasse infillings*). All of these are built of crudely bedded gravel and sand, showing that they are features for which glacial streams were responsible.

Kames are isolated or clustered mounds, each of which represents a steep-faced localized alluvial cone or delta built up by a stream emerging at a high level from a temporarily stagnant ice front. As the ice receded, the unsupported back or sides of the accumulation slumped down, leaving a mound with slopes corresponding to the angle of repose of gravel or sand. If such a stream, instead of

FIG. 9–32
Kettle hole near Finstown, WNW. of Kirkwall, Orkney. (*H.M. Geological Survey*)

FIG. 9–33
Esker at Holylee, Tweed valley, 12 miles (19 km) W. of Melrose, Scotland. (*R. J. A. Eckford, H.M. Geological Survey*)

FIG. 9–34
The Marielen See. an
ice-dammed lake held up by
the Aletch Glacier, between
the Jungfrau and the Upper
Rhone, Switzerland.
(*Hans Steiner*)

being short and temporary, were long and persistent, then the deposit continuously formed at its mouth would grow backwards as the ice retreated, thus extending into a winding ridge that would reproduce the course of the stream. Some *eskers* may have originated in this way. But such a stream would also deposit sediment while flowing through its tunnel in the ice, thus gradually raising its floor. Most eskers are therefore regarded as the infillings of the tunnels of unusually long sub-glacial streams. In some cases, where later outwash drift has lapped against them, it is obvious that thcy originated within the ice before it receded. Eskers characteristically disregard the underlying topography, which they cross like long railway embankments, this form being assumed as a result of the inevitable slumping of the original sides. Their courses, though winding, are generally aligned more or less at right angles to the receding ice front (Fig. 9–10). In glaciated lands riddled with lakes and marshes, like Finland, Sweden, and Canada, eskers provide natural causeways across many districts where road and railway construction would otherwise be difficult. In Ireland, roads and railways are similarly constructed on eskers in order to cross bogs. One extending from Dublin to Galway carries the railway, and long ago was used as the post road. To the south-west of Belfast a north-easterly trending esker is used by the road and railway.

Ridges that differ from eskers in being short and straight are interpreted as the in-fillings of crevasses that remained in a frontal or isolated sheet of ice when it became stagnant during the last stages of melting away.

ICE-DAMMED MARGINAL LAKES AND DIVERTED DRAINAGE

A glacier occupying a main valley may obstruct the mouth of a tributary valley and so impound the drainage and make a lake. The Marjelen See, held up in this way by the Aletsch Glacier (between the Jungfrau and the Upper Rhone) is a small-scale example (Fig. 9–34), and there are many others, large and small, in Norway, Iceland, and Greenland. Where the ice barrier is sufficiently high and massive the lake rises to the col or pass at the head of its valley and escapes through an *overflow channel* into the valley on the other side of the divide. During the degeneration of an ice cap into valley glaciers, the higher ridges of a divide between two neighbouring valleys may be uncovered, while the ice still extends across the divide at a lower level. Melt water then accumulates along the margin of the ice against the flanks of the hills, and if it overflows from one side of the ridge to the other, a channel is cut in the ridge, which thus becomes notched. Notching by marginal overflow channels may be repeated again and again at successively lower levels while the ice is retreating.

During the recession of the great Pleistocene ice sheets enormous numbers of ice-dammed lakes came into temporary existence some of

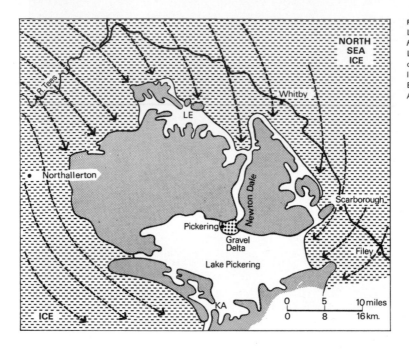

FIG. 9–35
Lake Pickering (*After P. F. Kendall, 1902*). White—Lake; Grey—land not covered by ice; dashed or broken lines—ice. L.E.—Lake Eskdale. K.A.—Kirkham Abbey.

them being immensely larger than any of the lakes of the present day. They formed wherever a drainage basin sloped down towards an obstructing ice dam. Some of these marginal lakes overflowed at successively lower levels before they eventually disappeared, each stand of the lake being determined by the height of the lowest outlet available at any given stage during the wasting away of the ice barrier. The features and deposits left behind by such lakes (thereby providing evidence of their former existence) include: (*a*) overflow channels at the outlets, often eroded into conspicuous valleys and gorges (now dry) situated at the heads of the valleys from which the lake waters escaped, or across the ridges and spurs between neighbouring valleys; (*b*) shore-line deposits and terraces, formed by the action of waves and currents; (*c*) deltas deposited by streams flowing into the lake; and (*d*) lake-floor sediments.

In the north of England several large lakes were formed when drainage was locally ponded back by Pleistocene ice sheets. Lakes Humber and Ouse were formed when the Humber and Wash were blocked by North Sea ice, whilst many smaller lakes were ponded back in the south-west Pennines. Two former ice-damned lakes, Lake Harrison and Lake Pickering, jointly illustrate all the features, listed above, that provide evidence of the former existence of lakes. Prior to the glacial period the Vale of Pickering was

drained by the River Derwent which then flowed eastwards reaching the sea at Filey. When the Vale of Pickering was blocked at its eastern end by North Sea ice and at its western end by Pennine ice, its drainage was ponded back and Lake Pickering was formed, on the floor of which finely laminated lake clay was deposited. (Fig. 9–35). The lake rose to about 225 feet O.D. (69 m) and overflowed on its southern side near Kirkham Abbey, cutting an overflow channel, the Kirkham Abbey gorge, through which the Derwent now flows southwards to the Humber. Another overflow channel, Newton Dale, cuts right across the Cleveland Hills. This is a typical overflow channel with steep sides and a flat floor. During the glacial period it drained ice-damned lakes, on the northern side of the Cleveland Hills, into Lake Pickering, and where the overflow entered Lake Pickering a large gravel delta was formed on which the town of Pickering now stands (Fig. 9–35).

Lake Harrison, named after W. J. Harrison (1898) by whom its former existence was first recognized, was located in Warwickshire (Fig. 9–36). It was ponded back by ice sheets approaching from the north-west, west, and north-east, and was bounded on its south-eastern side by high land (the Chalk Wolds of today). Evidence for the former existence of this lake is provided by lake clays deposited on its floor (Shotten, 1913, 1953), and by an erosion terrace (Dury, 1951) cut on the south-eastern side of the lake at a level of 410 feet (125 m) above present sea level. The lake terrace is up to a quarter of a mile wide and extends for about 35 miles from the northern Cotswolds to a point south of Rugby. It is a wave-cut platform, formed at a time when the lake spilled through the Fenny Compton gap; a col in the highlands bounding the south-eastern side of the lake. The lake terrace continues into the Fenny Compton gap which controlled the level of the lake.

Prior to the existence of Lake Harrison, the drainage from the area flowed north-eastward via the river Soar, which at that time was much longer than it is today, and so into the River Trent discharging into the Humber. This drainage route to the north-east was closed at the time when ice ponded back the waters of Lake Harrison, and because the ice on the south-western side of the lake was the first to retreat, the lake eventually drained away in that direction. So began the Warwick-

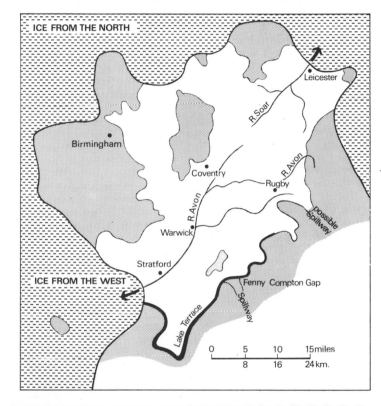

FIG. 9–36
Lake Harrison (*After F. Shotten, 1913 and G. Dury, 1951*). White— Lake; Grey—Land not covered by ice; dashed or broken lines—ice. The rivers are those of the present day.

FIG. 9–37
The Parallel Roads of Glen Roy. (*H.M. Geological Survey*)

shire Avon which to this day drains south-westward to join the Severn flowing into the Bristol Channel.

The most celebrated lake terraces formed around ice-damned lakes are the Parallel Roads of Glen Roy, Inverness (Fig. 9–37). These are beaches about 40 to 50 feet wide which follow the contours at the levels shown on the map (Fig. 9–38). Each beach can be traced to the head of a valley, where a spill-way (overflow channel) is found corresponding to the level at which the lake overflowed while the beach was being formed. Ice extending from Ben Nevis across the valleys to the north blocked the entrances to Glen Roy and Glen Gloy. The highest lake (1,165 feet: 355 m), that

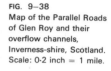

FIG. 9–38
Map of the Parallel Roads of Glen Roy and their overflow channels, Inverness-shire, Scotland. Scale: 0·2 inch = 1 mile.

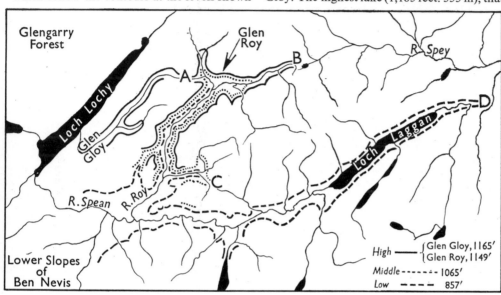

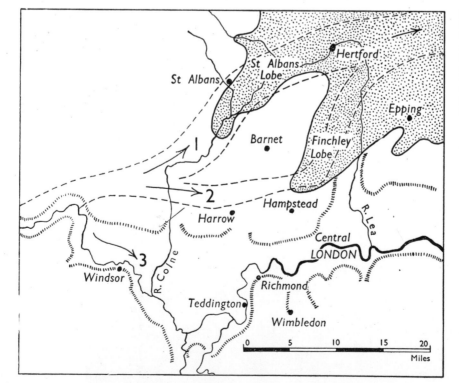

FIG. 9–39
Successive courses of the River Thames from early Pleistocene times: 1. through the Vale of St Albans; 2. through the Finchley gap; 3. through the present valley. Ice sheet (dotted) projecting as lobes along valleys 1 and 2.

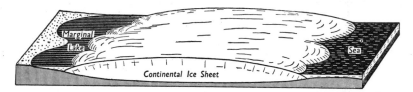

FIG. 9–40
Diagram illustrating the isostatic depression of a land surface by a continental ice sheet, and the consequent development of marginal lakes during the recession of the ice.

of Glen Gloy, discharged across the watershed at A into the Glen Roy lake (1,149 feet: 350 m) which overflowed into the river Spey at B. Later, an outlet into a tributary of Glen Spean was uncovered at C (1,065 feet: 322 m), and the lake rapidly drained to that level. This stage, during which the waters escaped over the eastward-sloping surface of the Glen Spean ice, lasted until further withdrawal of the ice allowed the lake to extend along Glen Spean, whence it overflowed through D (857 feet: 261 m), the outlet at its head. In due course the lobe of ice that blocked the lower part of the valley dwindled away sufficiently to allow the lake to drain towards the sea (Loch Linnhe) and so, finally, to disappear.

The lower course of the River Thames was twice diverted during Pleistocene times, but in each case it followed a new route and no ice-damned lake was formed. During early Pleistocene times the Thames flowed through the Vale of St Albans, and when this route became blocked, either as a result of gentle up-arching across the valley or by an advancing ice sheet, the river found a new route through the Finchley depression and joined its old course to the east of Hertford (Fig. 9–39). The Thames continued to use the Finchley loop for perhaps half a million years, and then ice advancing into the London basin blocked its passage across Essex to the sea, and sent ice lobes, up both the Finchley depression and the Vale of St Albans (Fig. 9–39). Thus the Thames was forced into the more southerly course which has become its present valley.

During the recession of the continental ice sheets of Europe and North America conditions were highly favourable to the development of widespread marginal lakes (Fig. 9–40). At the time of maximum extension of the ice the less mountainous parts of the underlying floor were depressed into a shallow bowl by the isostatic effect of the load of ice. The thickness of the ice reached 8,000 feet or more, tapering off towards the margins. The corresponding subsidence of the crust, where the load was greatest, would therefore be over 2,000 feet; sufficient, that is, to depress vast areas of the rock surface well below sea level. Such is the condition of Antarctica today. During the

retreat of the ice the crust was gradually unloaded and isostatic recovery worked in from the margins, though with a considerable lag. Consequently, for thousands of years there were large tracts, abandoned by the ice, that sloped towards and beneath the receding ice front. Many of these became giant lakes, while others were invaded by the sea. The isostatic recovery already achieved since the disappearance of the ice is clearly demonstrated by the occurrence of raised beaches (Figs. 2–7 and 2–8) at various heights above sea level and by the tilted attitude of many lake terraces. Moreover, the fact that the shores of Hudson Bay and the Gulf of Bothnia are steadily rising even now shows that the process of restoring isostatic equilibrium is still going on. The deeper depressions within the areas that were formerly inundated are, of course, still occupied by lakes or by the sea. The Great Lakes of North America and the Baltic Sea are outstanding examples.

LAKES: A GENERAL SUMMARY

It will already have been gathered that lakes are amongst the most characteristic features of the landscape of glaciated regions. Finland is renowned for its innumerable lakes, 55,000 of which have been mapped. Very appropriately, the Finns call their country *Suomi*— the Land of Lakes. Many parts of Ontario and the neighbouring Provinces and States are riddled with a comparable network of lakes and waterways. The extraordinary abundance at the present time of lakes of glacial origin— they are far more numerous than all other types put together—is a result of two circumstances: (*a*) immense numbers occupy hollows, excavated in the less resistant rocks by ice scouring, or irregular concavities in the drift surface left behind by the retreating ice; and (*b*) these lakes originated so recently that only some of the shallower ones have since been silted up and replaced by lacustrine flats (Fig. 7–11).

THE ORIGIN OF LAKE BASINS

Given a supply of water in excess of the amounts lost by evaporation or by seepage through the floor and sides, a lake continues to exist so long as the floor of its basin remains below the lowest part of the rim. Lakes are therefore conveniently classified according to the mode of origin of their basins.

LAKE BASINS DUE TO GLACIAL ACTIVITY

Lakes of glacial origin may occupy:

(*a*) ice-eroded rock basins in valleys or cirques with or without morainic fringes (Fig. 9–17);

(*b*) valleys obstructed by morainic barriers (Fig. 9–27);

(*c*) depressions due to surface irregularities of glacial drift.

(*d*) kettle holes left by the melting of buried or partly buried masses of stagnant ice (Fig. 9–32);

(*e*) valleys obstructed by ice barriers (Fig. 9–34).

Lake basins owing their origin to other geological processes are described in the appropriate chapters, but for convenience the following summary is added here.

LAKE BASINS DUE TO EARTH MOVEMENTS

Tectonic depressions are responsible for the largest of the world's lakes (Caspian Sea), the deepest (L. Tanganiyka), the lowest (Dead Sea), and amongst those of notable size the highest (L. Titicaca, Bolivian plateau), as well as for many shallow lakes, both large (L. Victoria) and small (local sinkings of the ground accompanying earthquakes). In terms of origin the chief types are due to:

(*a*) *Crustal Warping* (L. Victoria, page 236; Lough Neagh, Fig. 14–14) and the backtilting of valley systems (L. Kyoga, Fig. 13–24).

(*b*) *Folding* across pre-existing valleys.

(*c*) *Differential Faulting*, especially in the African Rift Valleys and in the Great Basin of the Western States.

(*d*) *Tear Faults* across a pre-existing valley, whereby it may be obstructed by a hill range (L. Joux, Jura Mountains; Fahlensee, Santis Alps). The lakes (lochs) along the Great Glen in Scotland are sited along a tear-fault (Figs. 4–26 and 4–27).

LAKE BASINS DUE TO VOLCANIC ACTIVITY

(*a*) *Craters* and *Calderas* of extinct or dormant volcanoes (Crater Lake, Oregon, Fig. 14–13).

(*b*) *Lava Flows* forming barriers across valleys (Sea of Galilee; L. Kivu, Fig. 13–26).

LAKE BASINS DUE TO DEPOSITION OF SEDIMENTS

Obstruction of valleys and river channels may be brought about by:

(*a*) *Landslides* (page 101) and occasionally by avalanches and screes.

(*b*) *River Deposits*: Alluvial fans from relatively vigorous side streams (Fig. 7–33) The sealing off at both ends of abandoned meander loops (ox-bow lakes, Fig. 13–27). Levee building in general (flood-plain lakes and swamps and delta lagoons).

(*c*) *Glacial Deposits* (see above).

(*d*) *Wind Deposits*: Coastal sand dunes enclosing lagoons and marshes (as in the Landes of south-west France).

(*e*) *Marine Deposits*: Closed bars and barrier beaches enclosing coastal lagoons (p. 202).

LAKE BASINS DUE TO DENUDATION

(*a*) *Solvent Action of Groundwater*: Swallow holes, of which the outlets have been clogged by residual clays. Surface subsidences due to underground solution of limestone or of rock salt (the meres of Cheshire).

(*b*) *Solvent Action of Rivers*: Expansion and deepenings of river beds by surface solution of limestone (some of the Alpine lakes; Lough Derg, an expansion of the River Shannon).

(*c*) *Glacial Erosion* (see above).

(*d*) *Wind Deflation*: Hollows excavated in arid regions to a depth where an adequate supply of groundwater is tapped.

LAKE BASINS DUE TO ORGANIC AND HUMAN ACTIVITIES

(*a*) *Growth of Coral Reefs*: Lagoons cut off from the sea by a continuous ring of coral rock, or by the emergence of atolls or barrier reefs above sea level.

(*b*) *Beaver Dams* (Beaver Lake, Yellowstone Park)

(*c*) *Dams built by Man* (L. Mead, Colorado river)

(*d*) *Excavations made by Man*: Some reservoirs; many abandoned peat diggings (Norfolk Broads, Fig. 8–22).

LAKE BASINS DUE TO IMPACT OF LARGE METEORITES

Many of the resulting craters are dry but some have become lakes,—for example, the meteorite crater of New Quebec; the largest known is the Ashanti Crater (Lake Bosumtwi) in Ghana, with a diameter of six miles.

10
Wind Action and Desert Landscapes

CIRCULATION OF THE ATMOSPHERE

The circulation responsible for the winds is primarily a result of the familiar fact that air is cold over the polar regions and hot over the equatorial belt. If the earth did not rotate, heated air would ascend at the equator and blow towards the poles where, having become chilled and heavy, it would descend and return towards the equator, becoming steadily warmer as it followed the meridians into lower latitudes. But because the earth is rotating, a powerful deflecting force is at work, called the *Coriolis force* after the physicist who first recognized it in 1835. If anything moves relatively freely from south to north in the northern hemisphere (*e.g.* air, water, a projectile) it starts from a place where it shares the earth's rotational velocity to the east (over 1,000 miles an hour at the equator) and passes through places where the velocity is much lower, according to the latitude (*e.g.* about 800 miles an hour for New York; 650 for London; 0 for the North Pole). Consequently the moving mass or object tends to travel eastward faster than the earth immediately beneath it, and the farther north it goes the more it turns towards the east. Similarly if the movement is towards the equator, where the rotational velocity is higher, the moving object tends to be left behind by the earth— that is, to turn increasingly westward. Put more generally, the deflection is always to the right in the northern hemisphere, to the left in the southern hemisphere.

The Coriolis force is one of the minor factors concerned in river erosion, the channel being more effectively undercut on the side towards which the force is directed. The less confined movements of projectiles and aeroplanes, and of the winds themselves, are far more powerfully affected. The high-altitude winds that blow from the equator to the poles are deflected to the east. The return winds, which complete the convective circulation near the ground, would therefore be expected to be deflected to the west—that is, to be "easterlies". And so they are across a broad belt on each side of the equator (the north-east and south-east trade winds) and, less regularly, in the polar regions. But we find that in each hemisphere there is a belt of disorderly "westerlies" separating the polar easterlies from the tropical easterlies (the trade winds).

To account for the westerly winds we must consider another global effect. Heated air ascending from the equatorial "doldrums" turns polewards at a height of about 6 or 8 miles, and passes into latitudes that are shorter than the equator. Latitude 30°, for example, is 13 per cent shorter than the equator. At about this position, but ranging between 25° and 35° (north or south according to the season), crowding of the air has become sufficient to raise the pressure so that air is obliged to descend towards the surface. Here, then, are the high-pressure sub-tropical calm belts that came to be known as the "Horse Latitudes" in the old days of sailing ships. At the surface the descending air divides into (*a*) the trade winds that blow towards the equator (so completing the tropical convection cells A and A′ of Fig. 10–1), and (*b*) the disorderly westerlies that spiral *towards* the poles in cell B. But surface winds are already blowing *from* the poles, in cell C, and where the two opposing wind systems B and C meet, the weather becomes very disturbed and variable. The cold polar air tends to wedge itself southwards, while the warm moist air from lower latitudes flows up the surface of this wedge and so becomes cloudy and a source of rain or snow, often accompanied by strong winds. The surface of the cold wedge is called the *polar front*.

In the northern hemisphere the polar front advances far to the south in winter and retreats to the north in the summer, its range over land being much wider than over the oceans, which have a stabilizing effect because of the relative slowness with which water gains and loses heat. A corresponding winter advance to the north and summer retreat to the south takes place in the southern hemisphere. We now have the basic scheme of a threefold tandem arrangement of convection cells in each hemisphere (A, B, and C in Fig. 10–1). But there are many further complications. The high-altitude westerlies are found to be concentrated in jet-like streams between the tropics and the poles. Instead of maintaining a nearly uniform direction as they blow towards the

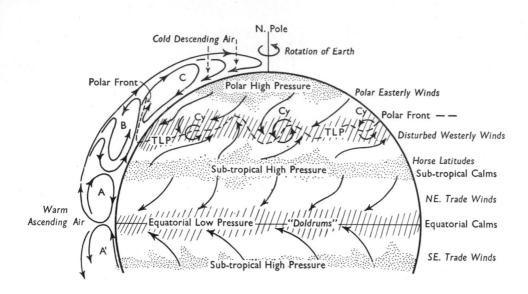

FIG. 10–1
The general planetary circulation of the lower atmosphere in three main cells, A, B, and C in the Northern Hemisphere (and similarly A′, B′, and C′ in the Southern Hemisphere). TLP, Temperate low pressure belt; Cy, Cyclones.

poles, the air streams follow sinuous courses, alternately surging far to the north and south of their mean directions. These surges are probably mainly responsible for the atmospheric eddies familiar as cyclones (with lowest pressure at the centre) and anticyclones (with highest pressure at the centre). Each cyclone is like an enormous vortex with winds spiralling round in an anticlockwise direction in the northern hemisphere and clockwise in the southern hemisphere. For anticyclones these directions are reversed, the general rule being a direct consequence of the Coriolis force. It is because of the continual recurrence of these broad eddies that the westerlies are described as "disturbed" or "disorderly". In the British Isles our most settled type of weather is, paradoxically, "unsettled".

TROPICAL WHIRLWINDS

Over tropical oceanic areas that have been abnormally heated, rapidly ascending streams of air generate the devastating vortices of winds known as *hurricanes* in the Atlantic and its great Mexican, Caribbean, and Mediterranean embayments. The very term *hurricane* comes from a Caribbean word meaning "the spirit of evil". In the West Pacific, similar violent whirlwinds are called *typhoons*, after the malevolent monster Typhon, of Greek mythology. In the Indian Ocean they are commonly referred to as *tropical cyclones*. Whereas the comparatively mild cyclones of temperate regions are usually 1,000 miles (1,600 km) or more across, the hurricane and typhoon systems may be only 200 or 300 miles

(300 to 500 km) in diameter. This means that from the outside, where the pressure is highest, to the relatively calm but menacing "eye" in the centre, where the pressure is lowest, the pressure gradient is correspondingly steeper. The resulting winds of hot moist air drawn into the spiralling updraught reach speeds of 75 to 150 or even 200 miles (120 to 300 km) an hour, and as the rising air expands and cools its water vapour condenses and falls in an overwhelming deluge of rain. After passing their climax hurricanes tend to broaden out into ordinary cyclones as they travel away from the tropics. Some cross the Atlantic and bring stormy weather to Western Europe.

The *tornado* (Spanish *tornar*, to twist or turn), which commonly begins on land, often as a satellite to a severe hurricane, is a very much narrower column or funnel of swiftly spinning air which may be up to 1,000 yards (900 m) across but is generally much less. The fiercely twisting winds create such havoc that any instruments that might have measured their speeds are inevitably destroyed. Estimates based on the fantastic effects of the winds sound incredible. The general destruction is due not only to the extreme violence of the winds, but also to the phenomenal reduction of pressure that takes place in the heart of a tornado. This results from the intensity of the surrounding rotation, just as happens, in a downward direction, in the vortex that develops in the water above the plug-hole when a bath is being emptied. When a house is suddenly struck by a tornado it may be literally burst open by the excess of its internal air pressure, although the latter is likely to be something less than normal. A characteristic feature of a tornado is the long black funnel-shaped or snaky cloud that stretches towards the ground from the great thunder cloud riding above the storm. This sinuous column is made visible by the presence of moisture, deposited as a result of the decreased pressure. Over the sea the pendant column swings about like an elephant's trunk and finally joins up with leaping peaks of water and spray to form a *waterspout* (Fig. 10–2). The sea makes its contribution where the pressure is so low that a kind of temporary isostasy comes into play. In response to the relief of pressure the water spurts upwards to complete its swirling union with the cloud from which the bulk of the waterspout is derived.

WIND, THE WATER DISTRIBUTOR

In addition to the basic scheme illustrated by Fig. 10–1, the circulation of the atmosphere also depends on the distribution of land and sea. Of these, only the Asiatic monsoon circulation need be mentioned here. Essentially, this is due to the intense winter cold of Siberia and the high plateaux, and ranges of central Asia, alternating with the extremely hot summers of the continent. In winter the outflowing monsoon strengthens the north-east trade winds and brings cool air over India. In summer the directions of the monsoon winds are reversed; moisture-bearing winds then blow in from the oceans—for example, from the south-west over India—and so control the rainy season.

Because the wind distributes moisture over the face of the earth it is one of the primary factors responsible for weather and the weathering of rocks, and for the maintenance of rivers and glaciers. The more northerly and southerly of the atmospheric surges mentioned in the previous section introduce streams of moist oceanic air far into Greenland and Antarctica respectively, so providing sources of precipitation for the nourishment of the ice sheets. Moreover, in blowing over the oceans and other bodies of water the wind transfers part of its energy to the surface waters and so becomes responsible for waves and their erosive work. Hurricanes and typhoons, in particular, generate unusually high waves and locally increase the height of high tides by driving water towards the land, so adding much coastal flooding to their catalogue of destruction.

THE GEOLOGICAL WORK OF WIND

As an agent of transport, and therefore of erosion and deposition, the work of the wind is familiar wherever loose surface materials are unprotected by a covering of vegetation. The raising of clouds of dust from ploughed fields after a spell of dry weather and the drift of wind-swept sand along a dry beach are known to everyone.

In humid regions, except along the seashore, wind erosion is limited by the prevalent cover of grass and trees and by the binding action of moisture in the soil. But the trials of exploration, warfare, and prospecting in the desert have made it hardly necessary to stress

FIG. 10–2
Waterspout off the Island of Rhodes, Greece, October 1930. (*Syndication International*)

FIG. 10—3
Dust storm approaching Port
Sudan, west coast of Red
Sea. (*Paul Popper, Ltd*)

the fact that in arid regions the effects of the wind are unrestrained. The "scorching sand-laden breath of the desert" wages its own war of nerves. Dust storms darken the sky, transform the air into a suffocating blast, and carry enormous quantities of material over great distances (Fig. 10–3). Vessels passing through the Red Sea often receive a baptism of fine sand from the desert winds of Arabia; and dunes have accumulated in the Canary Islands from sand blown across the sea from the Sahara.

By itself the wind can remove only dry incoherent deposits. This process of lowering the land surface is called *deflation* (L. *deflatus*, blowing away). Armed with the sand grains thus acquired, the wind near the ground becomes a powerful scouring or abrading agent. The resulting erosion is described as *wind abrasion*. By innumerable impacts the grains themselves are gradually worn down and rounded. This third aspect of wind erosion, the wear and tear of the "tools", is distinguished as *attrition*.

The winnowing action of the wind effectively sorts out the transported particles according to their sizes. This is well illustrated in the desert wherever mixed deposits of gravel, sand, and mud are worked over by the wind. Such materials are continually liberated by weathering and abrasion from bedrock surfaces, but far larger supplies are furnished by sheets of poorly assorted alluvium spread over the desert floor by the occasional torrents that flush out the wadis. Particles of silt and

dust are whirled high into the air and transported far from their source, to accumulate beyond the desert as deposits of loess (page 179). Sand grains are swept along near the surface, travelling by leaps and bounds, until the wind drops or some obstacle is encountered. The dunes and other accumulations of wind-blown sand thus come to be composed of clean and uniform grains, the finer particles having been sifted out and the larger fragments left behind. It follows that pebbles and gravel are steadily concentrated on the wind-swept surfaces of the original mantle of rock waste.

As a result of wind erosion, transport, and deposition three distinctive types of desert surface are produced:

(*a*) the rocky desert (the *hammada* or *hamada* of the Sahara), a desolate surface of bedrock with local patches of rubble and sand (Fig. 10–4),

(*b*) the stony desert, with a surface of rubble, gravel, or pebbles (the *reg* of the Algerian Sahara; the *serir* of Libya and Egypt); and

(*c*) the sandy desert (the *erg* of the Sahara).

Complementary to these is the loess of the bordering steppes, deposited from the dust-laden winds that blow from the desert.

WIND EROSION

The most serious effects of wind deflation—from the human point of view—are ex-

FIG. 10—4
The rocky wastes of Ahmar
Kreddou, viewed from the
Col de Sfa, Algerian
Sahara. (*Paul Popper Ltd*)

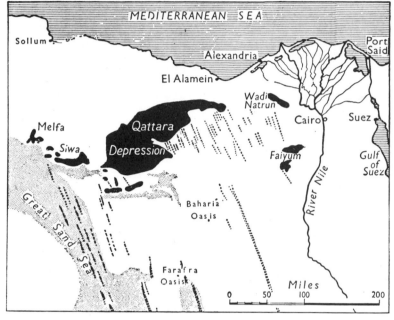

FIG. 10—5
Map showing depressions,
sand seas, and lines of
dunes in the Egyptian
Desert.

perienced in semi-arid regions like the Great Plains of the United States, where during this century vast quantities of soil have been blown and washed away from thousands of formerly productive wheat-growing farms. Originally an unbroken cover of grass stabilized the ground, but long-continued ploughing and over-exploitation finally destroyed the binding power of the soil and exposed it as a loose powder to the driving force of the wind. This national menace became critical during a period of severe droughts, culminating in 1934–35, when great dust storms originating in the "Dust Bowl" of Kansas and adjoining States swept eastwards towards the Atlantic. Rainwash and the progressive spread badland erosion extended the devastation. Widespread measures of

reclamation and protection have been taken to minimize the growing wastage and to conserve and improve the soil that remains. Wherever rain is deficient, deforestation, overgrazing, or other misuse of land inevitably leads to soil erosion. In the Mediterranean area, with its long dry summers, the green lands have been shrinking for centuries, especially in Spain and Algeria. Only recently has a start been made to break this vicious circle by afforestation and irrigation, and the application, enforced if necessary, of the "balanced" use of land. The over-hasty development of agriculture in parts of the U.S.S.R. quickly ran into similar difficulties, dramatically indicated by the great dust-storms of a few years ago, blowing out of the semi-arid lands east of the Caspian and Aral Seas. These

171

troubles are now being successfully corrected, and the lesson is being rapidly taken to heart in the new countries in Africa and elsewhere.

A characteristic result of deflation, especially over regions where unconsolidated clays and friable shales are exposed, is the production of wide plains and basin-like depressions. The excavation of hollows is limited only by the fact that even in deserts underground water may be present. Once the desert floor has been lowered to the level of the groundwater, the wind can no longer pick up the moistened particles, though it may drive pebbles across the surface when blowing hard and continuously. The base level for wind action is that of the water table, which may be far below sea level. The "pans" of South Africa and the Kalahari, and the depressions of the North African and Mongolian deserts, have all been excavated by deflation.

Westward from Cairo there is a remarkable series of basins with their floors well below sea level (Fig. 10–5), reaching − 420 feet in the salt marshes of the immense Qattara depression. Some of the smaller basins tap a copious supply of ground-water at depths of − 50 to − 100 feet, and have become fertile oases. To the north the surface rises by abrupt escarpments to terraced tablelands formed of hard sandstones and limestones which formerly extended across the softer rocks of the depressions. To the south, following the direction of the prevailing wind, long stretches of sand dunes represent part of the removed materials. The other well-known oases of Egypt—Baharia, Farafra, Dakhla, and Kharga—are above sea level, but they have originated in the same way. All of them are margined by steep escarpments of resistant strata, underlain by shales in which the floors have been excavated. These depressions are not crustal downwards, nor have they been hollowed out by water, for the sheet floods due to rare cloudbursts tend to fill them with debris. The wind has been the sole excavator.

The effects of wind abrasion are unmistakably expressed in the forms and surfaces of the desert bedrocks. Just as an artificial sand blast is used to clean and polish building stones and to etch glass, so the natural sand blast of the wind attacks destructively everything that lies across its path. Cars driven against wind-blown sand may have their windscreens frosted and their paint scoured off. The action on exposed rocks is highly selective. Like a delicate etching tool, the sand blast picks out every detail of the structure. Hard pebbles, nodules, and fossils are left protruding from their softer matrix until they fall out. Variably cemented rocks are fretted and honeycombed like fantastic carvings. Where there are thin alternations of hard and soft strata, the soft bands are scoured away more rapidly than the hard,

FIG. 10–6
Pillars of well-jointed red sandstone, Monument Valley, Utah. (*Dorien Leigh Ltd*)

FIG. 10–7
Pebbles from the Egyptian Desert faceted by sand blast (dreikanter or ventifacts). (*M. V. Binosi*)

which thus come to stand out in strong relief, like fluted shelves and cornices with deep grooves between. Where the wind blows steadily in one direction over strata of this kind, especially if the beds are tilted rather than flat, the softer materials are excavated into long passageways (parallel to the dominant wind direction) separating deeply undercut, overhanging ridges. Such fantastically carved "cockscomb" ridges are common in certain parts of the Asiatic deserts, where they are called *yardangs*.

Undercutting is everywhere a marked feature of wind abrasion, owing to the fact that the process is most effective just above the surface, where the sand is most abundant. Telegraph poles in sandy stretches of desert have to be protected by piles of stones against the cutting action of the sand grains hurled against them. Along the base of escarpments, alcoves and small caverns may be hollowed out. As always, the effect of undercutting on slowly weathered formations is to maintain steep slopes. Joints are readily attacked and opened up and these commonly determine the outlines of rock towers and pinnacles, left isolated like detached bastions in front of the receding wall of an escarpment (Fig. 10–6).

Where the bedrock of the desert floor is exposed to blown sand it may be smoothed or pitted or furrowed, according to its structure. Compact limestones become polished, massive granites are smoothed or pitted, and gneisses and schists are ribbed and fluted, especially where their foliation approximates in direction to that of the dominant winds. Where pebbles have become sufficiently concentrated by removal of finer material they become closely packed, and in time their upper surfaces are ground flat. In this way mosaic-like tracts of *desert-pavement* are developed. Isolated pebbles or rock fragments strewn on the desert surface are bevelled on the windward side until a smooth face is cut. If the direction of the wind changes seasonally, or if the pebble is undermined and turned over, two or more facets may be cut, each pair meeting in a sharp edge. Such wind-faceted pebbles, which often resemble Brazil nuts, except that their surfaces are polished, are known as *dreikanter* or *ventifacts* (Fig. 10–7).

As a result of continual attrition due to the friction of rolling and impact the sand grains themselves are gradually worn down and rounded. The prolonged action of wind is far more effective in rounding sand grains than that of running water, because of (*a*) the greater velocity of the wind; (*b*) the greater distances traversed by the grains as they bound and roll and collide with each other backwards and forwards across wide stretches of desert; and (*c*) the absence of a protective sheath of water. Some of the *millet seed sands* of the desert are almost perfect spheres with a mat surface like that of ground glass. It is also noteworthy that visible flakes of mica, such as are commonly seen in water-deposited sands and sandstones, are very rare in desert sands and dunes. The easy cleavage of mica facilitates constant fraying during the wear and tear of wind action. Mica is thus reduced to an impalpable powder that is winnowed

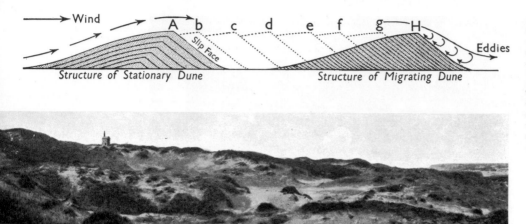

Wind

A b c d e f g H

Slip Face

Eddies

Structure of Stationary Dune   Structure of Migrating Dune

FIG. 10–8
Sections to illustrate the growth, migration, and stratification of sand dunes. A stationary dune, A, grows in height with a forward and upward advance of the crest. When the sand supply and wind velocity involve migration of the dune, the crest advances to successive positions such as b, c, . . . g, and H.

FIG. 10–9
Penhale sand dunes, north of Perranporth, Cornwall, largely composed of minute fragments of marine shells; illustrating migration from the sea floor and beach, partial fixation by marram grass, and "blow-outs" by severe gales. (*H.M. Geological Survey*)

away from the heavier sand grains. These contrasts between water-laid and aeolian sands are of great value in deciding whether ancient sandstones have been formed in deserts or under water. The Penrith Sandstone of the Eden valley is a well-known example of a Permian desert sand. Its rounded grains, the absence of mica, and the cross-bedding (p. 178) of the formation all testify to the desert conditions of the time.

COASTAL DUNES AND SANDHILLS

Along low-lying stretches of sandy coasts and lake shores, where the prevailing winds are onshore, drifting sand is blown landwards and piled up into dunes which form a natural bulwark of sandhills. Any mound or ridge of sand with a crest or definite summit is called a *dune*. Deposition begins wherever the force of the wind is broken by obstructive irregularities of the surface, including grasses and trees. In humid regions the conditions governing growth and removal are very complex. The wind varies in strength and direction. Vegetation and moisture tend to trap and fix the sand, but fixation is often incomplete. During severe gales old dunes may be breached and scooped out into deep "blow outs". The resulting confused assemblage of hummocks and hollows gives coastal

sandhills a characteristically chaotic relief. Where the water table is reached the ground becomes marshy.

A typical well-developed dune has a long windward slope rising to a crest and a much steeper leeward slope (Fig. 10–8). The latter is determined by the fact that sand blown over the crest falls into a wind shadow, and comes to rest at its natural angle of repose—about 30° to 35° for dry sand. The windward slope is often beautifully rippled (Fig. 10–11). In situations where dunes are not effectively arrested by vegetation, or kept within bounds by winds from opposing quarters, they slowly migrate in the direction of the prevailing wind. When the wind is not fully loaded with newly acquired sand it sweeps up more from the windward slope, and drops it over the crest, where it streams down the "slipface". By subtraction of sand from one side and addition to the other the dune travels forward.

As one belt of dunes is driven inland away from the beach, another arises in its place "so that a series of huge sandy billows, as it were, is continually on the move from the seamargin towards the interior" (Fig. 2–4). Very wide belts of sandhills have spread inland in this way from low-lying coasts well supplied with sand, such as those of Holland and North Germany, the Landes of Gascony adjoining the Bay of Biscay, and the coastal desert of South-West Africa. Landward migration from the sea floor is convincingly demonstrated by the existence of beaches and dunes that are largely composed of ground-up marine shells. Excellent examples occur at St Ives and Perranporth along the north-west coast of Cornwall (Fig. 10–9).

The Culbin and Maviston sandhills, near the mouth of the Findhorn on the southern shore of the Moray Firth, furnish a classic example of the destruction of cultivated lands and habitations by advancing sand. Prior to 1694 the sandhills had already reached the fringe of the Culbin estate. In that year a great storm started a phase of accelerated encroachment which finally led to the complete obliteration of houses, farms, and orchards, and even to the burial of fir plantations (Fig. 10–10).

In most threatened regions of agricultural value active measures are now taken to restrain the advance of the dunes. Tough binding-grasses such as bent or marram are excellent for this purpose, and since they thrive best where they are most needed they commonly acclimatize themselves naturally and can easily be added to, if necessary. The harsh tufts check the wind, trap oncoming supplies of sand, and continue to grow upwards as the entangled sand accumulates, leaving the underlying sand fortified with an intricate network of long roots. Such protected dunes become locally turfed over and their subsequent growth tends to be seawards rather than landwards. When great storms cause severe blow-outs that undo or delay the work of stabilization, dunes can be anchored more

securely by starting plantations of suitable trees on the landward side and gradually extending them across the sand already partially fixed by grasses. In recent years large areas of the Culbin and Maviston sandhills have been successfully afforested with conifers in this way.

DESERT DUNES AND SAND SHEETS

About a fifth of the earth's land surface is desert, and on an average about a fifth of the desert areas is mantled with sand. A high proportion of the desert floor is an erosion surface of bedrock, locally strewn with coarse rock-waste (Fig. 10–4). Regions of shale and limestone provide little or no sand, but where sandstone is being disintegrated or mixed alluvium is being deflated, the wind picks up the loose grains and concentrates them into vast sand wastes (Fig. 10–11) and long chains of dunes.

Complications due to vegetation and moisture arise only around oases or in the transition zones where the desert merges into steppe or savannah country. In the heart of the desert the wind has free play. Nevertheless the factors controlling the form of the sand accumulations are far from simple. They include the nature, extent, and rate of erosion of the source of supply; the sizes of the sand grains and associated fragments; the varying strength and direction of the wind; and the roughness or smoothness of the surface (*e.g.* the presence or absence of pebbles) across which the sand is drifted and deposited. Of the resulting sand forms four main types can be distinguished:

FIG. 10–10
Remains of an exhumed plantation formerly buried by sand which has now migrated farther; Maviston Sands, Moray. (*H.M. Geological Survey*)

(*a*) *Sand drifts*, which form temporarily in the wind shadows of protruding rocks or cliffs.

(*b*) *Crescentic dunes* or *barchans* (a Turkestan name which has been generally adopted), which occur as isolated units (Fig. 10–12), either sporadically or in long chain-like swarms, or as colonies, more or less linked together laterally, which advance across the desert like gigantic but irregular ripples (Figs. 10–13 and 10–14).

(*c*) *Linear ridges* or *longitudinal dunes* (known as *seifs* in the Sahara), which commonly occur in long parallel ranges, each diversified by peak after peak "in regular succession like the teeth of a monstrous saw."

(*d*) *Sand sheets* of wide extent, which may be flat or undulating or diversified with more or less crude examples of (*b*) or (*c*).

Dunes arise wherever a sand-laden wind deposits sand on the windward slopes of a random patch. The mound grows in height until a "slip-face" is established by avalanching on the sheltered leeward side. As the dune migrates, the extremities, offering less resistance to the wind than the summit region, advance more rapidly, until they extend into wings of such a length that their total obstructive power becomes equal to that of the middle of the dune. The resulting crescentic form then persists with only minor modifications of shape and size, so long as the wind blows from the same quarter. The width of a barchan is commonly about a dozen times the height, which ranges up to a maximum of 100 feet or so. Winds blowing continually from nearly the same direction are essential for the growth and stability of barchans. The north-east trade winds in the N. African deserts satisfy

FIG. 10–11
Characteristic surface features of a sand sea in the Egyptian Desert. (*M. V. Binosi*)

FIG. 10–12
A typical barchan (drawing from a photograph).

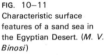

FIG. 10–13
Plan of a typical procession of barchans in the Libyan Desert.

FIG. 10–14
A colony of barchans in Mauritania, West Africa, advancing towards the south-west (*I.F.A.N.*)

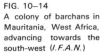

FIG. 10–15
Diagram to illustrate the shepherding effect of wind on sand ridges. The wind is strongest between the ridges and is retarded by friction against them; eddies are therefore set up, as shown.

this condition. Given such winds and an adequate supply of sand, colonies and elongated swarms of barchans march slowly forward, like a stream of vehicles in a one-way street (Figs. 10–13 and 10–14). The rate of progress varies up to 20 feet a year for high dunes, and up to 50 feet a year for small ones.

Where the prevailing wind is occasionally interrupted by strong cross winds which drive in sand from the sides, the conditions are like those of a one-way street which becomes densely crowded and choked by the inflow of traffic from every cross-road. Instead of a chain of barchans, a long seif dune is developed, a continuous, but serrated ridge parallel to the direction of the prevailing wind, with crests that may reach a height of several hundred feet. South of the Qattara depression (Fig. 10–5) there is a long tract of parallel seifs with corridors of bare desert floor between. South of the area shown in Fig. 10–5 the seifs come into the belt of north-east

trades and, accordingly, they wheel round towards the south-west, and pass progressively into barchans.

One of the most remarkable features of desert dunes is their apparent power of collecting all the sand in their neighbourhood. The explanation appears to be that the wind exerts a shepherding effect. If the surface between the dunes is fairly smooth, the drag on the wind there is less than it is along the edge of the dune. Eddies are thus set up which blow towards the dune, and so keep the intervening surface swept clean (Fig. 10–15).

In the development of great "sand seas", like that shown by Fig. 10–11, other factors come into operation, dependent on the quantity and nature of the materials on which the wind has to work. The surface may be variegated with poorly developed sief dunes or, more commonly, with groups of irregular barchans. Where the dunes are not too crowded, they rise from a platform of coarser

FIG. 10–16
An erosion plain (pediplain) of
semi-arid "desert scrub" with
basalt-capped mesa behind;
NE. of The Solitario, Texas.
(*G. C. Gilbert, United States
Geological Survey*)

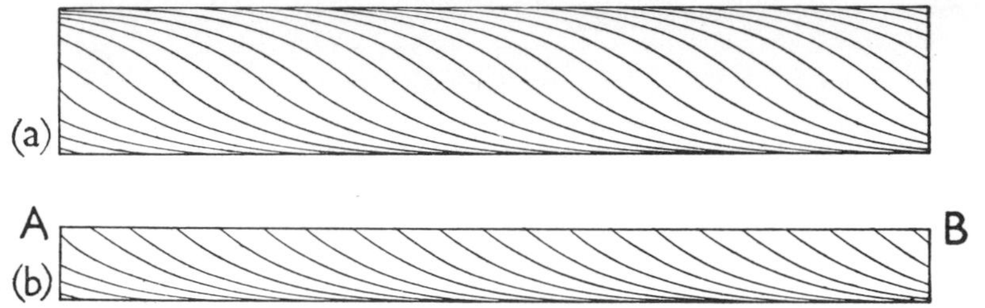

(a)

A   B

(b)

FIG. 10–17
Sections to illustrate
current-bedding. In (*a*)
the structure is complete.
In (*b*) the upper part has
been eroded down to AB and
the current-bedding pattern
is truncated.

sand. The finer sand has always a better chance to be driven up the slopes. Where a sprinkling of pebbles is present, the wind disperses chance mounds of sand instead of building them into dunes, and wide, almost feature-less, sheets of sand then accumulate. A patch of pebbles increases the drag on the wind to such an extent that the velocity near the ground is less than it is over a patch of clean sand. The resulting eddies therefore blow from the patch towards the pebbly surface until the sand is again evenly distributed between the pebbles. Widespread sand sheets are also characteristically developed on the borders of deserts, where a scanty vegetation diversifies the surface (Fig. 10–16). Grass and scrub break the force of the wind and inblown sand is more or less evenly distributed.

CURRENT-BEDDING: WIND DIRECTIONS OF PAST AGES

Since sand dunes advance by removal of sand from their windward slopes and its deposition on their slip faces (Fig. 10–8), the bedding of migrating sand dunes is inclined in the direction towards which the prevailing wind blows, at angles of about 30° to 35°.

Similarly the bedding of a growing sand bank, in shallow water, follows the gently curved slopes on which the sand is dropped, giving a pattern in cross-section which, under ideal conditions, resembles that shown in Fig. 10–17*a*. With changing conditions, possibly during a storm, the upper part of a sand bank or sand dune is swept away, and the bedding planes are sharply truncated by an erosion surface such as AB in Fig. 10–17*b*. Later on another dune or sand bank may be deposited on the eroded surface. So, in a quarry or cliff exposure of sandstone deposited by currents of air or water we find that within certain bands the bedding is oblique and variously inclined to the general dip of the formation as a whole (Fig. 10–18). This structure, which is original and not due to tilting or folding, is called *current-bedding* or *cross-bedding*, and in ancient sand dunes it reproduces, wholly or in part, the characteristic outlines of dunes.

By making a statistical study of the dips of the current-bedding of a group of barchans of ancient origin, it is possible to ascertain the mean directions of advance, and therefore of the wind direction at the time concerned. This ingenious method of determining the direction of "fossil winds" was initiated by F. W.

Shotton and successfully applied in 1937 to the aeolian sands of the New Red Sandstone (mainly Permian) of Britain (Fig. 10–19). Shotton has found that the various remnants of these British desert sands (*e.g.* in Shropshire and the adjoining Midlands, northern England, south-western Scotland, Arran, and Morayshire) are accumulations of barchans, indicating that they were most probably formed under the influence of the north-east trade winds of the time. Figure 10–19 shows the mean directions of dune advance as determined by Shotton and the corresponding direction of the inferred north-east trade wind. If this inference is correct the evidence indicates that in Permian times these dunes lay within about 30° of the equator. If so, the British area has not only changed its latitude by moving 25° or more to the north, relative to the present position of the North Pole, but it has also rotated about 40° (see p. 11).

LOESS

We must next consider what happens to the vast quantities of dust which have been winnowed from the desert sands and exported by the wind. From the deserts of Asia the wind carries the dust to the south and south-east over the grassy regions of China, where it is deposited and accumulated as a thick blanket of *loess* (Fig. 10–20). Farther west, loess accumulates against the foothills of the Pamir plateau, where it provides a narrow belt of well-irrigated and fertile soil which has recently become one of the most densely populated agricultural regions of the world. From the deserts of North Africa much of the dust reaches the countries to the south and west, such as the Southern Sudan, the Northern Congo, Nigeria, and Mali, where it adds to and is retained by the soil. Some of the dust blows over the Atlantic, some is trapped by the Mediterranean, and the Red Sea receives contributions from Arabia.

Other very important supplies of fine silt and dust were formerly provided by the rock flour of glacial and glaciofluvial deposits. During and after the retreat of each of the successive ice sheets, the finer material was sifted out by the wind and deposited over the surrounding country (Fig. 10–20). Thus it happens that a long belt of loess, mainly derived from glacial material in the west and from desert waste in the east, stretches from France to China. The term *loess* comes

FIG. 10–18
Current-bedding of barchan type in desert sandstone of Permian age. Mauchline Quarries, Ayrshire, Scotland. (*H.M. Geological Survey*)

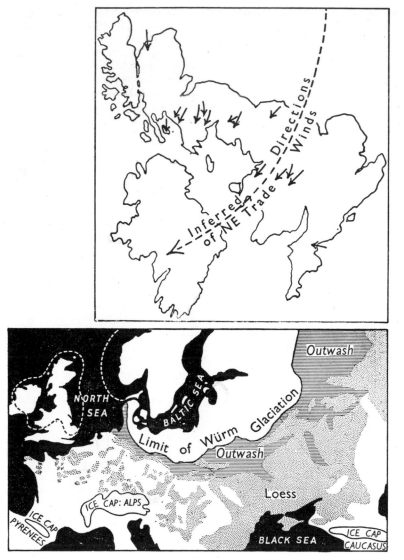

FIG. 10–19
Map showing the directions of dune advance in the Permian desert of Britain. The map is orientated so that the corresponding wind directions would be those of the north-east trade winds of the time. (*After F. W. Shotton and S. K. Runcorn*)

FIG. 10–20
Map showing the distribution in Europe of loess and loamy soil formed from it, and the marginal relation to the last major glaciation. (*After S. von Bubnoff*)

from a town of that name in Alsace. Beginning as local patches in France and Germany, the deposit becomes thicker and more extensive as it is traced across Russia and Turkestan, until in Shansi and the adjoining provinces of China it reaches its maximum development.

Loess is an accumulation of wind-borne dust and silt, washed down from the air by rain, and retained by the protective grip of the grasses of the steppe. Each spring the grass grows a little higher on any material collected during the previous year, leaving behind a ramifying system of withered roots. Over immense areas many hundreds of feet have accumulated, whole landscapes having been buried, except where the higher peaks project above the blanket of loess. The material itself is yellowish or light buff, very fine grained, and devoid of stratification. Although it is friable and porous, the successive generations of grass roots, now represented by narrow tubes partly occupied by calcium carbonate, make it sufficiently coherent to stand up in vertical walls which do not crumble unless they are disturbed. The passage of traffic along country roads loosens the material, clouds of dust are removed by the wind, and the roads are worn down into steep-walled gullies and miniature canyons.

In the loess provinces of China rain and small streams carve the surface into a maze of ravines and badland topography (Fig. 10–21). The larger rivers flow in broad and fertile alluvial plains bordered by vertical bluffs. Here and in the lowland and deltaic plains to

FIG. 10—21
"Badland" erosion of loess
in Kansu province, North
China, brought about largely
through destruction of timber
and over-cultivation in the
past. Terrace conservation
has checked the wastage in
the valley, which is drained
by a tributary of the upper
Hwang Ho. (J. P. Coster)

the east most of the alluvium is simply loess redistributed by water. In the loess uplands cultivation of the slopes is made possible by terracing. The steep-sided cliffs and walls, whether natural or artificial, are often riddled with entrances to cave dwellings, many of which have their chimneys opening into the fields above. This mode of habitation has occasionally led to great disasters. In 1556, for example, widespread landslides and floods were started by a catastrophic earthquake and nearly a million peasants lost their lives.

In the Midwest of the United States there are deposits of loess, locally called *adobe*, that correspond in all essentials to those of Europe and Asia. In Kansas and Nebraska much of the wind-blown silt has come from the semi-arid lands of the west. Elsewhere it consists largely of rock flour (winnowed by the wind from the outwash and temporary lake deposits left by the shrinking ice sheets of the Pleistocene) which found lodgement on grass-protected surfaces like the prairies. By subsequent erosion much of the original loess of the upper Mississippi basin has contributed to the alluvium of the downstream flood plains. Where these dry up in times of drought, they form an important source for a second generation of loess.

WEATHERING AND STREAM WORK IN THE DESERT

The belt of deserts between the Atlantic and the Persian Gulf lies mainly to the south of latitude 30° N. Here the high-pressure descending air is dry (Fig. 10–1) and the resulting trade winds become increasingly desiccating so long as they are blowing over land. This belt continues north of latitude 30° from Iran to the Gobi desert of central Asia, though with several interruptions, rainfall being low because of, distance from the oceans or the intervention of mountainous rain barriers. High mountains near the western coasts are mainly responsible for the deserts of North and South America. In all these arid regions the rainfall is rare and sporadic, both temperature and wind intensity are subject to violent daily and seasonal fluctuations and vegetation is extremely scanty or entirely lacking.

Under these conditions mechanical weathering is dominant, involving the splitting, exfoliation, and crumbling of rocks by alternations of scorching heat and icy cold (Fig. 5–3). Nevertheless chemical weathering, though extremely slow, plays some part. By decomposition and solution, rocks that would otherwise successfully resist the stresses set up by temperature changes are gradually weakened until they can be shattered. By evaporation minute quantities of dissolved matter are brought to the surface. The loose salts are blown away, but oxides of iron, accompanied by traces of manganese and other similar oxides, form a red, brown, or black film which is firmly retained. The surfaces of long-exposed rocks and pebbles thus acquire a characteristic coat of "desert varnish".

Although most desert localities remain entirely unvisited by rain for years on end, no part can be regarded as permanently free from rain. Over a representative period of years the rainfall is limited to an average of a few inches per annum, 10 inches being the limit, reached only on the desert margins. In the adjoining semi-arid regions the annual rainfall rises to 10–20 inches, but even here long periods of drought are usual.

The capacity for evaporation far exceeds the rainfall in the desert. Permanent streams cannot originate under such conditions, although well-nourished rivers, like the Nile, with adequate sources in humid regions, may cross the desert without entirely dwindling away. Outflowing streams are otherwise short and intermittent, and confined to coastal districts where, moreover, the rainfall is less scanty. The desert drainage is almost wholly internal, and directed towards the lowest parts of the many depressions which, owing to earth movements and wind erosion, characterize the desert surface. Evaporation prevents the growth of lakes from which, as in humid regions, the overflow could find an exit. The poetical generalization that "the weariest river winds somewhere safe to sea" does not apply to arid regions.

There are many indications that running water was formerly far more actively concerned than it is today in developing the landforms of the desert which we actually see: the gorges and steep-sided wadis that dissect the desert uplands (Fig. 10–22); some of the extinct "waterfalls"; the alluvial spreads that floor the depressions; the salt deposits and terraces of vanished lakes; the buried soils that can so easily be brought into cultivation; the rock carvings and paintings of prehistoric artists, and other relics of ancient man from stone implements to actual habitations, all point to previous pluvial climates. The Sahara has been described as "the corpse of a once well-watered landscape". But whereas man originally retreated before the spreading aridity, he is now returning for oil, gas, iron ores, and above all for the essential artesian water that alone can restore the long-vanished fertility and make the desert locally habitable. Between the Hoggar and Mauritania there is a vast expanse of desert-varnished *reg* or gravel desert, known as the Tanezrouft and hardly heard of until the French exploded their first atom bombs. Here, during the preliminary quest for water, French geologists discovered a thick fossil soil just below the surface. Pollen from the soil is of vegetation of the kinds that now flourish in a Mediterranean climate, and radio-carbon dating shows the soil to be about 7,000 years old. Drilling has revealed deep-lying water-bearing sandstones fed by the rain that falls on the Atlas ranges to the north, where the intake area extends for hundreds of miles along the upturned edges of the strata. On the northern side of the Sahara this great aquifer already supplies artesian water to all the newly developed oilfields, turning the growing settlements into market gardens of amazing fertility. Throughout this region official policy—not everywhere strictly adhered to—is that the rate of withdrawal of water for irrigation, industrial, and social purposes must not exceed the rate of replenishment along the intake area.

Despite the multiplication of artificial oases, the extreme desiccation of the desert is still its most striking natural feature, and it is puzzling that rare rainstorms and the resulting spasmodic stream action should occur at all. They probably result from cyclonic, funnel-shaped break-throughs from the moist air of

FIG. 10–22
Gorge of the Wadi Barud, Egyptian Desert. (*O. H. Little*)

FIG. 10–23
Alluvial fan, east wall of
Death Valley, south of Bad-
water, California, passing
into a deposit of salt and mud
in the foreground. (*J. S.
Shelton and R. C. Frampton*)

high-level westerlies (Fig. 10–1). The chief characteristics of the rare desert rainstorms are their erratic distribution and brief duration, and—apart from occasional light showers—their intense violence. Houses of dried salt mud are turned into a miry pulp and washed away when a sudden "cloudburst" descends on an oasis. Travellers have been drowned in the floods that race down the dry wadis with little or no warning. Such torrents, swiftly generated in a distant upland rainstorm, carry a heavy load of mixed debris, prepared for them by years of weathering and

wind erosion. At the foot of the mountains or escarpments, where carrying power is reduced by seepage or loss of gradient, the debris is dropped in order of decreasing size to form alluvial fans (Fig. 10–23) and "deltaic" deposits. Between the pediment or sediment-filled depression that commonly surrounds a desert mountain group or flanks an escarpment, there may be a more or less continuous slope of waste formed by the coalescence of alluvial fans; this feature is called a *bahada* or *bajada*.

Choked by their own deposits the short-lived streams subdivide into innumerable channels and spread out laterally across the plain, which thus becomes covered with a veneer of finer sediment. If the rain falls on the gentle slopes of a depression, a shallow sheet flood may carry a mud flow towards the middle of the depression. If the water reaches the lowest part before it is lost by further seepage and evaporation a temporary lake is formed. There the dissolved material is concentrated by evaporation and finally deposited to form salt muds or glistening white sheets of rock salt, gypsum, and other salts. In Western America the resulting alluvial plains of arid or semi-arid enclosed basins are called *playas*, and the more saline tracts are distinguished as *salinas* (Fig. 10–24). So long as more material is brought in by rare torrents and sheet floods than is removed by wind, the depressions continue to be filled.

THE CYCLE OF EROSION IN ARID REGIONS

A still unexplained aspect of the present wide extension of deserts is that arid conditions spread not only during, but long after, the retreat of the last great ice sheets, and may still be extending. One of the most striking historical proofs of such climatic change within the last 2,300 years is the account of the prodigious campaign of Alexander the Great (356–233 B.C.) to the Punjab and back. His route passed through lands that were then sufficiently well watered and forested to provide the needs (including shipbuilding) of an army of 110,000 men; today they include the Thar desert of Rajasthan and are "so desolate that they cannot support passing caravans of even 100 men and animals" (D. N. Wadia, 1960).

Just as ice sheets extended themselves for a time by a self-accelerating process, so, it appears, do desert areas. Wind erosion strips away the fertile soil formed during a preceding pluvial phase and turns the adjoining grasslands into sand-covered wastes. The destructive activities of mankind have powerfully contributed to the loss of fertile land in many places. Elsewhere natural changes in the air and water circulations of the globe have promoted increasing desiccation, but it is not understood how this is brought about. In these circumstances it is natural that there should be considerable doubt about the relative importance of the effects of wind and water in deserts that have remained arid long enough to have passed through an arid cycle of erosion. Most present-day deserts have had so short or so interrupted a life that some of their landscape features are of hybrid origin. However, the following outline serves to indicate how the processes known to operate in the desert could ultimately reduce a given region of uplands and depressions to a desert plain.

Youth is on the whole characterized by decrease of the original relief. Given sufficient time the rare and short-lived flash floods cut gullies in the uplands. These develop into wadis and canyons, from which rock waste is spread over the depressions, by way of alluvial fans where the uplands are bordered by escarpments. The escarpments gradually recede through wind erosion, and because the "sandblast" operates most effectively at the base, desert scarps are characteristically steep. So long as more material is carried into the depressions by intermittent streams than is removed by wind, the depressions continue to be filled, so passing into playas or salinas. The only features that offset the prevalent reduction of relief are (*a*) hollows excavated by the wind in beds of soft and dry materials, and (*b*) sand dunes.

Between the uplands and the playas the growing alluvial fans coalesce into bajadas which steadily increase in thickness as they encroach on the wind-swept escarpments. *Maturity* may be said to begin when the mountains become like islands half submerged in their own waste products. Now the lower depressions begin to tap the higher ones by incipient wadis that slowly extend themselves headwards. While they are being eroded away, the soft deposits of a higher basin are likely for a time to develop badland topography, with the "constant slope" much in evidence. The more resistant rocks of the escarpments, however, flanked by outlying buttes and inselbergs, rise abruptly with the "free face" of bare rock as their most prominent slope element.

During *old age* the higher "basins" contribute materials to the lower ones until they all unite and the relics of uplands dwindle away, provided the cycle is not interrupted by earth movements or a change of climate, or brought to an end wherever the surface is reduced to the base level of wind erosion, the water table. And so the region is reduced to an erosion surface, closely related to a pediplain but of more complex structure, being composed not only of bare rock, thinly strewn with debris, but of smooth tracts of mosaic- or desert-pavement and vast wastes of sand.

11
Coastal Scenery and the Work of the Sea

SHORE LINES

Nearly all coast lines have been initiated by relative movements between land and sea. A rise of sea level or a depression of the land, leads to the submergence of a landscape already moulded by sub-aerial agents. The drowning of a region of hills and valleys gives an indented coast line of bays, estuaries, gulfs, fjords, and straits, separated by headlands, peninsulas, and off-lying islands. Very broad bays, like the Great Australian Bight, result from the submergence of plains. Coasts that have originated in these ways are called *coasts of submergence* (Fig. 8–17). Conversely a fall of sea level or an elevation of the land and adjoining continental shelf leads to retreat of the sea and emergence of part of the sea floor. As the sea floor is essentially a realm of sedimentation its surface is generally smooth (Fig. 11–1), and the resulting *coasts of emergence* have correspondingly simple, broadly flowing outlines.

Structurally there are two contrasted varieties of coast distinguished as Atlantic and Pacific types. Coasts of *Atlantic* or *transverse* type are those where the trend lines of an orogenic belt are transverse to the coast (Fig. 11–2). Submergence of Atlantic-type coasts therefore gives rise to an alternation of long

promontories and bays. The bays are called *rias* (Spanish *ria*, estuary), the name given them in Spain where they occur south of Cape Finisterre. The south-west coast of Ireland is a perfect example of this type (Fig. 11–2). Coasts of *Pacific* or *longitudinal* type have the structural grain parallel to the coast, and long islands and inlets parallel to the structural grain are characteristic. When partially drowned, such coasts are said to be of Dalmatian type because they are exemplified by the Dalmatian coast of the Adriatic (Fig. 11–3).

Coasts can also be classified as *advancing* or *retreating*, according to whether land is being gained or lost. Loss can result from either submergence or erosion, and coastal retreat tends to reach its maximum when these two act in combination. Similarly, gain of land can result from either emergence or deposition, and coastal advance tends to reach its maximum when these two processes co-operate. But there are many coasts in which the operative processes are in opposition; it is then the dominant one that determines whether on balance, over a suitably long period of years, the coast advances or retreats.

The general outlines of a newly formed coast

FIG. 11–1
A coastal plain of emergence, North Canterbury, New Zealand. Relatively rapid upheaval is indicated by a cover of shelly deposits. Indented cliffs of older rocks are seen at the bottom right. (*V. C. Browne*)

are soon modified by marine erosion and deposition, with development of a wide variety of shore features and coastal scenery. By the incessant pounding of waves, which break up the rocks and wear back the cliffs, the sea cuts its way into the land like a horizontal saw. The liberated rock fragments are rounded by innumerable impacts and continual grinding as the line of breakers is carried backwards and forwards over the foreshore by the ebb and flow of the tide. The worn-down material is transported by the waves and the currents. Most of the finer sediment, including contributions from rivers and glaciers and the wind, is carried into deeper water before coming to rest on the sea floor. The coarser sediment is swept towards or drifted along the shore to form shoals and beaches or to build out spits and bars (long embarkments of sand and shingle), where the coast line abruptly changes its direction. Inlets and lagoons sheltered from the sea in this way develop into marshes, which in time are silted up by contributions from the landward side, or blanketed with sand dunes that advance from the seaward side. In these and other ways new land is added to the fringe of the old in compensation for the losses suffered elsewhere.

The seas and oceans readily respond by movement to wind brushing over the surface; to variations of temperature and salinity; to the gravitational attraction of the moon and sun; and to the Coriolis force (see p. 167). The work of erosion, transport, and deposition carried out by the sea depends on the varied and often highly complex interplay of the waves, currents, and tides that result from these movements.

It may be noted in passing that lakes, especially the larger ones, behave in much the same way as enclosed seas. In consequence, the shore features of lakes and seas have much in common. A lake formed by obstruction (*e.g.* Lake Kyoga, p. 236 and Fig. 13–24) drowns the surrounding land and so acquires a shore line of the submergence type. A lake which has shrunk from its former extent in response to climatic or other changes (*e.g.* the Great Salt Lake of Utah) is margined by flats and terraces of sediment, and so acquires a shore line of the emergence type. Tides are negligible in lakes, but seasonal variations of rainfall may cause the water to advance and recede over a tract of shore which is alternately covered and exposed, though less frequently than the tideswept foreshore of a coast. Waves and currents operate exactly as in land-locked seas of similar extent and depth, and are responsible for erosion and deposition on a corres-

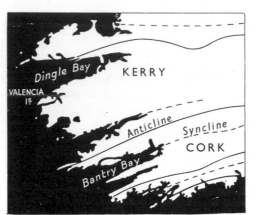

FIG. 11–2
Submerged Atlantic-type coast, SW. Ireland.

FIG. 11–3
Submerged Pacific-type coast (Dalmatian type), Yugoslavia.

ponding scale. There are, of course, important biological contrasts. The swamps into which shallow lakes degenerate, with their luxuriant growth of aquatic vegetation and accumulations of peat, are very different from the mangrove swamps and tidal marshes that locally border the sea. On the other hand, lake shores have nothing to compare with the coral reefs of tropical seas.

TIDES AND CURRENTS

The tide is the periodic rise and fall of the sea which, on an average, occurs every 12 hours 26 minutes. Tides are essentially due to the passage around the earth, as it rotates, of two antipodal bulges of water produced by the differential attraction of the moon and sun. The bulges are the crests of a gigantic wave, low in height but of enormous wave length. It is easy to understand that the water facing the moon should bulge up a little, but it is less obvious why there should be a similar bulge in the opposite direction on the other side of the earth. The basis of the explanation is that the

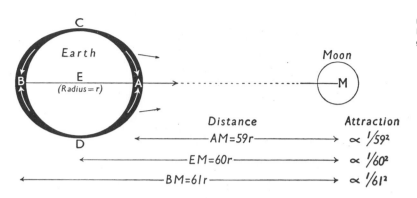

FIG. 11—4
Diagram to illustrate the
generation of tides.

water centred at A (Fig. 11–4) is attracted towards the moon more than the earth, centred at E, while the earth, in turn, is attracted more than the water centred at B. The water at the far side is thus left behind to almost the same extent as the water on the near side is pulled forward. From places such as C and D the water is drawn away and low tide results. As the earth rotates each meridian comes in turn beneath the position of high and low tide nearly twice a day; not exactly twice, because allowance must be made for the forward movement of the moon. Nor are these positions exactly in line with the moon (as for simplicity they are shown in the diagram), because the tides are affected by (*a*) the earth's rotation; (*b*) the great continental obstructions met with during their circuit of the globe, and (*c*) friction against the sea floor, especially in shallow seas.

The effect of the sun is similar to that of the moon, but considerably less powerful. When the earth, moon, and sun fall along the same straight line, the tide-raising forces of sun and moon help each other, and tides of maximum range, known as *spring tides*, result. The moon is then either new or full. When the sun and moon are at right angles relative to the earth, the moon produces high tides when the sun produces low. The tides are then less high and low than usual and are called *neap tides*.

In the open ocean the difference in level between high and low tide is only a few feet. Enclosed basins have still weaker tides—only a foot or so in the Mediterranean and no more than 4 inches in the Black Sea. In shallow seas, however, and especially where the tide is concentrated between converging shores, ranges of 20 to 30 feet are common and tidal currents are generated. The tides around the British Isles are of special interest. After passing up the western coasts the crest of the tidal wave swings round into the North Sea and proceeds southwards. The Coriolis force drives the water towards the right, that is the British side, which in consequence has far

FIG. 11—5
The Seven *bore* advancing
up-river at the peak of a
spring tide. (*Keystone
Press Agency Ltd*)

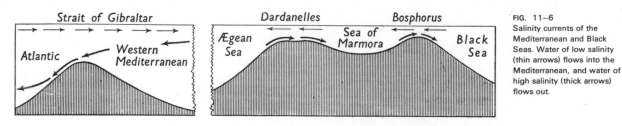

FIG. 11–6
Salinity currents of the Mediterranean and Black Seas. Water of low salinity (thin arrows) flows into the Mediterranean, and water of high salinity (thick arrows) flows out.

higher tides than Norway and Denmark. In passing northwards up the Irish Sea the Coriolis force results in the tides being at least twice as high on the Welsh and English coasts as on the Irish side. Similarly, the tides running up the English Channel are also forced to the right, giving the French coasts the higher tides. It will be readily appreciated that conditions of exceptional complexity arise in the Straits of Dover and the southern part of the North Sea.

A current of about 2 knots accompanies the flood tide as it advances up the English Channel. In the Bristol Channel, which is like a wide funnel leading into the Seven, the in-flowing tide is forced into a rapidly narrowing passage. It therefore rises in height. Spring tides may reach a height of 42 feet and the in-ward current may attain a speed of 10 knots. In these circumstances, and especially if the wind co-operates, the overcrowded tidal waters eventually travel bodily up the river with a wall-like front of roaring surf. This is the Seven *bore*, a vigorously advancing flood of powerful waves and breakers (Fig. 11–5) which may ride up the river almost as far as Gloucester before subsiding completely.

Near the shore and between islands, tidal currents are often sufficiently powerful to transport sand and even shingle, and so to scour and erode the sea floor. In estuaries, where the outward flow of river water is added to the ebb current, transport is dominantly seaward. But since the fresh river water, carrying a load of silt and mud, tends to slide out over the heavier salt water that has crept in along the bottom, it is mainly the upper suspended load that is swept out to sea, while the coarser debris is stranded and tends to accumulate as sand bars.

Powerful currents are generated by differences of salinity. Salinity is decreased by inflow of rivers, rainfall, and the melting of ice, and increased by evaporation. Evaporation over the Mediterranean lowers its surface and increases the salinity and density. Surface currents therefore flow into the Mediterranean through the Dardanelles from the Sea of Marmora and the Black Sea (where the evaporation is more than neutralized by the inflow

of rivers), and through the Straits of Gibraltar from the Atlantic (Fig. 11–6). In each case undercurrents of higher salinity flow outwards from the Mediterranean along the bottom. Shore deposits are affected by the surface currents, while in deeper water the floor is scoured by the bottom current. A similar interchange of water takes place between the highly saline Red Sea and the Indian Ocean, and also between the comparatively fresh Baltic and the North Sea. Since the less saline and lighter water always tends to spread over the more saline and heavier water, the surface current flows in all cases towards the region of higher salinity, while the bottom current is in the opposite direction.

The main current systems of the oceans are primarily of a convectional nature, brought about (*a*) by density differences due to heating in the tropics and cooling in the polar regions, and (*b*) by variations in salinity. They are greatly modified by the configuration of the continents and the dominant winds. Apart from the superficial movements charted in every atlas, there is much to be learnt about ocean circulation in three dimensions. The discoveries now being made as the oceanic depths are explored are, as usual, surprisingly different from expectations. Cold water from the Arctic spreads south at depths between 1,000 and 1,500 fathoms, is warmed by the undercurrent from the Straits of Gibraltar, and continues south until it rises over the cold currents moving northwards from Antarctica. The latter can be traced into all the oceans, including the North Atlantic, while deep Arctic and Atlantic water also passes into the Pacific and Indian Oceans.

WAVES

The ordinary waves seen on the sea are almost entirely due to winds sweeping over the surface of the water. The exceptions are the far-travelled descendants of giant waves which result from the sudden displacement of immense volumes of ocean water by catastrophic "accidents" such as earthquakes, volcanic eruptions, submarine landslides,

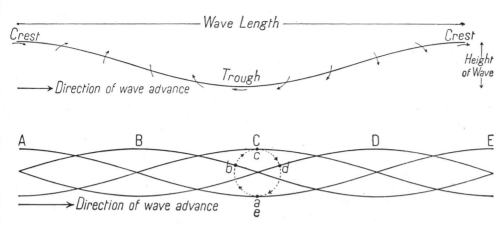

FIG. 11—7
Profile of an ideal wave of oscillation from crest to crest, showing the direction of movement of water particles at various points.

FIG. 11—8
Diagram showing the orbit of a water particle during the passage of a wave of oscillation. A, B, C, D, E mark successive positions of the crest as the wave moves forward; a, b, c, d, e are the corresponding positions of the particle. AE = wave length; Ca = height of wave.

and avalanches of rock from high cliffs or steep mountain sides into deep water. Here we are concerned with waves that derive their motion and energy from the wind. Wind ruffles the surface into undulations which move forwards and gradually increase in height and speed. The *height* of a wave is the vertical distance from trough to crest (Fig. 11–7). The horizontal distance from crest to crest—or from trough to trough—is called the *wave length*. The height ultimately attained by a wind-driven wave, where it is not restricted by shallowing water, depends on the strength, duration, and *fetch* of the wind, the fetch being the length of the open stretch of water across which the wind is blowing. When the loss of energy involved in the propagation of the waves through the water is just balanced by the amount of energy supplied from the wind, the height reaches its maximum.

In the open ocean heights of 5 to 15 feet are common, increasing to 40 or 50 feet in high seas. The corresponding wave lengths range from 200 to 800 feet, but as they flatten out into swell they may reach 1,000 feet or more, about 2,500 feet being the maximum ever recorded, with a speed of nearly 80 miles per hour.

The sea waves we watch from the shore are generally a mixture of swells from distant storms, and "seas" from local winds. In other words, they can be described as a *spectrum* of "trains" of waves of different lengths, just as sunlight is a blend of light waves of different lengths which, when separated (as in the rainbow), appear as a spectrum of different colours.

It is important to realize that in the open sea—apart from wind drift—it is only the wave form that moves forward, not the water itself. Each particle of water moves round a circular orbit during the passage of each complete

wave, the diameter being equal to the height of the wave (Fig. 11–8). This is demonstrated by the behaviour of a floating cork under which a train of waves is passing. Each time the cork rises and falls it also sways to and fro, without advancing appreciably from its mean position. Such waves are called *waves of oscillation*. If the wind is strong, however, each water particle advances a little farther than it recedes. Similarly, in shallow water, where friction against the bottom begins to be felt, each particle recedes a little less than it advances. In both cases the orbit, instead of being a closed circle, resembles an ellipse which is not quite closed and a certain proportion of the water slowly drifts forward in the direction of wave advance.

When gusts of wind brush over a field of corn the stalks repeatedly bend forward and recover, and waves visibly spread across the surface. Here it is obvious that the wave motion is not confined to the surface, since it is shared by the stalks right down to the ground. In the same way the energy contributed by the wind to a body of water is transmitted downwards as well as along the surface. Owing to friction the diameters of the orbits rapidly diminish in depth until at a depth of the same order as the wave length they become negligible. The greatest depth at which sediment on the sea floor can just be stirred by the oscillating water is called the *wave base*. This depth was formerly thought to be about 600 feet, but it is now known to be considerably less, at least for surface waves. Ripple marks have been photographed at depths of thousands of feet, but such effects are far beyond the influence of surface waves. There are, however, deeper waves generated at the boundaries of currents travelling in opposing directions, and of these we know very little as yet.

WAVES IN SHALLOW WATER

As waves approach the shore and pass into shallow water, they gradually slow down as they begin to "feel the bottom", each wave progressing more slowly than the one behind. The wave lengths are also gradually reduced in proportion to the decreasing velocity, and the resulting tendency of the wave fronts to crowd together as the shore is approached can often be clearly seen. Consequently when the waves approach a shelving shore obliquely, as in Fig. 11–9, the crest lines swing towards parallelism with the shore. This change of direction with change of speed is called *refraction*; it is essentially the same phenomenon as the sudden bending of a ray of light when it passes from air into, say, glass in which its speed is reduced by 30 per cent or more. Refraction of oblique waves around a head-

land and islet into a bay is well illustrated by Fig. 11–10.

The effect of wave retardation off an indented coast is illustrated by Fig. 11–11. The waves advance more rapidly through the deeper water opposite a bay than through the shallower water opposite a headland. Thus the crest of a wave at *a* moves to *a'*, while the crest at *b* moves only to *b'*. Each wave crest in turn begins to approximate to the curves of the shore line. Consequently, when the shore is reached by a wave such as *a b c d e*, all the energy from the long stretch *ac* is concentrated on the headland AC (and that from *de* on DE). In contrast, the very much smaller amount of energy from the short stretch *cd* is spread around the shores of the bay from C to D. Thus, while headlands are being vigorously

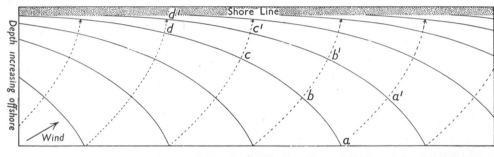

FIG. 11–9
Wave refraction. Diagram to illustrate the swing of oblique waves towards parallelism with the shore. While the crest at *a* advances to *a'*, the crest at *b* (in shallower water) advances a shorter distance to *b'*, and so on. The crest lines *abcd* thus become curved as shown.

FIG. 11–10
Aerial photograph showing the refraction of waves around a headland and islet into a bay at San Clemente Island, California. (*Official U.S. Navy photograph*)

attacked by powerful waves, the bays are less disturbed and their waters provide safe anchorage for vessels sheltering from a storm. In the same way waves entering a harbour between the piers spread out and merely ruffle the water inside.

When a wave reaches the foreshore and enters shallow water, so that its velocity and wave length are reduced, it becomes higher, and at the same time the wave front becomes steeper. Finally a critical point is reached when the volume of water in front is insufficient to complete the wave form as required by the orbital movement. The crest of the uncompleted wave is then left unsupported and breaks. What were *waves of oscillation* have now passed into *waves of translation* in which the water advances bodily up the shore. This sheet of surf may form into smaller waves that break again higher up, so that there may be a *zone of breakers* rather than a single *break point*. The final translation of water up the beach is

called the *uprush* or *swash*. The return of water down the slope is called the *backwash* (Fig. 11–12). Between the landward zone of swash and backwash, and the seaward zone of breakers, there may be a surf zone, the presence of which has made some holiday resorts, (*e.g.* Perranporth, Cornwall) famous for the sport of surf riding. Where the shore profile slopes gently, a surf zone is generally present, but where it slopes steeply, the depth of water is such that the break point lies close to land and there is no surf zone. There are of course gradations between these two extremes of shore profile where surf zones are intermittantly present.

Two contrasted types of breakers have been recognized, namely the spilling breaker and the plunging breaker, between which there are all gradations. A *spilling breaker* advances over a gently shelving floor with a foaming crest. As it advances its wave front steepens until the crest spills over into the trough in

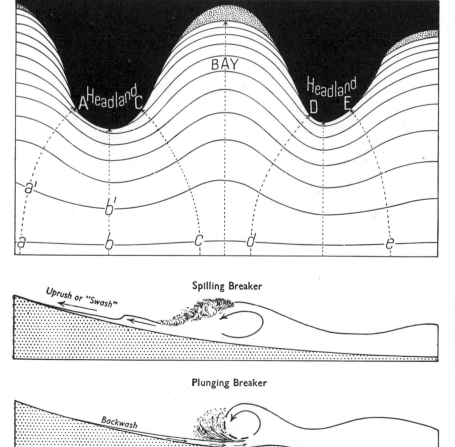

FIG. 11–11
Diagram to show the effect of wave retardation off an indented coast.

FIG. 11–12
Diagrammatic illustration of the difference between a spilling breaker with an effective uprush (constructive type) and a plunging breaker with an effective backwash (destructive type). (*Modified after W. V. Lewis*)

front, and surges up the beach as swash (Fig. 11–12). A *plunging breaker* advances over a more steeply sloping floor and the wave front steepens until an unstable-looking hollow appears in front. Over this the crest begins to curl, sometimes hovering a little while the wave continues to advance. But finally it plunges down, often with great violence, and considerable volumes of air may be rapidly trapped by the plunging breaker and compressed so strongly that the air escapes with explosive violence "atomizing" the water into masses of foaming spray. When a plunging breaker breaks close to a cliff or sea-wall the shock-pressures resulting from the explosive escape of air entrapped between the breaker and the cliff or wall may cause marked erosion.

In 1931 Lewis distinguished between constructive and destructive waves of translation. Constructive waves of translation are those with a strong swash that carries material up the beach, and a relatively ineffective backwash: spilling breakers provide an example (Fig. 11–12). Destructive waves of translation are those with a strong backwash that removes material from the beach, and a relatively ineffective swash: plunging breakers provide an example. There are, of course, all gradations between constructive and destructive waves, and much work has been done, including experimental investigations within tanks, to determine their characteristics. Generally speaking high, steep-fronted waves are destructive and tend to carry a beach away, whilst flat waves are constructive and build up a beach.

MARINE EROSION

The sea operates as an agent of erosion in four different ways:

(*a*) by the *hydraulic action* of the water itself, involving the picking up of loose material by currents and waves, and the shattering of rocks as the waves crash, like giant water-hammers, against the cliffs;

(*b*) by *corrasion*, when waves, armed with rock fragments, hurl them against the cliffs and, co-operating with currents, drag them to and fro across the rocks of the foreshore;

(*c*) by *attrition*, as the fragments or "tools" are themselves worn down by impact and friction; and

(*d*) by *corrosion*, that is solvent and chemical action, which in the case of sea water is of limited importance, except on limestone coasts.

The destructive impact of breakers against obstructions is often far greater than is generally realized. The pressure exerted by Atlantic waves averages over 2,000 lb/ft² (nearly 10,000 kg/m²) during the winter; in great storms it may exceed even 6,000. Thus, not only cliffs, but also sea walls, breakwaters, and exposed lighthouses are subjected to shocks of enormous intensity. Cracks and crevices are quickly opened up and extended. Water, often in the form of high-pressure spray, is forcibly driven into every opening, tightly compressing the air confined within the rocks. As each wave recedes the compressed air suddenly expands with explosive force, and large blocks as well as small thus become loosened and ultimately blown out by pressure from the back. The combined activity of bombardment and blasting is most effective as a quarrying process on rocks that are already divided into blocks by jointing and bedding, or otherwise fractured, for example, along faults and crush zones. A result of such quarrying action is well illustrated by Lulworth Cove in Dorset (Fig. 11–13). Here, the strata strike parallel to the coast, and the general dip is inland. A long coastal strip of hard, folded Jurassic limestone is followed inland by soft Lower Cretaceous beds, bounded on the landward side by an upland of Chalk. In places the sea has breached the well-jointed Jurassic limestone and scooped out the softer rocks behind. Lulworth Cove is a beautiful example of a scooped-out bay, and the Stair Hole, just to the west, illustrates an earlier stage in such a development. At the Stair Hole (Fig. 2–12) the sea has no more than gained access to the soft rocks by tunnelling through the Jurassic Limestone which still stands as a battered and crumbling rampart against the sea.

Cliffs originate by the undercutting action of waves against the slopes of coastal land. By collapse of the rocks overhanging the notch which is excavated at the base of the cliffs, the latter gradually recede and present a steep face towards the advancing sea. But where the cliffs are protected for a time by fallen debris, and especially if they are composed of poorly consolidated rocks, the upper slopes may be worn back by weathering, rainwash, and slumping. At any given place the actual form of the cliff depends on the nature and structure of the rocks there exposed, and on the relative rates of marine erosion and sub-aerial denudation.

The most striking evidence of undermining is provided by caves. There are few stretches of coast along which the rocks are equally resistant to wave action, and caves are excavated along belts of weakness of all kinds; especially where the rocks are strongly jointed (Fig. 11–14). By subsequent roof collapse and removal of the debris, long narrow inlets develop (Fig. 11–16). In Scotland and the Faroes such a tidal inlet (Fig. 11–15) is called a *geo* ("g" hard—Norse, *gya*, a creek). A cave at the landward end of a geo—or indeed any sea cave—may communicate with the surface by way of a vertical shaft which may be some distance from the edge of the cliff. A natural chimney of this kind is known as a *blow hole* or *gloup* (a throat). The opening is formed by the falling in of joint blocks loosened by the hydraulic action of wave-compressed air already described. The name *blow hole* refers to the fact that during storms spray is forcibly blown into the air each time a foaming breaker surges through the cave beneath.

When two caves on opposite sides of a head-land unite, a natural arch results, and may persist for a time (Fig. 11–17). Later the arch falls in, and the seaward portion of the head-land then remains as an isolated stack. Well-known examples of stacks are the Chalk pinnacles at the western extremity of the Isle of Wight, known as the Needles, the more stalwart Old Harry Rocks of Swanage (Figs. 11–16 and 11–17 which illustrate two stages in a continuous process of marine erosion), and the impressive towers of Old Red Sandstone near John o'Groats and in the Orkneys.

As the cliffs are worn back a *wave-cut plat-form* is left in front (Fig. 11–18), the upper part of which is visible as the rocky foreshore exposed at low tide (Fig. 11–19). There may be patches of sand and pebbles in depressions, and beach-like fringes strewn with fallen debris along the foot of the cliffs, but all such material is continually being broken up by the waves, and swept to and fro across the platform which becomes further abraded, until the abrasive materials themselves are eventually ground down to sizes that can be carried away by currents. Since the outer parts of the wave-cut platform have been sub-jected to scouring longer than the inner, a gentle seaward slope develops. In massive and resistant rocks this is an extremely slow process.

As the cliffs recede and the platform be-comes very wide, the waves have to cross a broad expanse of shallow water, so that when they reach the cliffs most of their energy has already been used in transporting the abraded materials. Thus the rate of coast erosion is automatically reduced. In high latitudes, how-ever, the cliffs may still continue to be worn back by frost and thaw, provided that the waves are able to remove what would other-wise become a protective apron of scree. The wave-cut platform off the rocky coast of West and North-West Norway—there known as the *strandflat*—has reached an exceptional width by this co-operation of processes, locally up to as much as 37 miles (Fig. 11–20). The most extensive level now stands 50 to 60 feet above sea level because of recent isostatic uplift.

On the other hand, where the sea is en-

FIG. 11–13
Lulworth Cove, a beautifully curved bay scooped out by the sea after the breaching of the resistant barrier of Portland beds, which still form the cliffs on both sides of the entrance to the Cove.

FIG. 11–14
Fingal's Cave, Island of Staffa, west of Mull, Argyllshire. The cave has been eroded from part of a basaltic lava flow showing columnar jointing.
(Paul Popper)

FIG. 11–15
Inlets developed by roof collapse of caves formed by marine erosion of Old Red Sandstone. The Wife Geo, near Duncansby Head, NE. of Caithness, Scotland, looking seawards. (H.M. Geological Survey)

FIG. 11–16
Inlets eroded along belts of relatively closely jointed Chalk, and sea stacks developed from the intervening promontories. Old Harry Rocks, Swanage. (*John Hinde Studios*)

FIG. 11–17
Showing stages in the development of sea stacks from a Chalk promontory in Fig. 11–16: 1. caves; 2. arches; and 3. sea stacks after the collapse of the roofs of arches. Old Harry Rocks, Swanage. (*John Hinde Studios*)

FIG. 11–18
Idealized section illustrating a temporary stage in the development of a sea cliff, wave-cut platform, and wave-built terrace.

195

croaching on a coast of poorly consolidated rocks, the platform in front is quickly abraded and normal coast erosion proceeds vigorously. In some localities the inroads of the sea reach alarming proportions. In Britain serious loss of land is suffered in parts of East Anglia and along the Yorkshire coast south of Flamborough Head, where the waves have the easy task of demolishing glacial deposits of sand, gravel, and boulder clay. Since Roman times the Holderness coast has been worn back 2½ to 3 miles, and many villages and ancient landmarks have been swept away (Fig. 11–21). During the last hundred years the average rate of cliff recession has been 5 or 6 feet per year. The rate is not uniform, however, for severe storms and localized cliff falls are more destructive in a short time than the normal erosion of several average

years, while recent erection of coast defences has resulted in small gains in one or two areas.

The North Sea surge of 1953 provides an extreme example of rapid coast erosion. A *surge* is an abnormal rise of sea level that occurs when spring tides, wind, and storm waves all act together in the same direction in a more or less confined and shallow sea. On the last day of January 1953 very low atmospheric pressure over part of the North Sea caused a rise of sea level which, though only a foot or two, meant the inflowing of immense volumes of water from the Atlantic where the atmospheric pressure was higher. At the same time a violent gale from the north drifted the surface water southwards. Only a limited amount of the excess water could escape through the Straits of Dover and the sea poured in through countless breaches in the coastal defences of

FIG. 11–19
Wave-cut platform cut across steeply dipping Silurian strata, near Abb's Head, Berwickshire, SE. Scotland. (*H.M. Geological Survey*)

S.W.　　　　　　　　　　　　　　　　　　　　　　　N.E.

Fedje Fjord　　　　　　　　　　　　Fens Fjord

Lindås
Peninsula
Igneous and Metamorphic Rocks

FIG. 11–20
Section across the *strandflat* north of Bergen, Norway. Length of section 32 miles (52 Km). (*After Fridtjof Nansen*)

the Netherlands, devastating the low-lying areas previously reclaimed from the sea. Along the lowlands of East Anglia and the Thames estuary the disaster, though less widespread, was locally just as destructive. Seven miles south of Lowestoft, for example, a 25-foot cliff was cut back 35 feet in two hours.

SHORE PROFILES

In appropriate circumstances some of the sediment in transit across the wave-cut platform accumulates in the deeper water beyond, to form a *shoreface terrace* which grows forward like a broad embankment with its upper surface in smooth continuity with the platform (Fig. 11–18). The combined shore and offshore surface in this case, as in others, is a product of the joint action of erosion and deposition, each of which varies considerably from time to time and from place to place. The supply of sediment, for example, is irregular both in rate and distribution, since contributions are received from rivers and currents as well as from cliff wastage and platform abrasion, all fluctuating sources of income. The processes concerned in the removal of sediment—also widely variable—are themselves largely controlled by the slope of the shore and its seaward continuation—that is to say, by the profile of the surface taken at right angles to the shore. A relatively steep slope favours destructive waves of translation and removal of sediment from the landward side, so that the slope becomes less steep. Conversely, a relatively gentle slope favours constructive waves of translation and beach deposition on the landward side, so that the slope becomes steeper. The surface is therefore being continually modified, and in such a way that at each point it tends to acquire just the right slope to ensure that incoming supplies of sediment can be carried away as fast as they are received. A profile so adjusted that this fluctuating state of balance is approximately achieved is called a *profile of equilibrium*. Because of the alternating changes from tide to tide and from season to season, and the particularly marked changes from calm to storm, however, only a short-lived approximation to equilibrium can ever be achieved. The actual profile is continually being modified, especially along shores fringed with sand or shingle, loose materials which are easily moved.

The concept of the ideal profile of equilibrium has its uses, however. At any given time the seaward slope at a given place may be either steeper or gentler than this ideal.

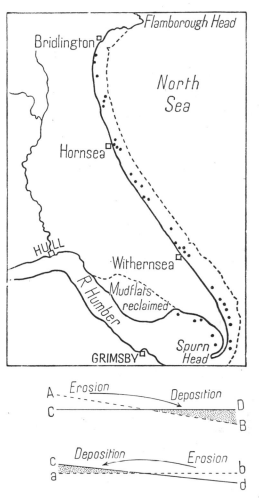

FIG. 11–21
Sketch map showing the loss of land and villages by marine erosion along the Holderness coast of SE. Yorkshire. The broken line indicates the approximate position of the coast in Roman times; former settlements are shown by black dots. (*After T. Sheppard*)

FIG. 11–22
The development of a profile of equilibrium CD from a more steeply sloping initial surface, AB.

FIG. 11–23
The development of a profile of equilibrium cd from a more gently sloping initial surface, ab.

Suppose *AB* in Fig. 11–22, represents a relatively steep initial slope on a shore of submergence. In transforming this as nearly as possible into a profile of equilibrium *CD*, the waves cut a cliff-backed platform, while the resulting sediment is deposited as an offshore terrace, as already illustrated in Fig. 11–18. Next, suppose *ab* in Fig. 11–23 represents a relatively gentle initial slope, as when a broad valley floor becomes a bay of submergence. In transforming this into a profile of equilibrium *cd*, waves and currents build up a beach around the shores of the bay. It must be emphasized that Figs. 11–22 and 11–23 are merely diagrams to illustrate some basic principles. The real profiles are commonly far from simple.

TRANSPORT AND DEPOSITION TRANSVERSE TO THE SHORE

The study of the landward and seaward migra-

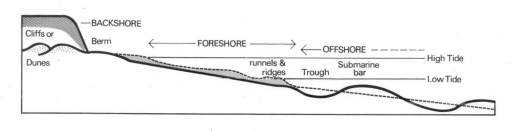

FIG. 11–24
Diagrammatic representation
of the subdivisions of a shore,
with characteristic beach and
offshore profiles after a period
of beach construction (broken
line) and of beach destruction
(full line) when the berm is
cut back. The diagram is based
on information derived from
experiments in tanks. On
natural shores submarine bars
and foreshore ridges may
both be present, but one
or other of these may be
waxing while the other is
waning.

tion of beach material received great stimulus from the preparations for D-day, during the second World War, when it was a necessary preliminary for landing on the Normandy beaches to know just how the profiles changed under varying conditions. Since then many other types of shore have been studied, and various techniques have been developed to aid observation. Pebbles and sand grains have been dyed various colours in order that they may be recognized and their movements traced. Radioactive tracer materials have been added, sometimes in the form of artificial grains of glass charged with a radio-active isotope, and after transport these grains have been located with the aid of a Geiger counter. Fluorescent dyes have been used on sand that has been liberated at intervals of a few weeks on the beaches from which it was collected. This method of using the actual shore materials which will move in the same way as the natural sand may be expected to give the best results.

Experimental investigations, in tanks, have also been made but, although they have added much to our knowledge of the movements of shore materials, they can never be a substitute for the study of actual beaches themselves. In experimental investigations the fluctuating conditions of sea shores cannot be reproduced, and the question of scale raises difficulties. For an experiment to be true to scale the hydrodynamical processes and the size and specific gravity of the sediment should simultaneously be scaled down so that they hold the same ratios to one another that they have on a natural shore, and this has not proved to be practical. Nevertheless such experiments are very fruitful in the investigation of specific problems.

Although the conditions of beaches are highly variable and much more detailed investigation remains to be made, some general characteristics are emerging. For example, on the landward side of the break point or break zone of the waves the prevalent direction of movement of the beach materials depends on the predominant character of the waves through a season or more. Generally speaking low waves, with a strong swash, act constructively and carry sand and shingle up the beach, whilst high, steep waves, with a strong backwash, act destructively and carry beach materials down towards the break point.

During a constructive period when a mixed assemblage of sediment is swept up the beach, the coarser material is left stranded at the top in the backshore zone (Fig. 11–24), where it is piled up to form a terrace or a ridge with a gentle landward slope and a steeper slope leading down to the foreshore. This terrace or ridge is called a *berm* (Fig. 11–24). During periods of destructive waves the berm may be attacked and part of it carried away. Yet steep plunging breakers may be responsible for one constructive activity which, although rarely coming into operation, is of major importance over a long period. Violent splashes of spray from the most powerful of these breakers, generally occurring during winter storms and spring tides, may fling pebbles and boulders to the highest part of the berm or even beyond, so building up a strong coastal defence against all but highly exceptional attacks from the sea. In this way Chesil beach (Fig. 11–25) has been built up above normal high-water level.

Immediately outside the break point the movement of sand appears always to be landwards towards the break point, where it meets sand transported seawards from the shore. Beneath the break point of the waves this sand commonly collects and forms a bar the summit of which is always below water level (Fig. 11–24). Such a bar, known as a *submarine bar* or a *break-point bar*, is not a permanent feature since change of wave height and of the position of the break point may lead to its migration or destruction. On the landward side of a submarine bar a parallel trough is usually present (Fig. 11–24).

On the foreshore *ridges* are sometimes exposed at low tide, on the landward side of which there may be a *runnel* or a string of *long pools*. These ridges, sometimes called swash ridges, result from the accumulation of sand transported landwards by the swash and seawards by the backwash of waves. The beach at Blackpool is a good example of a beach with ridges. It was first investigated, during the last world war, because it resembled the Normandy beaches where ridges, below sea level at high tide, could have been dangerous for landing craft.

The contrasted conditions responsible for the construction and destruction of beaches tend to be correlated with quiet and stormy periods respectively, and therefore in a general way with summer and winter. The operation of "combing down"—thinning or removal of beaches by destructive breakers—is eventually followed by restoration of material by constructive waves. But beaches removed by a catastrophe like the North Sea surge of 1953 naturally take much longer to restore. On that occasion, for example, the beaches of Lincolnshire were completely scoured away in one night, and it was not until 1959 that their former condition was restored.

Both thinning and thickening of beaches may be effectively assisted by winds in the appropriate directions. Gales blowing strongly offshore cause a surface drift away from the coast. To balance this an undercurrent is directed towards the shore and, though feeble, it co-operates with the constructive waves. On the other hand, onshore gales not only whip up destructive waves, they also raise the hydraulic head of water along the shore and so strengthen the backwash and the outward currents that necessarily result from the piling-up of water against the shore. The growth and maintenance of beaches are therefore favoured by offshore winds.

Interference with natural profiles, for example, by offshore dredging, has dangerous results if it causes one-way changes outside the normal limits of thinning and thickening of beaches (Fig. 11–22). In 1897, for example, dredging began off the coast north of Start Point to furnish shingle for use in the harbour works then in progress at Plymouth. This caused thinning of the beach at Hallsands; by 1902 the beach had been lowered 12 feet and cliff erosion had become a steadily increasing menace. The licence to dredge offshore shingle was cancelled, but it was too late. Storm waves and resulting blow holes were already attacking the little fishing village of Hallsands, built on a 25-foot raised beach, and by 1917 only the walls of a few ruined cottages remained, which can still be seen.

Currents capable of transporting sediment seaward require some discussion. When breakers and onshore winds pile up water against the coast, the rising sea level must be counterbalanced by currents flowing away from the shore. These were formerly grouped together as undertow, but it is now known that most of the water flows seawards as localized currents, known as *rip currents*, which flow through depressions in the submarine bars. Near the shore all the water in a rip current, from sea floor to surface, flows seawards, but farther out to sea rip currents become surface currents. Rip currents are the only currents easily capable of transporting sediment out to

FIG. 11–25
Chesil Beach, showing the highest part or "berm" at Chesilton, which is 43 feet (13 m) above high-water level, viewed from the West Cliff, Portland, Dorset. (*Fox Photos Ltd*)

FIG. 11—26
Beach drift impeded by
groynes at Eastbourne, NE.
of Beachy Head, Sussex.
The direction of drifting
is to NE. *i.e.* up-Channel.
(*Aerofilms Ltd*)

sea. Seen from the cliff top they sometimes appear as long lanes of foaming turbid water stretching out to sea. They are highly dangerous to swimmers who can best escape from them by swimming parallel to the shore.

TRANSPORT AND DEPOSITION ALONG THE SHORE

Longshore drift of sediment takes place in two zones: (*a*) near the upper limit of wave action and (*b*) in the surf and breaker zones.

Broadly speaking, when waves are driven obliquely against the coast by strong winds, debris is carried up the beach by the swash, in a forward sweeping curve, and some of it is then swept back again by the backwash. The backwash may have a slight forward movement at the start, owing to the swing of the water as it turns, but otherwise it tends to drag the material down the steepest slope, until it is caught by the next uprush of swash. By the continual repetition of this zig-zag progress sand and shingle are drifted along the shore near the upper limit of wave action.

The direction of drifting may vary from time to time, but along many shores there is a cumulative movement in one direction, controlled by the dominant or most effective winds. A subsidiary factor which aids or

hinders beach drifting is the direction of the advancing flood tide.

Farther out from the shore, in the surf zone, oblique winds and waves co-operate in generating intermittent and fluctuating longshore currents. If the velocity of these currents is great enough, say greater than about 1 foot per second, they transport sediment alongshore, largely in suspension. In addition sediment always moves alongshore within the breaker zone, above any submarine bar that may be present.

In the English Channel the dominant winds and the inflowing tides both come from the south-west, and the prevailing direction of drift is up-Channel and through the Straits of Dover, almost to the estuary of the Thames. Down the east coast of Britain the drift is mainly southwards, the dominant winds being from the north-east and the flood tide advancing from the north. There are a few exceptions: for example, the north coast of Norfolk, west of Cromer, stands athwart the main drift which, striking the coast obliquely, is deflected and travels westwards towards the Wash, as is evidenced by the patterns of sand spits.

Wherever it is thought desirable to protect the coast by checking the drift of sand and shingle, barriers known as *groynes* are erected across the beach. On the side of the groyne

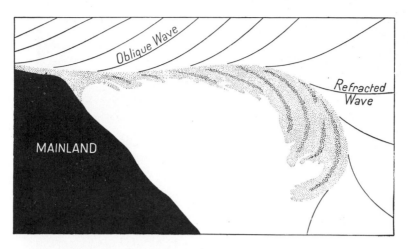

FIG. 11–27
Diagram to illustrate the development of a hooked spit by the refraction of oblique waves.

from which the beach drift comes, sediment is heaped up, while from the other side it is washed away, to be retained in turn by the next groyne (Fig. 11–26). The groynes as a whole interrupt the natural flow of material necessary to maintain the beaches farther along the coast. Where the beaches are starved and drift away, as a result of artificial interference with the balance of deposition and erosion elsewhere, the coast is exposed to more vigorous wave attack. To the east of Brighton and Newhaven, for example, the wastage of the Chalk cliffs has greatly increased since groynes were erected to protect these resorts.

SPITS AND BARS

Where shore drift is in progress along an indented coast, spits and bars are constructed as well as beaches. Where the coast turns in at the entrance to a bay or estuary the sediment transported by beach drift and longshore currents is carried more or less straight on and dropped into the deeper water beyond. The shoal thus started is gradually raised into an embankment. This grows in height by additions from its landward attachment until a ridge of sand or shingle is built above sea level in continuity with the shore from which the additions are contributed. The ridge increases in length by successive additions to its end, until waves or currents from some other quarter limit its forward growth.

If the ridge terminates in open water it is called a *spit*. Storm waves roll material over to the sheltered side, especially when they approach squarely, and spits thus tend to migrate landwards, often becoming curved in the process. Curvature is also brought about by the tendency of oblique waves to swing round the end (*i.e.* to be refracted) in places where the sea floor beyond shelves rapidly into deeper water. A spit may thus be developed into a *hook*, as indicated in Fig. 11–27. Cross currents may assist or modify hook formation, and it is usual for spits to lengthen by the addition of a number of successive hooks. Hooked spits of similar structure occur in large lakes where tides are absent and currents are negligible. This suggests that the dominant winds and waves are the agents essentially responsible for the curving of spits.

A good example of a curved spit is Spurn Head (Figs. 11–21 and 11–28), which extends into the Humber in streamlined continuity with the Holderness coast. The latter is almost everywhere fringed with sand and shingle that drifts steadily from north to south, fresh supplies being constantly furnished by the rapid erosion of the coast. Nearly all (97 per cent) the transported material is carried beyond Spurn Head, cumbering the estuary with shoals on its way towards the Lincolnshire coast, where it is added to the seaward-growing coastal flats.

Southward drift is also very active along the east coast of Norfolk and Suffolk. Ten centuries ago the Yarmouth sands had already spread across the estuary of the Yare, forming an obstruction which deflected the river towards the south (Fig. 11–29). The spit then continued to grow southwards, hugging the coast, with the river confined between itself and the mainland. By 1347 the end of the spit and the outlet of the river had reached Lowestoft. Since 1560, however, an artificial outlet has been maintained at Gorleston, where the spit now terminates. The truncated part has long ago drifted south. At Aldeburgh, half-way between Lowestoft and Harwich,

FIG. 11–28
Spurn Head, built by beach
drifting into the estuary of
the Humber in continuation of
the Yorkshire coast; looking
NNE. (*cf.* Fig. 11–21).
(*J. K. St Joseph*)

the longest spit on the east coast has similarly diverted the outlet of the Alde (Fig. 11–30).

A *bar* or *barrier beach* extends from one headland to another, or nearly so. When the bay inside is completely enclosed it becomes a marsh, or, if it receives streams from the mainland, a shore-line lake. More usually, however, a narrow and deep channel is kept open by tidal scour. Between Gdansk and Memel, on the south-east Baltic coast there are two very long bay-mouth bars, surmounted by sand dunes, with extensive tidal lagoons on the landward side (Fig. 11–31). A similar construction of sand or shingle connecting a headland to an island, or one island to another, is a *connecting bar* or *tombolo* (Italian).

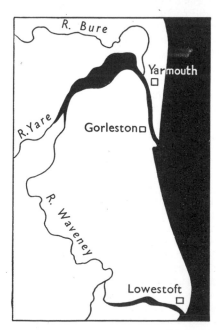

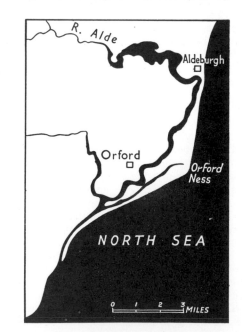

Examples of river deflection, in East Anglia, by the southern extension of sand and shingle spits. Both drawn to same scale.

FIG. 11–29 (far left)
River Yare, Norfolk.

FIG. 11–30
River Alde, Suffolk.

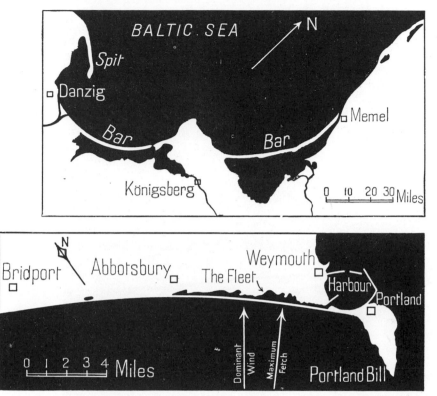

FIG. 11–31
A spit N. of Danzig (Gdansk) and two smoothly curved bay-mouth bars enclosing broad lagoons along the SE. Baltic coast of Poland and Lithuania (Königsberg and Memel are now called Kaliningrad and Klaipéda by the U.S.S.R.).

FIG. 11–32
Map of Chesil Beach, Dorset.

By far the most impressive barrier beach of shingle in Britain is Chesil Beach (Figs. 11–32 and 11–33). For six miles east of Bridport the beach fringes the Dorset coast. Near Abbotsbury the shore recedes and for the next eight miles the beach continues in front of the tidal lagoon of the Fleet as a bar well over 20 feet in height. Finally, becoming a tombolo, it crosses two miles of sea to the Isle of Portland, which is thus linked to the mainland. Chesil beach is a composite structure, its shingle having accumulated from local sources as well as by drift from each end. Although towards the Portland end the beach rises to the quite exceptional height of 43 feet, the sea sometimes bursts over it during great storms and pours through breaches into the low-lying area beyond. The beach is in fact slowly migrating towards the Fleet, as a cumulative result of its alignment almost exactly at right angles both to the direction of the average dominant winds and to that of the maximum fetch (Fig. 11–32).

Chesil beach is not an isolated example, for bars and spits are a characteristic feature on the south coast of England. On the east coast of Devon, Slapton Sands is another example of a bar or barrier beach. It extends north-north-eastwards as a bank of sand and shingle for more than two miles across an embayment at the head of Start Bay, and so forms a lake, Slapton Ley. A good example of a hooked spit occurs near Milford-on-Sea on the Hampshire coast. Three "double spits", the origins of which have proved puzzling, occur on the south coast. Two of them, near to Bournemouth, cut across the entrances to Poole and Christchurch harbours respectively. The third lies across the entrance to Pagham harbour, to the west of Bognor Regis on the Sussex coast. Fig. 11–34 shows how a "double spit" consists of two spits pointing towards one another. Such pairs of spits have suggested that there might be local longshore drift in opposite directions. At Poole, Christchurch, and Pagham, however, it has been established, from accumulations of sand against groynes, that the dominant longshore drift is eastwards or north-eastwards even where the spits point south-westward. After detailed field observations combined with study of old maps, revealing both the topographic and hydrographic evolutions of these "double spits" through more than a century, Robinson (1955) reached the conclusion that they were built mainly by on-shore storm waves in the same way that

203

bars are built. Indeed the total evidence suggests that these "double spits" originated as bars extending across the harbour embayments, a channel being kept open through the bar by the outflow of the respective rivers. The positions of the outlets at the entrances to Christchurch and Pagham harbours, however, is known to have varied considerably. Embayments cut off by bars and "double spits" gradually silt up if they are not kept open by dredging. On the other hand, the value of these embayments as sheltered harbours, (e.g. Poole harbour) is much enhanced by the protection of the "double spits".

FIG. 11—33
Chesil Beach, Dorset, viewed from the West Cliff, Portland (see also Fig. 11—25). (*H.M. Geological Survey*)

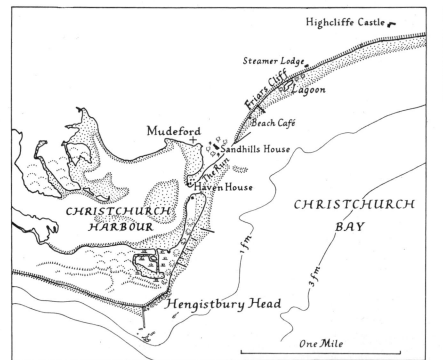

FIG. 11—34
"Double spit" at the entrance to Christchurch Harbour, Hampshire. Bathymetric contours in fathoms. (*A. H. W. Robinson, Geogr. J.* 121, 1955, p. 40, *by permission of the Royal Geographical Society*)

12

Submarine Landforms, Coral Reefs, and Marine Deposits

EXPLORATION OF THE FLOORS OF THE SEAS AND OCEANS

It may be recalled that the oceans are underlain by heavy rocks (sima) and that the continents, like icebergs, ride high because they are composed of relatively light rocks (sial, p. 5). The topographic transition from ocean floor to continental land is known as the *continental margin*, and is divisible into three parts. A gentle slope, the *continental rise*, connects the ocean floor with the *continental slope* which resembles an escarpment margining, the *continental shelf* (Fig. 12–21). Structurally, the ocean basins commence at the outer edge of the continental margin. The continental shelves, submerged beneath relatively shallow seas, and the deltas deposited upon them at the mouths of rivers too sluggish to

sweep their estuaries clean, have already been described. In this chapter it remains to consider submarine canyons, which traverse the continental slopes, and the topography of the floors of the oceans.

Exploration of the ocean floor by various geophysical techniques and by descents in bathyscapes, have added much to our knowledge of its topography. A generation ago the oceanic islands, mainly volcanic peaks and coral atolls rising from great depths, were supposed to be surrounded by almost featureless abyssal plains of enormous area. Today the ocean floors are known to be traversed by great submarine mountain ranges, the peaks of which sometimes rise above sea level as islands (Fig. 12–1). A great majority of the peaks fall short of the surface, however, and these are known as *seamounts* or, if they have nearly flat tops, like truncated cones, as table-mounts or *guyots* (Fig. 12–11).

Deep ocean trenches, like those margining the island arcs of the western Pacific, have been known since the *Challenger* Expedition of 1872–76, and recent investigations have not yet resolved the mystery of their origin (Fig. 1–5). A few submarine valleys carved into the slopes of the continental margins have long been known, but systematic echo sounding has revealed the presence of great numbers of deep submarine canyons with their tributary systems, and more are continually being charted.

SUBMARINE CANYONS

Nearly a century ago it was discovered by soundings that the Hudson and Congo valleys continue over the sea floor as submarine trenches which cut through the supposedly featureless floor of the continental shelf and become comparable in their dimensions with deep canyons where they traverse the continental slope beyond. One hundred and twenty miles south-east of New York the Hudson submarine canyon is 6 miles (10 km)

FIG. 12–1
An artist's impression of the Mid-Pacific Mountains. "If the Pacific Ocean were drained away, the mile-deep sunken islands would emerge as truncated volcanic cones. The original oil painting is by the distinguished scientific illustrator Chesley Bonestell and is based on part of the bathymetric chart of the Mid-Pacific range". (*E. L. Hamilton, 1956*)

across from rim to rim, and 3,700 feet (1,128 m) deep, measured from the rim. The Congo example is on an even vaster scale. These submarine canyons were naturally a source of great perplexity, and as other examples came to be found elsewhere the mystery of their origin presented geologists with a challenge of increasing urgency.

About 1920 sounding ceased to be a slow and tedious process with the invention of echo sounding. Since then the technique has been greatly improved and continuous soundings are now automatically recorded on a chart which shows a profile—called an *echogram* (Fig. 12–11)—of the sea or ocean floor over which the ship travels along an accurately known course. Although vast areas still remain to be systematically surveyed in this way, many hundreds of submarine canyons are now known in considerable detail. The margin of every continent provides examples. A very few begin as gorges within the estuaries of great rivers, like that of the Congo. A few are in line with rivers, but discontinuously, like that of the Indus which begins about 15 miles (24 km) from the land. But a large majority of the submarine canyons begin on the continental shelf or slope without any obvious relation to

the drainage of the land. All of them become features of vigorous relief on the steeper surfaces of the continental slopes, which turn out to be far more rugged than could have been expected. A dendritic system of tributary valleys, as illustrated in Fig. 12–2, is characteristic and the resulting submarine topography closely resembles that of a land surface dissected by youthful rivers. This similarity is strikingly exemplified by Fig. 12–3. The trunk canyons range between broad valleys with V-shaped profiles and gorges with steep or vertical sides. Some have been traced across the gentler slopes of the continental rise until they die out in the sediments of the abyssal plains beyond, at depths of up to 3,000

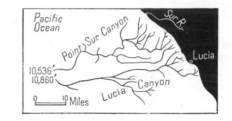

FIG. 12–2
Chart of submarine canyons off the Californian coast between San Francisco and Los Angeles, showing their tributaries and the depths to which they extend.

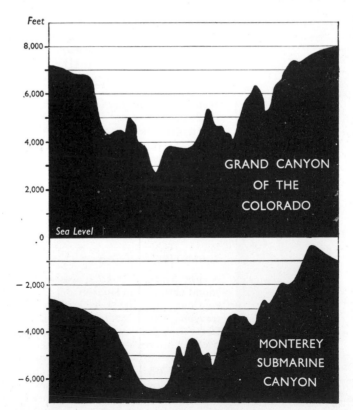

FIG. 12–3
Cross sections of the Grand Canyon of the Colorado River, and the submarine canyon of Monterey, off the Californian coast, to show the similarity of form and dimensions. Each section is 12·5 miles (20·1 km) across, and drawn to the same scale. (*After F. P. Shepherd*)

metres. Cores brought up from the canyon mouths and beyond include layers of shallow-water types of sediment, sometimes showing current bedding, and fossils which could only have got there by being transported through the canyons themselves. This implies that the canyons were cut by the erosive effects of some kind of current.

At one time there was much discussion as to whether the submarine canyons might be of subaerial origin rather than having been formed beneath the sea. Before the very great depths reached by the longer canyons had been discovered it was not unreasonable to suppose that they were drowned river valleys. If this were the explanation, some of the submarine canyons might be expected to terminate part way down the continental slopes, indicating the positions of the coast lines at the time when they were formed. However, none of them have been observed to do this. Since the average depth of the terminations of the best surveyed canyons, off the coast of California, is 1,820 m, and the world average is of the order of 2,117 m, the relative changes of level required by the subaerial hypothesis are of the order of 1,800 to 2,100m all over the continental margins.

The alternative hypothesis that most submarine canyons were formed beneath the sea had to be seriously considered. Detailed investigations of submarine canyons, off the coasts of California, Mexico, Japan, Hawaii, the Bahamas, Ceylon, and within the Mediterranean, have been made by members of the Scripps Institution of Oceanography, California. These investigations have revealed that the walls of submarine canyons are being intermittantly eroded at the present time. Currents have been found to flow in both directions along the canyons, stirring the bottom sediments, and ripple marks have been observed down to depths of 3,500 metres. The bottom sediments flooring the submarine canyons are known to move intermittently down the gradient and to build up fans where the submarine canyons terminate. It has not been observed how these sediments move, but it is commonly thought that they are transported by turbidity currents, and that by the erosive action of these currents the submarine canyons are formed.

TURBIDITY CURRENTS

Turbidity currents (Figs. 12–4 and 12–5), also known as density or suspension currents, are currents charged with suspended sediment. Sea water containing sediment in turbulent suspension has a higher density than the clear surrounding water and can form a relatively heavy underflow that will move rapidly downslope, with an accelerating speed determined by the density of the suspension and the angle of slope. By guiding and concentrating the flow of the loaded bottom water, chance

FIG 12–4
A small turbidity current flowing into the Pacific from the Santa Clara River, near Ventura, California, during a springtime flood. (*U.S. Department of Agriculture: Soil Conservation Service*)

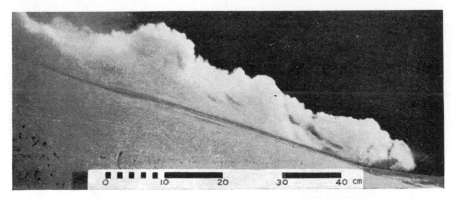

FIG. 12–5
An experimental turbidity current of fine sand and water flowing down a model valley excavated in fine sand in a laboratory tank. *(Ph. H. Kuenen)*

depressions may become selectively eroded into furrows which thereafter would canalize and accentuate the currents. On reaching the continental slope (with an average gradient of about 1 in 15) the currents would gather speed and thus gain additional erosive power. Once started, such submarine flows would be self-accelerating until the slope begins to flatten out. The inference is that on the continental slopes erosion would become more vigorous than on the shelf above. Given a subaqueous slope, the essential requirements for turbidity currents to form are a source of sediment and a trigger mechanism to start off the flow. These may be provided by a river in flood with a heavy load of sediment, or an earthquake may set off submarine landslides or shake loose unstable masses of sediment which then slump downslope. What was probably the most gigantic turbidity current of modern times was triggered off by the Grand Banks earthquake of 1929 (Fig. 12–6). Not only was the southern coast of Newfoundland devastated by this earthquake but twelve submarine cables were broken in at least twenty-three places. Nearly all the breakages occurred in pairs, near the edges of a trough-like submarine canyon. About twenty years later Heezen and Ewing had a hunch that turbidity currents might have broken the cables. If this were so the breaks should have occurred in a definite time sequence, dependent on the speed of the current concerned. On looking up the records of the earthquake they found, to their delight, that the evidence was just what they had anticipated (Fig. 12–7). In the words of Heezen:

"While the cables lying within 60 miles of the epicenter of the quake broke instantly, farther away the breaks came in a delayed sequence. For more than 13 hours after the earthquake, cables farther and farther to the south of the epicenter went on breaking one by one in regular succession. . . . It seems clear that this series of events must indicate

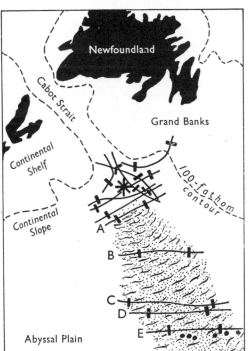

FIG. 12–6
Sketch map showing the original positions of the 12 broken telegraph cables crossing the deep continuation of the Cabot Strait submarine canyon at the time of the Grand Banks earthquake of 1929. Breakages are shown by cross bars. The shaded area represents the submarine canyon within which the cables marked A to E were broken. The large star at the head of the canyon marks the epicentre of the earthquake, *i.e.* the region immediately above its place of origin. *(After J. W. Gregory, Nature, 1929; and B. C. Heezen and M. Ewing, 1952)*

a submarine flow: the quake set in motion a gigantic avalanche of sediment on the steep continental slope, which broke the cables one after another as it rushed down-slope and flowed onto the abyssal plain".

From the time intervals between successive breaks and the related distances, the speed of the current can be calculated. Between A and B, for example, its average speed was over 40 miles (64 km) an hour (Fig. 12–7).

Turbidity currents transport a mixture of loose sediment, ranging in grain size from little pebbles, through sand to mud. When the sediment is deposited the large particles may be expected to sink first, followed in turn by

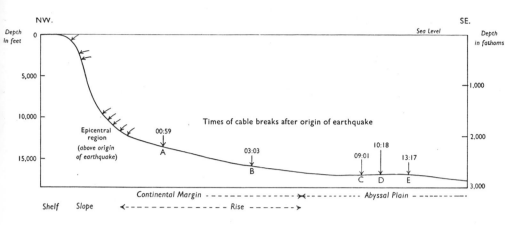

FIG. 12–7
Section along the floor of Cabot Strait submarine canyon, with arrows showing the places where the cables A to E were broken and the corresponding time intervals after the earthquake, which originated at 20:32 G.M.T. on 18 November, 1929. Length of section approximately 610 miles (981·5 km). (*After B. C. Heezen and M. Ewing, 1952*)

successively smaller ones. The resulting sedimentary rock should therefore be characterized by graded bedding, with coarse grit at the bottom of a bed grading gradually upwards to finer material at the top (Fig. 12–8). If the sediments on the floors of submarine canyons characteristically showed graded bedding, this would provide evidence that turbidity currents have been active there. Study, at the Scripps Institution, of beds of sand dredged up from the floors of submarine canyons has revealed that about 30 per cent of them show graded bedding of this kind, but that some of the other beds have inverse grading with the grain size increasing upwards. Submarine canyons still present problems.

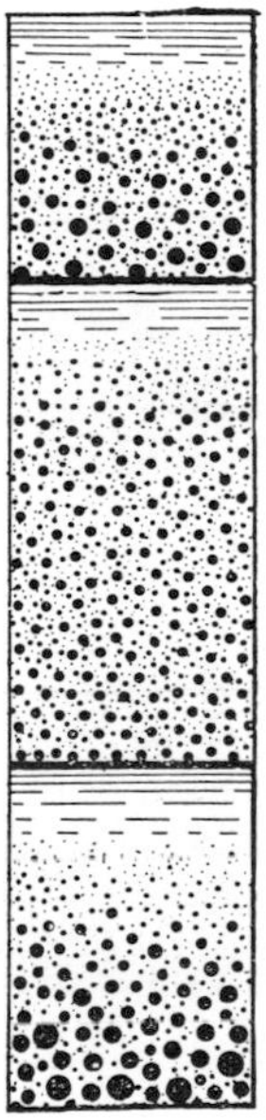

FIG. 12–8
Graded bedding.

OCEANIC RIDGES AND RISES

The well-known mid-Atlantic ridge, with a width varying between 500 and 800 miles, rises like a mountain range to a height of a mile or more above the deep basins between its flanks and the continental margins (Fig. 12–10). This ridge has now been found to be part of an almost continuous world-wide system of similar oceanic ridges (Fig. 12–9). Perhaps even more astonishing is the fact that the mid-Atlantic ridge is characterized by a summit rift valley comparable with the great African rift valleys (Fig. 12–10). In Iceland, which rises from the mid-Atlantic ridge, the rift valley can be seen. Traced to the extreme south the mid-Atlantic ridge passes between Africa and Antarctica and becomes the mid-Indian ocean ridge, which in places has also been found to have the characteristic median rift valley along its crest. This ridge is traceable into the Carlsbad ridge, which in turn is linked to rifts in the Gulf of Aden and the Red Sea.

While it is not impossible that sialic relics,

such as occur in Iceland and the Azores, may be found on some of the smaller islands that rise from the mid-Atlantic ridge, seismic evidence so far shows that the ridge is essentially basaltic and volcanic in origin. The volcanic activity displayed by Jan Mayen and Iceland in the north and by Tristan da Cunha in the south is a vigorous reminder that the process of growth of the ridge is far from having come to an end. Basaltic boulders have been dredged from various parts of the ridge, and the radiometric age of one from a depth of 14,000 feet (4,267 m), suggests that the boulder represents a lava flow erupted in mid-Tertiary times. The ridge has therefore been developing for a considerable length of time, mainly during the Tertiary.

The broad bulge known as the East Pacific

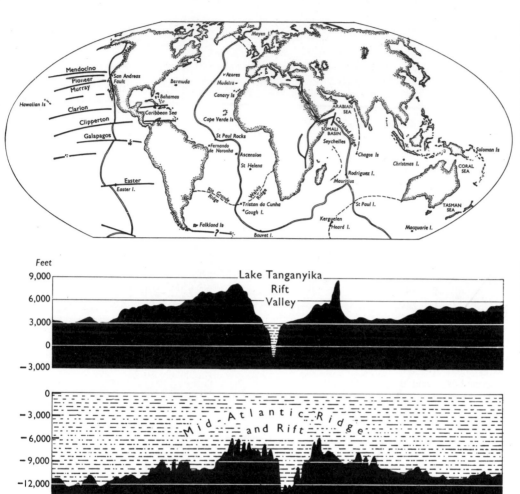

FIG. 12–9
The Mid-Atlantic Ridge and other mid-ocean ridges of the same type are shown by two parallel lines which schematically represent the summit rifts. The rift-valley system of East Africa and the Red Sea is shown in the same way. The transcurrent faults of the eastern Pacific floor, and the San Andreas fault are marked by bold lines.

FIG. 12–10
Diagram to illustrate the similarity of form and scale between the Tanganika rift of Africa and the submarine rift of the Mid-Atlantic Ridge. Each section is 450 miles (724 km) long. (*After B. C. Heezen, 1959*)

SEAMOUNTS AND GUYOTS

rise has a width of 2,000 to 4,000 km. Compared with the mid-Atlantic ridge the submarine topography in its southern part is relatively smooth with only occasional minor ridges and troughs parallel to the crest. The crest of the ridge passes into the Gulf of California, which is a rift valley on a grand scale, like the Red Sea (Fig. 12–9). An astonishing feature of the East Pacific rise is the east-west fault system shown on Fig. 12–9. The vertical displacements along these faults have produced submarine fault scarps rising thousands of feet above the ocean floor on the deeper side. The faults, however, are transcurrent (tear) faults and the blocks into which they have cut the rise have moved relative to each other like a series of trains running on parallel tracks at different speeds.

Conical peaks which rise from submarine mountain ranges, as well as from the ocean floor are known as *seamounts*. Some of them—*tablemounts*—that have nearly flat tops, so that they look like cones with their points cut off (Fig. 12–1), were called *guyots* by Hess, after Arnold Guyot, a Swiss Geographer of the eighteenth century (Fig. 12–11). Whilst on wartime service Hess saw from the echo-sounding records that at least twenty flat-topped seamounts had been crossed during his voyage, the depths of their summits ranging from 3,000 to 6,000 feet (900 to 1,800 m) below sea level. He interpreted these remarkable forms as volcanic islands which had been truncated by wave erosion and subsequently deeply submerged. This conclusion was substantiated after an intensive investigation of a great submarine mountain range, now known as the Mid-Pacific Mountains, which rises to a height of two and a half miles (4 km) or more above the adjacent ocean floor and strikes in an east-west direction for a distance of 1,500 miles or 2,400 km (Fig. 12–12). This great mountain range, of volcanic origin, is comparable with the younger Hawaiian chain to the north-east. By recording bottom profiles, and raising samples of materials both by coring and dredging, the seamounts and guyots were found to be the relics of basaltic volcanoes and volcanic ridges, many of which probably formed islets during the late Mesozoic, over 100 million years ago.

A typical example is Hess Guyot with a flat top, 12 by 8 miles (19 by 13 km), standing 5,500 feet (1,700 m) below sea level, but 10,000 feet (3,000 m) above the surrounding ocean floor. By far the commonest material dredged from the slopes and tops of the guyots was debris of basalt ranging from rounded boulders and pebbles to erosional products of smaller size. The date of the erosion is known to be Cretaceous from the fossil fauna that lived on the tops of the guyots. The evidence is clear that the guyots formed a chain of basaltic islands that were eroded down to sea level about 100 million years ago. Subsequently they were submerged to great depths and globigeria ooze of early

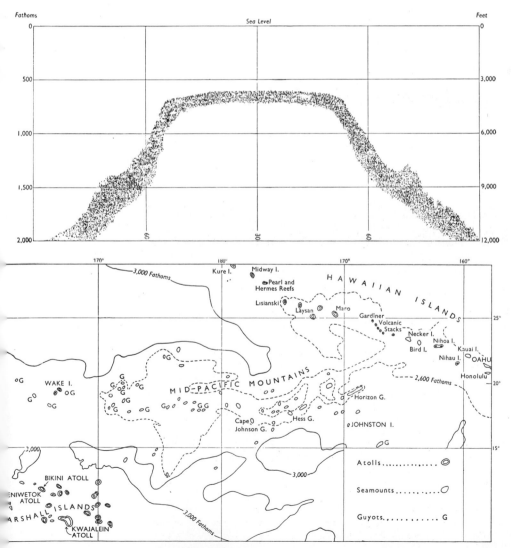

FIG. 12–11
Echo-sounding record across a typical guyot south of Eniwetok Atoll. The truncated platform at a depth of 620 fathoms is 9 miles (14·5 km) across. (*After H. H. Hess, 1946*)

FIG. 12–12
Simplified chart to show the sunken seamounts of the Mid-Pacific Mountains. The greater part of the Hawaiian Chain appears in the NE., and the northern group of the Marshall Islands in the SW. (*After E. L. Hamilton, 1956*)

Tertiary age, dredged from hollows and fissures in the flat tops of four of the guyots, shows that they were already deeply submerged 50 or 60 million years ago.

Not all guyots rise from submarine mountain ranges, however; those of Marshall Island (Fig. 12–12) rise as separate volcanoes from the ocean floor.

CORAL REEFS AND ATOLLS

In favourable situations in tropical seas, corals, together with all the organisms to which they give shelter and attachment, grow in such profusion that they build up reefs and islands of very considerable size. Clothed in vivid green, crowned by the coconut palm, and fringed with the white foam of the ceaseless surf, the "low islands" of the Elizabethan mariners have a reputation for dazzling but treacherous beauty (Fig. 12–13). Dangerous to navigation and difficult to explore, they have been equally tantalizing to geologists who sought to account for their existence. Darwin was the first to face the problems in a scientific spirit and by him coral reefs were divided into three main classes:

(*a*) *Fringing reefs* consist of a veneer or platform of coral which at low tide is seen to be in continuity with the shore, or nearly so (Fig. 12–14). The width may be half a mile or

FIG. 12–13
Hao Atoll, Tuamotu Archipelago (half-way between Fiji and Peru). (*J. P. Capin, American Museum of Natural History, New York*)

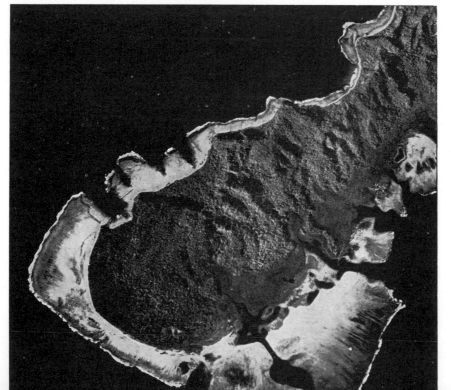

FIG. 12–14
Fringing reef, British Solomon Islands. (*Overseas Geological Surveys*)

more, and where the reef is facing the open sea the windward side may have a protective algal ridge before sloping steeply down to the surrounding sea floor, which is commonly deep. Many fringing reefs, however, have grown on the inner side of relatively shallow lagoons enclosed by barrier reefs (Fig. 12–15).

(*b*) *Barrier reefs* are situated up to several miles off-shore, with an intervening lagoon. The thousand-mile complex of reefs known as the Great Barrier Reef, which forms a gigantic natural breakwater off the north-east coast of Australia, is by far the greatest coral structure in the world (Fig. 12–16). Most barrier reefs, however, of which there are countless examples, are island-encircling structures forming irregular rings of variable

width, more or less interrupted by open passages on the leeward side (Fig. 12–15).

(*c*) *Atolls* resemble barrier reefs, but are without the central island (Figs. 12–14 and 12–17). They are essentially lowlying ring-shaped islands enclosing a lagoon which again is generally connected with the open sea by passages on the leeward side.

Reef-building corals live in colonies of thousands of tiny individuals (polyps), each occupying a cup-shaped depression in a calcareous framework which is common to the whole colony. As the successive generations of corals grow upwards and outwards through the restless waters in their competition for food, the stony framework also branches up-

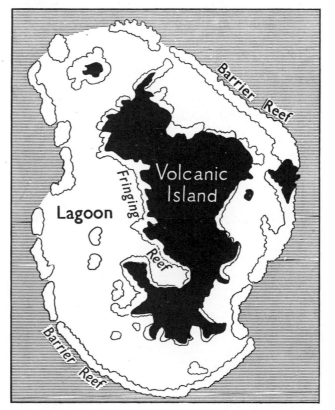

FIG. 12–15
Fringing and barrier coral reefs of Mayotta, Comoro Islands, north end of Mozambique Channel. The embayed outlines of the islands indicate subsidence.

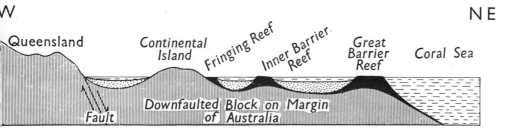

FIG. 12–16
Schematic section to show the relationship of the Great Barrier Reef and its associated islands to the mainland of Queensland. Reef rock, black; lagoon and channel sediments dotted. (*After J. A. Steers*)

wards and outwards and grows into forms that resemble plants, some being like shrubs and others like cushioned rock plants (Fig. 12–18). The interspaces between the dead structures are cemented and bound together by coralline algae called nullipores. These precipitate calcium carbonate within themselves, and still more as incrustations which coat their surfaces and cover the coral growths to which they are attached. Other calcareous con-

tributions are made by shelled molluscs, foraminifera, worms, and bacteria. The whole assemblage forms a white porous limestone which gradually becomes more coherent as it is buried and subjected to prolonged saturation by sea water.

The development and maintenance of coral reefs depend upon the conditions that favour a vigorous growth of the living colonies. A thriving reef has to contend not only with

FIG. 12–17
South-western reef of Ifaluk Atoll, western Caroline Islands, western Pacific. (*U.S. Navy*)

FIG. 12–18
Coral growths exposed at low tide on a fringing reef off the coast of Queensland, near Port Denison. (*American Museum of Natural History, New York*)

the waves, but also with boring organisms and voracious crustaceans that feed on the bodies of the individual corals. The reef represents the margin of success in a never-ceasing struggle against death and extinction. Not only have the corals and nullipores to supply material to maintain a flourishing living face, they have also to provide the broken masses of coral rock and other debris that accumulate to form the low land surface of the reef and its seaward foundations. The seaward face of the living reef passes downwards into a talus slope that may descend steeply to very great depths. On the lagoon or landward side of the growing face is the *reef flat*. This may be a platform with isolated clumps or patches of coral that remain submerged except at low tide, or it may be an irregular built-up surface consisting of material thrown up by breakers to a height of about 10 to 15 feet. A certain amount of debris is also washed into the lagoon when the reef is swept by heavy seas.

Reef-building corals flourish best where the mean temperature of the surface water is about 23° to 25°C (73° to 77°F), with 18°C (64°F) as the lower limit of tolerance—and that not for long. Reefs and atolls are therefore restricted to a zone lying between latitudes 30°N. and S., except locally where warm currents carry higher temperatures to the north or south of these limits. The reefs of the Bermudas, for example, are dependent upon the warmth of the Gulf Stream. Along the torrid belts of the oceans the equatorial currents drift towards the west, becoming warmer on the way, and consequently reefs flourish far more successfully in the western parts of the oceans than on their colder eastern shores.

The water must be clear and salt. Opposite the mouths of rivers, where the diluted sea water carries suspended silt and mud, corals cannot live and no reefs appear. Conversely, reefs grow best on the seaward side of the reef, where splashing waves, rising tides, and warm currents bring them constantly renewed supplies of oxygen and food. Corals cannot long survive exposure above the water, and consequently living reefs can never grow much above low-tide level. Dead reefs are found above sea level, but they have been uplifted into such positions by earth movements, to which they are therefore a most reliable index. On the other hand, reef-building corals require sunlight and do not grow freely at depths greater than about 100 feet. Coralline algae are similarly restricted to shallow water, because they too are dependent on an adequate supply of radiant energy. Light intensity diminishes rapidly with depth and also with distance from the tropics, becoming negligible during the long nights of the polar regions. A clear indication that reef builders can flourish only in warm, shallow, sunlit seas lies in the fact that reefs and atolls are easily "drowned" if their upward growth cannot keep pace with any submergence that may be in progress. Many examples of reefs and atolls that have been killed off in this way have been discovered on the sea floor. The average rate of coral growth varies with the species, the range being from 6 to 45 mm per year. The average rate of reef growth is about 14 mm a year—that is, approximately 1 foot in 20 years.

THE ORIGIN OF REEFS AND ATOLLS

From the growth requirements of corals, outlined above it follows that an essential condition for the initiation of a coral reef is the pre-existence of a submarine platform not far below sea level. The origin of fringing reefs is easy to understand. Minute coral larvae and spores of coralline algae drift with the ocean currents, and those that reach suitable shores find attachment and start new reefs that gradually develop seawards. Barrier reefs and atolls, however, are remarkable in that they generally rise from depths where no reef-building corals or coralline algae could live. There are two possibilities: either the reefs have grown upwards from submerged banks within 100 or perhaps 200 feet of the surface, or they have grown upwards and outwards from fringing reefs during the submergence of the land or island to which they were originally attached. Another feature that calls for explanation is that the lagoons have nearly flat floors (Fig. 12–19) and depths that vary with the widths, the range being from about 270 feet (82 m) for the larger examples (50–100 miles across) to 150 feet (46 m) for the smaller ones.

The first general explanation was offered by Darwin in 1837 as a result of the observations he made during his celebrated voyage in the *Beagle*. He visualized all reefs and atolls as different stages in a single process (Fig. 12–20). Growth begins with the building of a fringing reef around, let us say, a volcanic island. Subsidence of the island combined with continuous growth converts the reef into a barrier reef. Since reefs can grow upwards at a rate of about a foot in twenty years it will rarely happen that they are unable to keep pace with the movement. The submerged area between the island and the rim of coral rock forms the lagoon. By further subsidence the summit of the central island sinks out of sight, and the barrier reef becomes an atoll.

Darwin's simple theory has not passed unchallenged, but it satisfactorily accounts for most of the features associated with reefs. The reality of subsidence, or at least of a change of sea level, is proved by the embayed shore lines and drowned valleys of land areas encircled by the lagoons of barrier reefs. Darwin's theory, however, leaves the problem, as to how the lagoons of the present day come to be so remarkably uniform in depth, unsolved. Figure 12–20 shows the enormous quantity of lagoon sediment necessary to fill in the "moat" around a subsiding volcanic island.

The flat lagoon floors of atolls and island-encircled barrier reefs suggest that the corals grew upwards from the seaward faces of plat-

forms worn down by marine erosion and since submerged. In 1910, Daly showed that these features result from changes of climate and sea level. During the glacial period, when water was frozen in ice sheets, the level of the oceans was about 300 feet (90 m) lower than it is today. Pre-glacial volcanic islands and reefs were consequently attacked by the waves and commonly reduced to platforms of marine erosion. From the outer slopes of these guyots (Fig. 12–11), which with the melting of the ice began to be submerged, corals would grow upwards, keeping close to the surface as the sea level rose. With a guyot as its foundation the lagoon encircled by a coral atoll would have a flat floor and therefore a uniform depth from the start. The lagoons, however, must have been progressively shallowed by deposition, and this is consistently matched by the fact that the depths of submerged plat-

FIG. 12–19
Map of the Suva Diva Atoll (about 50 by 40 miles: about 80 by 64 km) Indian Ocean, showing the depths of the lagoon floor in fathoms. (R. A. Daly)

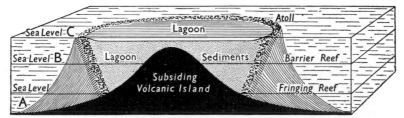

FIG. 12–20
Diagram to illustrate Darwin's theory of the successive development of fringing reef, barrier reef, and atoll around a subsiding island.

forms outside the coral seas are correspondingly greater. This is because where there are no encircling coral reefs only a little sediment is deposited on the platforms, and that is likely to be swept away by currents.

Final confirmation of the correctness of the subsidence theory as an explanation of barrier reefs and atolls has now been provided by borings and dredgings. Bikina, an atoll at the northern end of the Marshall group, became notorious when it was decided to test nuclear weapons there. Since 1946 it has been studied in detail. Corals and other organisms of shallow-water type were found in boreholes down to a depth of 2,556 feet (778 m). This convincing evidence of subsidence was followed by seismic exploration. The results indicated that the sediments were supported by a basement of hard rock, probably basaltic, at depths between 8,000 and 10,000 feet (2,400 and 3,000 m) beneath the lagoon. The suspected nature of the foundation was confirmed in 1950 when basaltic rocks were dredged from the slopes of Bikini at various depths between 6,000 and 12,000 feet (1,800 and 3,600 m).

In 1952, two borings were put down in Eniwetok, an atoll west of Bikini. One on the northern part of the rim passed through reef rock and coralline sediments and encountered hard basement rock at a depth of 4,610 feet (1,405 m), but samples of the basement were not recovered. The second boring, on the south-eastern part of the rim, passed through a similar sequence and reached a basaltic foundation at a depth of 4,208 feet (1,252 m). This time 14 feet (4·3 m) of olivine basalt were recovered. Thus it was definitely established that the basement supporting this atoll is a volcanic edifice, the summit of which is still more than 11,000 feet (3,300 m) above the surrounding ocean floor. So, after a long

period of doubt and controversy, Darwin's explanation of coral reefs can now be hailed as one of the few Victorian "theories" that has not become a casualty as a result of modern discoveries.

MARINE DEPOSITS

According to the source of their materials, marine deposits fall into two groups: *terrigenous*—derived from the land by river transport and coast erosion; and *organic*—comprising the calcareous and siliceous shells and other remains of marine organisms.

The terrigenous deposits are naturally found in greatest bulk bordering the lands, in the littoral and shallow-water zones (Fig. 12–21). Littoral deposits are those formed between high and low tides and are familiar to everyone as pebble strands, sandy beaches and, near river estuaries, as mud. The marine organisms that contribute most conspicuously to the sediments of the littoral and shallow-water zones belong to a group known collectively as the *benthos* (bottom dwellers). This includes seaweeds, molluscs, sea urchins and corals, and other forms that live on the sea floor. Many of them are firmly attached to the bottom. Deposits of shells or of their wave-concentrated fragments are formed in great abundance in favourable situations, while elsewhere similar remains are dispersed as fossils through the terrigenous deposits. The North Sea is mainly floored with terrigenous material, but off the Kentish coast and between the Thames and the Hook of Holland there are patches of several square miles consisting almost entirely of large shells. The shelly sands of some of the Cornish beaches have already been mentioned (p. 175). These are but relatively small examples of shelly limestones in the making. Far more extensive accumulations occur off limestone coasts and

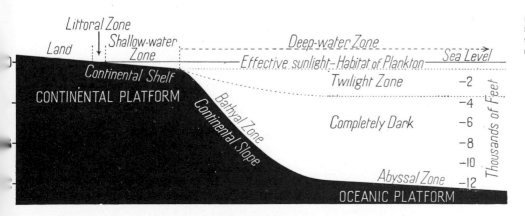

FIG. 12–21
Schematic section to show the zones of marine sedimentation.

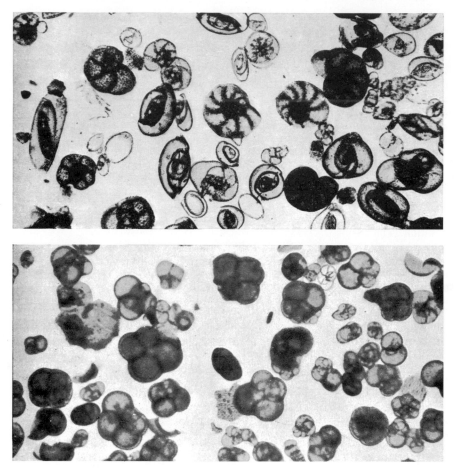

FIG. 12—22
Foraminifera from Ooze,
Equatorial Pacific. 40 times
natural size. (*R. M. Craig*)

FIG. 12—23
Globigerina from Ooze,
Porcupine Bank, Atlantic,
west of Ireland. 34 times
natural size. (*R. M. Craig*)

in other situations where the organic remains are not smothered by sand and mud. The reefs and atolls built up by corals and their associates in the shallow water of warm, uncontaminated seas illustrate limestone-building on a spectacular scale. Terrigenous and organic deposits like those just described which have accumulated off continental shores, represent the materials from which the sedimentary rocks of the continental land areas were made by cementation.

Beyond the edge of the continental shelf muds and oozes form the *deep-sea deposits*. The deposits on the continental slope, in the bathyal zone (Fig. 12–21) are mainly muds of terrestial origin, but at greater depths the deposits of the abyssal zone are the deep-sea oozes and the red clay, called *pelagic* deposits (Gr. *pelagos*, the sea). The oozes are largely composed of the remains of free-floating marine organisms belonging to a group called the *plankton* (the wanderers) (Figs. 12–22, 12–23, and 12–24). This includes the single-celled marine plants (diatoms) and animals (foraminifera, of which *Globigerina* is the commonest genus, and radiolaria); certain floating molluscs known as "sea butterflies" or pteropods; most of the eggs and larvæ of the benthos and other marine organisms; and all other forms which, unlike fishes, have no means of self-locomotion. The pteropods are blown along the surface by the wind, but the others, nearly all microscopically small, are passively suspended in the water. Diatoms, being plants, cannot live below the depth of effective sunlight penetration, which in the open ocean reaches a maximum of several hundred feet. Though individually quite invisible to the unaided eye, the diatoms are present in such prodigious numbers that they turn the sea in which they live into a kind of thin vegetable soup. This forms the main food supply of the rest of the plankton, whose habitat is therefore similarly confined to the sunlit zone.

From this prolific overhead source the sea floor receives a slow but steady rain of plankton shells which have escaped destruction by being eaten or by being dissolved in the sea water as they sank. In the shallow-water zone the tiny shells are generally lost in an overwhelming abundance of terrigenous and neritic materials. In the bathyal zone, where the rate of supply of terrigenous sediment is less overpowering, they make a bigger show and can be readily found in the blue and green muds, both of which are characteristically calcareous deposits. In the abyssal zone, however, the plankton shells accumulate with little contamination from other sources, to form the deep-sea oozes which, together with the red clay, constitute the pelagic deposits.

Fishes, whales, and other marine animals which go actively after their food supply are grouped as the *nekton* (swimmers). These contribute to all the marine deposits on a limited scale, but concentrations of their remains are quite rare.

It is of great significance that no representatives of the abyssal deposits of former ages have been found among the formations now exposed on the continent, except in certain marginal islands. This means that there is nowhere any indication that the floor of the ocean has become part of a continental region.

THE INTERPLAY BETWEEN EXTERNAL AND INTERNAL PROCESSES

In the interest of clarity the geological processes have been classified, in this book, as those of external origin, such as denudation and deposition, and those of internal origin, such as igneous activity and earth movements, to be described in Part III. These two groups of processes, however, are intimately geared together. For example, as illustrated by Fig. 8–21, lowering of the earth's surface by denudation brings into play the internal process of isostatic adjustment resulting in elevation. Indeed it is only the practical necessity of dealing with one aspect of the subject at a time that in any way justifies the separation of external from internal processes. In the present chapter this separation has not been followed for, if it were, the oceanic rises, seamounts, and guyots, being of volcanic origin, should be left for consideration in Part III together with volcanoes. The interests of clarity here seem to be better served by describing these topographic features of the ocean floor together with other marine phenomena resulting from external processes.

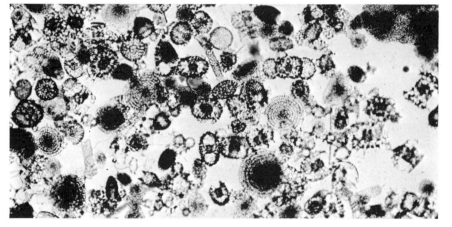

FIG. 12–24
Radiolaria. 50 times natural size.

Part 3
Internal Processes: Major Architectural Forms

13
Earth Movements

FOLD MOUNTAINS: OROGENIC BELTS

As indicated in Fig. 4–32 great mountain-building movements have been particularly active during certain periods of the earth's history, when the rocks of long belts of the crust have been folded, crumpled, cleaved, overthrust, and elevated to become ranges of fold mountains like the Alps and the Himalayas. Earth movements of this kind, and the resulting folded belts, are described as *orogenic* (Gr. *oros*, mountain). Mountain building, in the purely structural sense, without reference to the subsequent effects of denudation, is referred to as *orogenesis*. Most of the great ranges of fold mountains of today are parts of orogenic belts that came into existence at various times of crustal unrest since the Jurassic period, and particularly during the Tertiary period. Others, like the Appalachians and the mountains of Scandinavia and Britain, represent older orogenic belts that were deeply eroded long ago but have since been rejuvenated, so to speak, by uplift.

While all the present-day ranges of folded mountains represent orogenic belts, it must be clearly realized that by no means all orogenic belts are now mountainous. Most of the Pre-Cambrian orogenic belts and certain stretches of the later ones have lost their original mountainous relief by long-continued denudation, so that the rocks now exposed to view (*e.g.* along the mainland and island shores of southern Finland, Fig. 13–1) are those which were formed by metamorphism and igneous activity far below the surface at the time when the region was undergoing active deformation. Some sections of orogenic belts are submerged below sea level. Between Scandinavia and Britain, for example, the Caledonian orogenic belt lies beneath the North Sea. From the floor of the Black Sea, which has only recently been formed by subsidence, Pliocene land deposits have been dredged which probably overlie and hide the submerged connecting links between the Caucasus and the Crimea and the Balkan mountains. It is therefore essential to distinguish carefully between the geographical concept of a mountain range or system and the geological concept of an orogenic belt: the one refers to the height and relief of the land; the other to the structure of the rocks, whether the region be high, low, or submerged.

By the work of several generations of geologists it has been firmly established that the orogenic belts of each geological era originated in long downwarps of the crust in which extraordinarily thick deposits of sedimentary rocks accumulated during the era (or eras) that

FIG. 13–1
Fold structures depicting the grain of an old Precambrian orogenic belt, now a wave-swept erosion plane, Finland. (*E. Wegmann*)

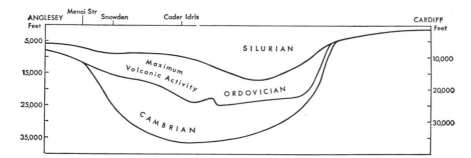

FIG. 13–2
Section across a geosyncline
that existed in Wales during
Lower Palaeozoic times
where it preceded the
Caledonian orogeny. Length
of section 140 miles
(230 km). (*O. T. Jones,
1955*)

preceded the orogenic revolution. The first important step towards understanding the natural history of folded mountains was taken over a century ago by the famous American geologist, James Hall. From his study of the northern Appalachians he discovered that the folded sediments out of which the ranges are built are shallow-water marine types which reach a thickness of 40,000 feet (just over 12 km). In the unfolded regions of the Interior Lowlands to the west the sediments of corresponding age are only a tenth or a twentieth as thick. The accumulation of so thick a sequence of sandstones, shales, and limestones clearly implies that the original floor of the belt must have subsided by a like amount. The mountain building was evidently preceded by long periods of downwarping during which sedimentation more or less kept pace with the depression of the crust. Such elongated belts of long-continued subsidence were called *geosynclinals* by Dana in 1873. Later the modified form *geosyncline* came into general use (Fig. 13–2).

The early pioneers thought that the weight of the accumulating sediments was itself sufficient to depress the crust, so that room was automatically provided for still more sediments. Any such effect, however, is strictly limited. Suppose the initial depth of sea water to be 100 feet (stage A in Fig. 13–3) and that marine sediments of density 2·4 accumulated, and depressed the crust isostatically, until the region became completely silted up (stage B). Let the maximum thickness of sediments so deposited be h feet. The crust is depressed by $(h - 100)$ feet, and this must also be the thickness of the deep-seated sima, density 3·4, displaced at the base of the crust. At stage B

    the weight of sediment added is proportional to $2·4 \times h$
    the weight of water displaced is proportional to $1·0 \times 100$
    the weight of sima displaced is proportional to $3·4 \times (h - 100)$.

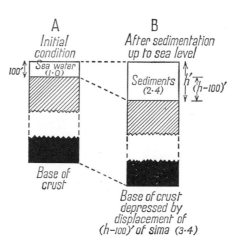

FIG. 13–3
Diagram to illustrate the
isostatic response of the
earth's crust to loading
by sedimentation.

For isostasy to be maintained the weight lost must be equal to the weight gained. Thus, we have

$$2·4 h = 100 + 3·4 \; h - 340; \text{ whence } h = 240$$

feet.

For 40,000 feet of Appalachian sediments to accumulate under such conditions, the initial depth of water would have had to be nearly 17,000 feet. Actually, however, the water was very shallow to begin with, as shown by the abundance of shore and deltaic deposits. It follows that the weight of sediments cannot be the main cause for the depression of the floors of geosynclines. It is independent downwarping of the crust that makes room for the sediments to accumulate. A geosyncline is essentially a result of earth movements.

It may be noticed in passing that the average rate of sinking of a geosyncline is extremely slow. In the Appalachian example, the deposition of 40,000 ft. of sediments in 300,000,000 years (Cambrian to early Permian) is only one foot (30·5 cm) in 7,500 years. However, this very slowness makes the cumulative effect seem even more remarkable.

FIG. 13—4
Recumbent folds in the
High Calcareous Alps. The
Axenstrasse, near Fluelen,
at the south end of Lake
Lucerne, Switzerland.
(*F. N. Ashcroft*)

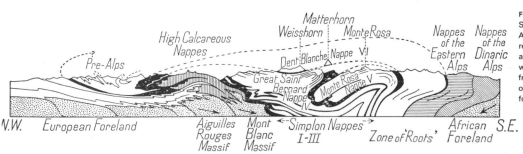

Matterhorn
Weisshorn   MonteRosa

High Calcareous
Nappes

Nappes
of the
Eastern
Alps

Nappes
of the
Dinaric
Alps

Pre-Alps

Dent Blanche Nappe VI

Great Saint
Bernard
Nappe
IV

Monte Rosa
Nappe V

N.W.   European Foreland

Aiguilles
Rouges
Massif

Mont
Blanc
Massif

←-Simplon Nappes-→
I-III

Zone of 'Roots'

African
Foreland

S.E.

FIG. 13—5
Section across the Western
Alps showing grand-scale
recumbent folds and nappes,
as interpreted by Argand,
who thought them to result
from a vice-like approach
of African and European
forelands.

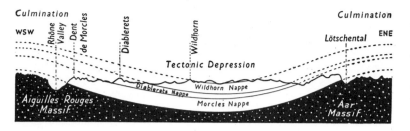

FIG. 13–6
Section at right angles to
Fig. 13–5, parallel to the
strike of the fold axes of the
grand-scale recumbent folds
and nappes, showing how they
undulate and give rise to
broad culminations and
depressions.

STRUCTURES OF OROGENIC BELTS

Some of the structures of orogenic belts that become impressed upon the vast thicknesses of geosynclinal sediments, and associated volcanic rocks have already been illustrated. These structures include alternations of more or less open anticlines and synclines (Figs. 4–3, 4–4 and 4–10), tightly compressed isoclinal folds, recumbent folds (Figs. 4–12 and 13–4), and great thrusts above which rock slices have sometimes travelled forward for many miles (Figs. 4–23 and 4–24). Such far-travelled rock-sheets are called *nappes*, and the crustal block towards which the movements were directed is called the *foreland*.

Although no two orogenic belts are identical in the details of their structures, the western Alps illustrate the most important general features. Here, as portrayed in Fig. 13–5, a series of gigantic recumbent folds and nappes, each of which has travelled forwards for many miles towards the foreland, are piled one upon another. The Alpine rivers have cut deeply into the folds and nappes, thus exposing the underlying rocks in many a steep-walled valley. If the nappes were everywhere at the same level, only the outer parts of the structure would be exposed to view in this way, and even the tunnels would add little more. But as the nappes are traced along the trend of the ranges from SW to NE they are found to undulate up and down in an alternating succession of broad *culminations* and *depressions* (Fig. 13–6). Where the depressions carry the nappes downwards, the uppermost ones are still well preserved. Where the culminations raised the upper nappes to levels now far above the highest peaks—that is to say, where they have already been swept away by erosion—the lower nappes come to the surface. Thus, although no single section across the mountains provides more than part of the picture, the whole complicated structure can be visualized by taking a series of several sections in order across the successive culminations and depressions.

THE UPRISE OF OROGENIC BELTS

At one time it was generally thought that the great folds and thrusts of orogenic belts were to be explained as a result of horizontal (tangential) compression (Fig. 13–5). The idea was that the crustal blocks on either side of the geosynclinal trough approached one another and, like the jaws of a vice, crushed the geosynclinal sediments so that they were forced upwards as complex folds and so formed a mountain range. This hypothesis, known as the *contraction hypothesis*, was a natural outcome of the idea that the earth was a cooling and shrinking globe. After the discovery of radioactivity it soon became obvious that although the earth is undoubtedly losing heat it is not necessarily cooling. Moreover, evidence is being recorded which suggests that the earth may be expanding, like the universe.

Although the contraction hypothesis still has many adherents, it is now widely known that the forms and internal structures of many of the folds and overfolds do not result from lateral compression. Evidence has been found that many of them are gravity glide folds formed by a bed of rock sliding extremely slowly down a slope under the influence of gravity (Fig. 13–7).

In the Swiss Alps the Morcles nappe (Fig. 13–8) was for several decades thought to be an overthrust and a result of contraction. This interpretation was based on the supposed identification of mylonite, formed by the grinding of granite, at the sole of the thrust. In 1947, however, it was recognized that the supposed mylonite is not a mylonite at all, but an ordinary sedimentary rock derived by the erosion of granite; Lugeon, a Swiss geologist of international fame, recognized the Morcle nappe to be a gravity glide fold that slipped down a gentle incline on the floor of the Alpine geosyncline. At a later period of time the old foundation rocks, which formed the floor of the geosyncline, rose upwards and the overlying Morcle nappe and its associates were uplifted and flexed so that they formed a carapace over the upbulged foundation rocks (Fig. 13–8). Fig. 13–9 illustrates the manner in which the old foundation rocks, near the foreland, moved upwards as a succession of gigantic steeply dipping slices and wedges, uplifting the overlying nappes of geosynclinal rocks and entrapping parts of them between the slices. In the heart of the evolving mountain range, however, where the foundation rocks rose from deeper and hotter levels, as in the Ticino area of the Alps, they moved upwards by rheid flow (p. 26) and at the same time become migmatized or actually converted into granite. The appearance of migmatite bodies that have risen upwards in this way in the core of the Caledonian orogenic belt in Greenland is illustrated in Fig. 4–45. As a whole complex of such migma-

tite bodies rose in Greenland, the overlying Caledonian geosynclinal rocks became infolded between them, and transformed to regional metamorphic rocks, whilst the highest covering rocks became unstable and slid slowly downwards, as gravity glide folds, on either side of the rising orogenic belt.

This brief discussion of the highly complex phenomena of the uprise of orogenic belts is far from complete. Moreover, as the world pattern of the Alpine orogenic belts suggests, the ultimate cause of fold mountains is likely to be of global dimensions. An important fact that needs to be emphasized here, however, is that long after the main fold movements have ceased, orogenic belts continue to rise upwards as is evidenced by the fact that the granites, migmatites, and regional metamorphic rocks, which were deeply buried

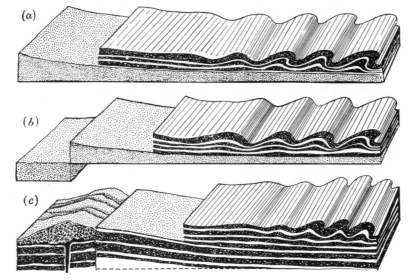

FIG. 13–7
Experimental gravity glide folds by E. Reyer, 1888.
(a) gravity gliding down an inclined bedding plane, as in submarine slumping
(b) gravity gliding resulting from uplift on the left
(c) gravity gliding of surface layers away from a belt of elevation. (E. Reyer)

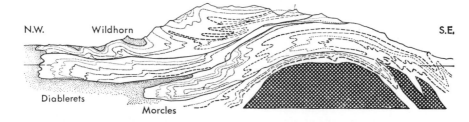

FIG. 13–8
Diagrammatic section, after Lugeon, illustrating the flexing of the grand-scale folds and nappes as a result of uprise of the old foundation rocks (dark shading) that formed the floor of the Alpine geosyncline.

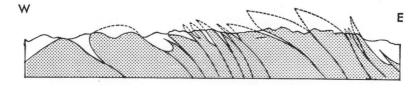

FIG. 13–9
Section through the Pelvoux massif, SW. France, showing how the foundation rocks, near the foreland, rise upwards as steeply dipping slices and wedges, and the overlying geosynclinal rocks become infolded and entrapped between them. (After J. Goguel)

FIG. 13–10
Illustrating the uprise of granite which now forms part of Mt McKinley, Alaska, the highest peak (20,300 feet; 6,187 m) of the Alaska Range which is 600 miles (965 km) long. Granite forms the walls of the central cirque up to the summit and is surrounded by folded slates and greywackes of Mesozoic age. *(Bradford Washburn)*

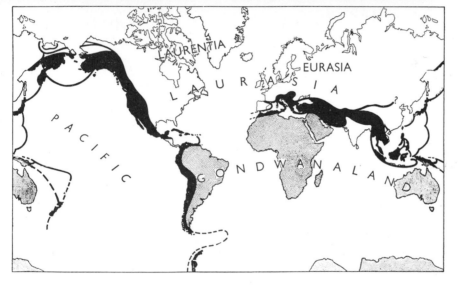

FIG. 13–11
Map showing the distribution of the Mediterranean and Circum-Pacific Alpine orogenic belts.

beneath the surface of the earth at the time when they were formed, now appear as the highest peaks of mountain ranges (Fig. 13–10). Fold mountains have deep sialic roots (see the Alps, Fig. 13–45) and their continued uprise results from isostatic readjustments.

THE WORLD PATTERN OF THE ALPINE OROGENIC BELTS

The cumulative effects of all the orogenic movements which have occurred at intervals since late Jurassic times are described as the Alpine orogenic belts. Geologically speaking these are young orogenic belts. The resulting assemblage of mountain systems combines into a world pattern of apparent simplicity. The pattern is usually described as a great ring encircling the Pacific, combined with a Mediterranean belt, of which the chief part is the Alpine-Himalayan system (Fig. 13–11). On the east the latter swings into the Circum-Pacific ring by way of Burma, Malaya, and Indonesia.

Another way of expressing the pattern is to describe it in terms of two gigantic rings (Figs. 13–12 and 13–13), one surrounding the northern continents of North America and Eurasia (known collectively as *Laurasia*), the other surrounding the southern land masses of South America, Africa, Arabia, India, Australia, and Antarctica (known collectively as *Gondwanaland*). The first of these rings includes the northern ranges of the Mediterranean belts and the northern half of the Circum-Pacific ring, while the second includes

227

the southern ranges of the Mediterranean belts and the southern half of the Circum-Pacific ring.

In plan Laurasia and Gondwanaland appear to have moved outwards (Figs. 13–12 and 13–13), suggesting that this movement would raise up peripheral orogenic belts. But this type of hypothesis fails to account for the geosynclines that preceded the actual mountains.

Within the peripheral ring of Laurasia lies the North Atlantic and its Arctic continuation. The coasts of these oceans are of the disruptive or *Atlantic type*—that is, due to fractures and faults that characteristically cut across the tectonic "grain" of the bordering lands

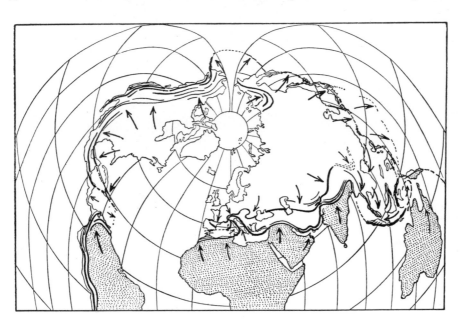

FIG. 13–12
Map showing the orogenic ring peripheral to the continental masses (unshaded) of Laurasia. The probable movements of the continents are roughly indicated by arrows.

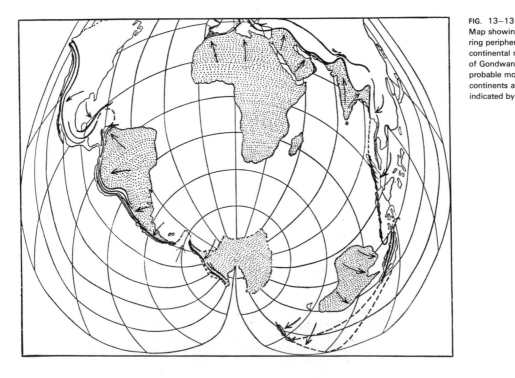

FIG. 13–13
Map showing the orogenic ring peripheral to the continental masses (dotted) of Gondwanaland. The probable movements of the continents are roughly indicated by arrows.

(Fig. 11–2). Locally, they are roughly parallel to some of the older orogenic belts (*e.g.* Norway, eastern North America and Greenland) as if the "grain" had to some extent determined the directions of the fractures. But the contrast with the *Pacific-type* coasts (Fig. 11–3) with the bordering mountain chains and island festoons, is sufficiently clear.

The peripheral ring of Gondwanaland is interrupted not only by the South Atlantic, but also by the Indian Ocean, and here again the coasts are of Atlantic type, except along the Burma arc.

OLDER OROGENIC BELTS AND SHIELD AREAS

Broad regions composed of ancient Precambrian rocks that have not been subjected to orogenic movements since Precambrian times are described as *shields*. The oldest part of Europe, for example, is the Baltic Shield (Fig. 13–14). In the early days of geology, the crystalline rocks of shield areas were thought to represent parts of the earth's original crust, but they are now known to be the granites and regional metamorphic rocks that formed the cores of geologically ancient

orogenic belts, of which four or five have been recognized in the Baltic Shield.

Most of the Precambrian orogenic belts, and many stretches of the later ones, have lost their original mountainous relief by long-continued denudation, but the "grain" of these orogenic belts commonly controls the trend of present-day topographic features. Since Precambrian times the Baltic Shield has fluctuated in level from time to time, but on the whole the movements have been slow gentle uplifts which maintained the surface above sea level, despite the ravages of denudation. Towards the east and south, however, the old rocks of the Shield are covered by a veneer of flat-lying sediments, deposited during the Palæozoic and later periods. This buried extension of the Shield, known as the Russian Platform, evidently subsided a little at intervals and was flooded by shallow seas, just as part of the Shield is flooded to-day by the Baltic. North of the Black Sea, and in a few other isolated spots where the sedimentary blanket has been removed, the shield rocks reappear at the surface. The north German plains and probably the English Midlands represent a westerly continuation of the Russian Platform, although in this section the crust was less stable.

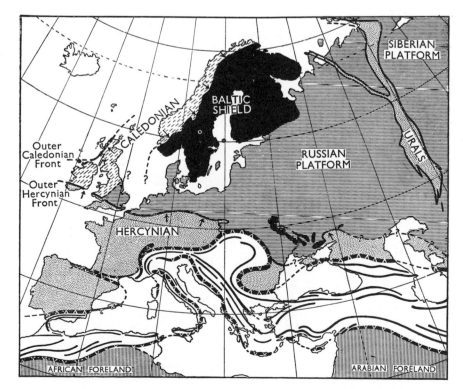

FIG. 13—14
Structural map of Europe. The Alpine orogenic belt is represented by the thick black lines.

The stable triangle of the Baltic Shield and Platform is bordered on its three sides by clearly defined orogenic belts, towards each of which it acted as a foreland. On the north-west the Caledonian belt extends through Scandinavia to Britain. The north-western front of the Caledonian belt is cut off by the Atlantic, except in the north-west Highlands of Scotland, where the thrusts illustrated in Fig. 4–23 splay out over another shield area, of which only a narrow strip now remains as land. The south-eastern front of the Caledonian belt is poorly defined in Britain, but well preserved in Scandinavia.

The mountainous Caledonian belts of Norway and Scotland present familiar present-day examples of ranges that owe their mountainous relief to the rejuvenation brought about by a renewal of uplift, following a long period of erosion, submergence, and burial.

While the Caledonian movements were in progress, other geosynclines began to develop and to fill up with sediment: (a) along the site of the Urals; and (b) across Central and Southern Europe from the promontories of south-west Ireland to north of the Sea of Azov. These became transformed into orogenic belts during Carboniferous and early Permian times. This orogenesis and the structures and mountains that resulted are known by the name *Hercynian* (after the Harz Mountains) (Fig. 13–14). Most of the Uralian belt is continuously preserved, but the much wider

Hercynian belt of the south has become broken into a series of isolated blocks or *massifs*. These include south-west Ireland, South Wales, and Cornwall and Devon; Brittany and the Central Plateau of France; the Ardennes, Vosges, and Black Forest and the Harz and Bohemian Mountains (Fig. 13–15). The depressed regions between are buried beneath later sediments, but here and there (*e.g.* in South-East England) the Hercynian foundation has been encountered in borings and mining operations. There is no doubt that all the uplifted massifs referred to are parts of a highly complex belt that was originally continuous.

In North America the Canadian Shield is a stable region of the same type as the Baltic Shield, and its buried continuation beneath the Interior Lowlands corresponds to the Russian Platform (Fig. 13–16). The south-eastern side of this stable triangle is bounded by the Appalachians, a complex of two mountain systems which roughly correspond to the Caledonian and Hercynian of Europe. The western side of the Shield and Platform is bounded by the geologically young ranges of the Alpine orogenic belts (Fig. 13–16).

BLOCK FAULT MOUNTAINS

The foundations of the continents, whether or not they are overlain by younger sediments, are constructed of interwoven orogenic belts

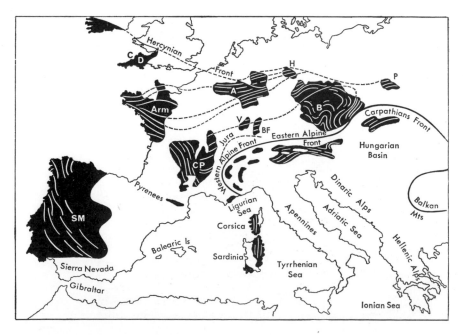

FIG. 13–15
Hercynian massifs of Europe (black) showing the dominant trend of the folding (white lines): A, Ardennes; Arm, *Armorica*; B, Bohemia; BF, Black Forest; CD, Cornwall and Devon (*Cornubia*) CP, Central Plateau of France (Massif Central); H, Harz Mts (*Hercynia*); P, Polish Massif; SM, Spanish Mesata; V, Vosges.

FIG. 13—16
Structural map of North
America.

of various ages, the individual structures of which are still recognizable after the mountain ranges have been worn away and the regions reduced to erosion plains. Overprinted on this primary framework, of which the orogenic belts form the "grain", there are later epeirogenic effects due to warping, fracturing, and faulting of the crust. The movements implied by *epeirogenesis*, continent-forming movements (Gr. *epeiros*, land, continent), are those by which extensive regions are gently elevated or depressed, with little or no folding apart from broad undulations.

The earth movements of all the shield areas and platforms, such as the Baltic Shield and Russian platform in Europe, and the Canadian Shield and Interior Lowlands in North America (Figs. 13–14 and 13–16), have been epeirogenic in type ever since Precambrian times. The crust of platforms and shields behaves somewhat like a badly cracked pavement on a poorly laid and shifting foundation. Widespread swells and sags—for example, plateaux and basins—are produced by differential warping on a regional scale and are usually accompanied by marginal and interior faults. The swells become intersected by ridges and troughs, for example, block mountains and rift valleys, produced by differential

movements of the fault-margined blocks and strips into which the crust has been broken.

Plateaux are broad uplands of considerable elevation: Tibet, the Colorado plateau, and the plateaux of Africa are outstanding examples. *Basins* are relatively depressed regions of roughly rounded or oval outlines. The term is used very widely and is applied to all broad sags of the crust, whatever the surface levels may be: from sea basins, like the Black Sea or the Celebes Sea, to mountain-rimmed plateaux which are often, like the Great Basin of Nevada, characterized by internal drainage. Ideally, the drainage from a plateau would be outwards and that of a basin inwards; but as many plateaux have locally dimpled or down-broken surfaces and many basins have drainage exits through marginal depressions in the rims, this simple criterion is far from being of general application. The term "basin" is also given to ancient crustal sags which have been filled with sediments and in some cases, as in Africa, subsequently uplifted into plateaux (Fig. 13–21).

Regions which have been divided by faulting into relatively elevated or depressed blocks are said to be *block faulted*. The upstanding fault blocks, which may be small plateaux or long ridge-like block mountains, are called *horsts* (Fig. 13–17). The Hercynian massifs of Europe, such as the Vosges and the Black Forest (Fig. 13–15) and the Harz Mountains, are horsts. Blocks which have been tilted, like many of the Great Basin ranges (Figs. 13–18 and 13–19), are sometimes distinguished as *tilt blocks*. The North Pennine region, as shown in Fig. 4–37, is an uptilted block sloping gently down towards the North Sea. Fault blocks depressed below their surroundings form minor basins or *fault troughs*. A long fault trough, forming a tectonic valley bordered by parallel fault scarps, is known as a *rift valley*. Between the horsts of the Vosges and the Black Forest the Rhine flows through a rift valley (the *Rheingraben*—Fig. 13–28). The river occupies the valley, but did not excavate it. The most renowned system of rift valleys, however, is that which traverses the East African plateaux from the Zambesi to the Red Sea and beyond (Fig. 13–26).

In the course of time the surface relief which results from epeirogenic movements becomes greatly modified by denudation and deposition, and locally by volcanic activity. Deep gorges are cut by rivers in high plateaux; fault scarps are gradually worn back by the sculpturing of erosion; block mountains are carved into hills and valleys, and sediments are accumulated in basins and troughs; but long ages must elapse before the broad out-lines of the topography of these regions cease to reflect the latest epeirogenic dislocations of the crust.

HORSTS AND TROUGHS

The Great Basin of North America (Figs. 13–18 and 13–19) provides excellent examples of block-fault mountains and intervening troughs and basins. For the most part it is an area of internal drainage made up of more than a hundred undrained troughs and basins lying between long horsts which trend approximately north and south. In the extreme southwest of the area the drainage escapes into the Colorado River at a point which is now the site of the great Boulder Dam. The upstanding blocks, known as the Basin Ranges, rise to heights of from 7,000 feet (2,134 m) to over 10,000 feet (3,048 m). Most of the ranges are tilted blocks, generally 18–24 miles (29–39 km) across, with steep fault scarps on one side and gentler back slopes on the other (Fig. 13–19). The bordering ranges, the Sierra Nevada on the west and the Wasatch Range on the east, are gigantic blocks of the same type, with their high fault scarps facing inwards in each case. The older scarps have been considerably eroded into ravines and spurs, and the lower slopes are commonly aproned with screes and fans of rock waste.

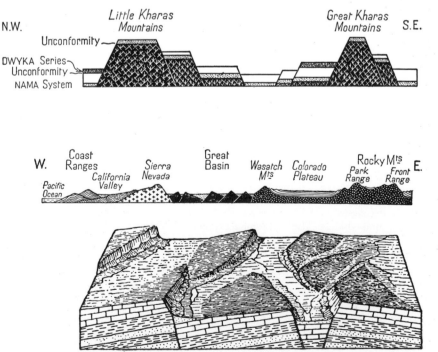

FIG. 13–17
Diagrammatic section to show the horsts and intervening rift valley or *graben* of the Kharas Mts, SW. of the Kalahari Desert, South-West Africa. Minor modifications of the topography by denudation and deposition are omitted. Length of section about 60 miles (97 km). (*After C. M. Schwellnus*)

FIG. 13–18
Schematic section across the Cordillera of the western United States. Length of section about 1,900 miles (3,057 km).

FIG. 13–19
Diagram to illustrate the fault-block structure of the ranges of the Great Basin, Utah. (*After W. M. Davis*)

Both these and the spurs are truncated by triangular facets along the lower slopes of some of the ranges, showing that the latest fault movements have been quite recent (Fig. 13–20).

The basins and troughs are mostly levelled up by sediments derived from the ranges, and in places by volcanic contributions, to heights that usually lie between 3,000 and 5,000 feet (914–1,524 m). Some are barren desert wastes, others support scanty vegetation, and a few contain lakes, mostly temporary and saline and surrounded by *salinas* or *playas* (p. 184). Great Salt Lake is the salt-saturated relic of a much larger freshwater lake, known to geologists as Lake Bonneville. The terraced shore lines of this ancestral lake make conspicuous horizontal features along the slopes of many ranges that formed its margins or stood out as islands above its surface. The Precambrian floors of the basins and troughs are generally far below sea level, and in places along the western margin even the present surface falls to exceptionally low levels. Death Valley, for example, is 280 feet (85 m) below sea level, although the range only a few miles to the west attains a height of over 11,000 feet (3,353 m).

The Great Basin forms a typical part of the "Basin and Range" province, a structural province, characterized by block faulting, which extends northwards into Oregon and southwards into Arizona. Nearly all the faults are normal faults indicating an extension of the crust in an east-west direction. For the Great Basin between the Wasatch Range and the Sierra Nevada, Eardley estimates that the faults imply an extension of 30 miles (50 km) during the last 15 million years. A few of the faults are transcurrent (tear) faults, and these again imply extension, but in another direction.

SWELLS AND SAGS

Africa, to which Arabia must be added from a structural point of view, is a vast continental shield, margined with younger folded mountains only in the extreme north and south (Fig. 13–21). Much of Africa has been land since Precambrian times. For hundreds of millions of years the movements of the shield have been persistently epeirogenic, giving a structural pattern of broad basins separated by irregular swells which rise towards the east to form a coalescing series of plateaux, the latter being traversed by a spectacular system of rift valleys (Fig. 13–26). The plateaux and swells have been intermittently uplifted and denuded, with the result that they now consist of old rocks which were formerly very deep seated. The basins have been the receptacles of thick deposits of continental sediments representing the material eroded from the uplifted tracts.

Some of the basins are arid regions of internal drainage. The *Chad* basin is one of the most remarkable. Lake Chad, fed by the Shari River from the swell to the south, is a shallow expanse of swamps and open water with no visible outlet. Yet the water is not stagnant, and although evaporation from its surface is high it does not become brackish. Despite appearances, Chad is not a terminal lake, for

FIG. 13–20
Fault scarp. The fault plane has truncated the spurs of the mountain range, showing the fault to be relatively recent. Teton Range, Wyoming, south of Yellowstone Park. The highest peak, 13,747 feet (4,190 m) is Grand Teton. (*United States National Park Service*)

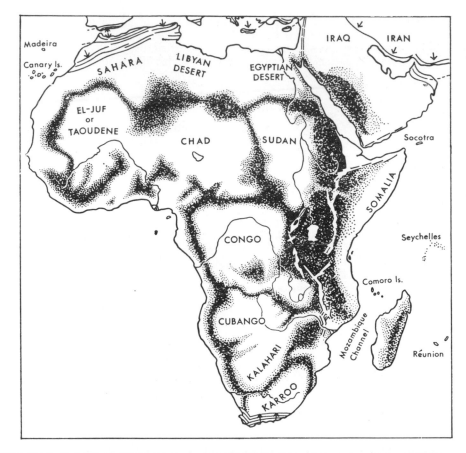

FIG. 13—21
Map showing in a generalized way the tectonic basins of Africa and the intervening swells, plateaux, and rift valleys.

FIG. 13—22
Aerial view of sudd formation on the Nile in the southern part of the Sudan. (*Dorien Leigh Ltd*)

FIG. 13–23
Section across Lake Victoria and the Western and Eastern Rifts. Length of section 500 miles (805 km).

FIG. 13–24
Map of Lake Kyoga, Uganda, to illustrate the reverse drainage caused by late Pleistocene back-tilting of the plateau east of the Western Rift.

it drains underground and feeds the oases of the lowlands south of Tibesti, 450 miles (724 km) to the north-east. *El Juf*, a vast desert depression north of Timbuktu, is one of the most awesome parts of the Sahara. On the other side of the Equator lies the *Kalahari* basin, partly grassy steppes and partly desert, with internal drainage in the north towards the brackish swamps of "lake" Ngami.

In striking contrast is the equatorial *Congo* basin, copiously watered by the great river system after which it is named. The whole region is underlain by thick continental sediments of late Carboniferous to Jurassic age (collectively known in Africa as the Karroo system). These everywhere dip gently inwards from the surrounding swells, as a result of warping which occurred in Tertiary times. The basin as a whole is slightly tilted towards the south-east. Where the Congo meets the swell on the coastal side it forms Stanley Pool, whence it escapes across the obstruction to the Atlantic by way of a series of cataracts. The basin of the *Sudan* is less easily traversed by the Nile. In the southern part of the basin the White Nile follows a sluggish and tortuous course through a wide expanse of papyrus swamps and lagoons. Thick floating accumu-

lations of vegetable remains, known as the *sudd* (Fig. 13–22), obstruct the interlacing channels. These hot reedy swamps are the relic of a former lake, the extent of which is marked by vast spreads of sediment. The level rose until the waters overflowed through a notch in the northern rim, to become the vigorous Nile of the six cataracts between Khartoum and Aswan.

To the east, from the head of the Red Sea to the Cape, Africa has been uplifted into a series of plateaux interrupted by occasional downwarps. To the south, the basin of the Karroo rises eastward to the Basuto Highlands, culminating in the basalt-capped crest of the Drakensberg escarpment. North of the Karroo basin is one of the oldest and best known of the world's structural basins, that of the Rand goldfields, which dates from nearly 3,000 million years ago. Johannesburg stands on its northern rim, where the gold-bearing strata of the Witwatersrand System dip southwards and, like the inward dipping beds on the eastern and western rims, are accessible to mining until they sink to depths where the rocks are too hot to be worked.

The region of the oval-shaped Central Plateau of Tanganyika, Kenya, and Uganda

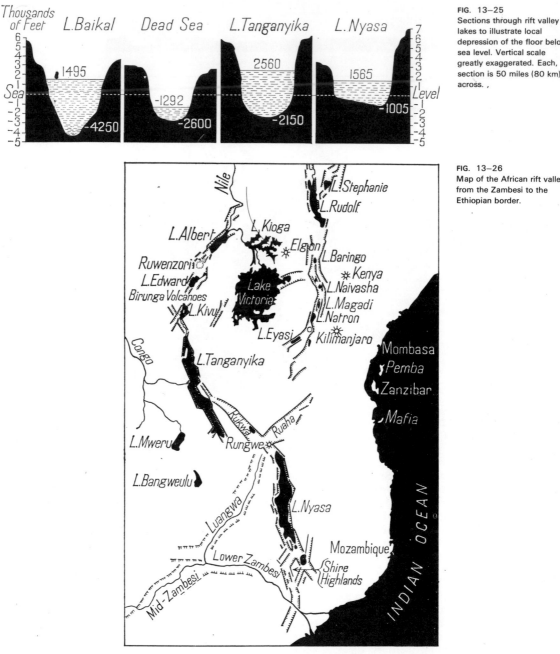

FIG. 13–25
Sections through rift valley lakes to illustrate local depression of the floor below sea level. Vertical scale greatly exaggerated. Each, section is 50 miles (80 km) across. ,

FIG. 13–26
Map of the African rift valleys from the Zambesi to the Ethiopian border.

was reduced to a pediplain in Miocene times, but since then it has been intermittently raised up as much as 5,000 or 6,000 feet (1,524–1,829 m) and fractured and trenched by an unrivalled series of rift valleys (Fig. 13–26). Superimposed on the broad upwarp of the Central Plateau there is an eastern and a western swell, each with a deep rift valley at its crest. Between the two upwarps is a shallow crustal sag occupied by Lake Victoria, which has gently shelving shores and a depth of no more than 270 feet (82 m) despite its enormous area (Fig. 13–23). The western upwarp is so recent that rivers are reversed, and flow inwards, draining either into Lake Victoria or into the Victoria Nile. The curious shape of Lake Kyoga and its swampy margins, filled with papyrus and sudd, is a clear indication that the Kafu River and its tributaries have been ponded back (Fig. 13–24).

RIFT VALLEYS

The term *rift valley* was introduced by Gregory for the "Great Rift Valley" of East Africa, which he was the first to recognize as a tectonic feature due to faulting. Gregory defined the term to mean a long strip of country let down between normal faults—or a parallel series of step faults—as if a fractured arch had been pulled apart by tension so that the keystone dropped in *en bloc* or in strips. The floors of some rift valleys have obviously subsided (Fig. 13–25), but in many cases it is equally clear that they have merely lagged behind the surface of the adjoining plateau in the course of a general uplift.

The rift valleys of Africa do not constitute one long continuous trough with a curving branch to the west (Fig. 13–26). Some of the individual faults can be traced for long distances, but others are shorter and commonly arranged *en échelon*. Nevertheless, the rift faults are all parts of a single system which extends from the Zambesi to the Red Sea, a distance of 1,800 miles (2,900 km). This distance is nearly doubled if the Red Sea depression and its continuation into Syria, via the Dead Sea, is included. There is a remarkable uniformity in the widths of most of the rift valleys, the average width being 45 km and the range from 30 to 60 km. Rift valleys in other continents have similar widths—for example, the Rhine rift valley is 30–45 km, and Lake Baikal south, 55, north 70 km. The Dead Sea-Jordan rift valley is, however, conspicuously narrower at 15–20 km (Fig. 13–27).

The Rhine rift valley, or *graben* as it is usually called, separates the horsts of the Vosges and the Black Forest, and, like the African rift valleys, it occurs at the crest of an upwarp, and is bounded by normal faults (Figs. 13–28 and 13–29). The Rhine rift valley was investigated by Hans Cloos, who designed experiments with the object of reproducing the rift valley and the adjoining horsts. He eventually succeeded by uparching and thus stretching layers of clay (Fig. 13–30). Figure 13–31 illustrates another of the ingenious experiments devised by Cloos. Here the updoming is imitated by the slow upheaving of the swelling surface of a rubber hot-water bottle coated with moist clay. The minute faults, produced by uplift and extension, faithfully reproduce the splaying-out pattern that is developed at each end of the Rhine graben and also characterizes the African rift valleys. The important conclusion to be drawn is that rift valleys are primarily a response to upwarp.

EARTHQUAKES

When a stone is thrown into a pool, a series of waves spreads through the water in all directions. Similarly, when rocks are suddenly disturbed, vibrations spread out in all directions from the source of the disturbance. An earthquake is the passage of these vibrations. In the neighbourhood of the disturbance itself the shaking of the ground can be felt and the effects may be catastrophic, but further away the tremors die down until they can be detected

FIG. 13–27
The River Jordan meandering through the Jordan Rift Valley (*Aerofilms Ltd*).

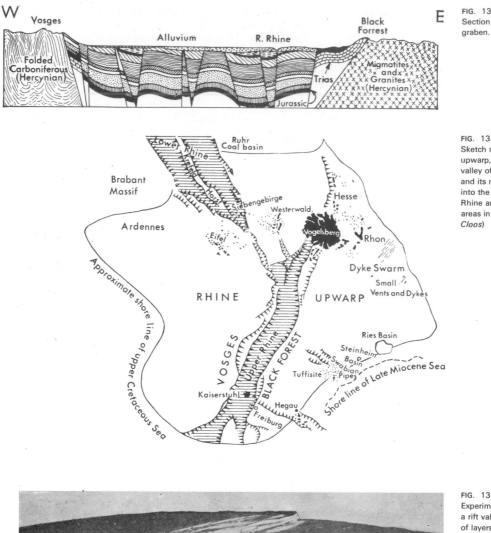

FIG. 13–28
Section through the Rhine graben.

FIG. 13–29
Sketch map of the Rhine upwarp, showing the rift valley of the Upper Rhine and its northerly bifurcations into the rifts of the Lower Rhine and Hesse. Volcanic areas in black. (*After Hans Cloos*)

FIG. 13–30
Experimental formation of a rift valley by slow upheaval of layers of moist clay. (*Hans Cloos,* 1939)

only by delicate instruments called seismographs (Gr. *seio*, to shake; *seismos*, an earthquake).

The destructiveness of an earthquake, known as its *intensity*, can be gauged at any distance from the source by the effect on buildings, on the ground (fissures and landslips), on people, and on seismographs. More accurately it can be measured by the maximum acceleration of the ground—that is, the maximum rate of change of the vibrations. The place of origin of an earthquake is called the *focus*, and the point or line on the surface vertically above is the *epicentre* or *epicentral line*. A line drawn through all places with the same intensity is an *isoseismal line* (Fig. 13–32). Each one generally encloses a roughly circular or elliptical area, according as the focus is point-like or elongated. By comparing the intensities at the epicentre and along an isoseismal line, as measured by the maximum acceleration of the ground, the depth of the focus can be calculated.

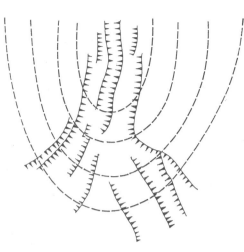

FIG. 13–31
Experimental reproduction of the typical pattern of rift faults by the swelling of a hot-water bottle coated with moist clay. (*After Hans Cloos*)

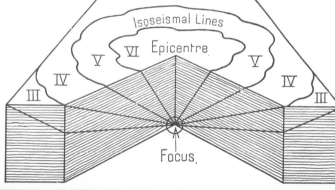

FIG. 13–32
Block diagram showing isoseismal lines and their relation to the epicentre and to the wave paths radiating from the focus of an earthquake.

FIG. 13–33
One of two parallel fault scarps formed at the time of a major earthquake that originated at a depth of 35 km beneath Quiches in the Andes of Peru in 1946. The scarp illustrated has a vertical throw of 12 feet (4 m) and a length of 5 km through country with a height of 12,000–13,000 feet (3,658–3,962 m). The zone between the two scarps subsided about 10 feet on average. (*Arnold Heim*)

Vibrations are set up in solid bodies by a sudden blow or rupture, or by the scraping together of two rough surfaces. Corresponding causes of earthquakes in the earth's crust are volcanic explosions, the initiation of faults, and the movements of the rocks along fault planes. Perceptible tremors are set up by the passage of trains and tanks, by avalanches and landslides, by rock falls in mines and caverns, and by explosions of all kinds. When a munition factory explodes, the intensity of the resulting earthquake may be comparable with that of volcanic earthquakes, while that of the shock waves through rocks set up by the underground testing of H-bombs may be far more severe. The majority of natural earthquakes, however, including all the most widespread and disastrous examples, are due to sudden earth movements, generally along faults (Fig. 13–33); these are distinguished as *tectonic* earthquakes. The term *tectonic* (Gr. *tekton*, a builder) refers to any structural change brought about by deformation or displacement of rocks (*cf.* architecture).

The cause of tectonic earthquakes is thus the building up of stresses in rocks until they are strained to breaking point, when they suddenly rupture and move. The fault movements themselves, as already described on pages 55–9, may be vertical, horizontal, or oblique. After the great Alaskan earthquake of 1899, it was possible from the presence of barnacles clinging to the uplifted rocks of Disenchantment Bay to measure the uplift, which in this case reached an exceptional maximum of 47 feet. Crustal blocks often move obliquely, both vertical and sideways movements being observed (Fig. 13–34). Surveys carried out after the Sagami Bay earthquake of 1923, when Tokyo and Yokohama were wrecked, showed that the floor of the Bay and the surrounding mainland had twisted round a little in a clockwise direction, the measured shift of Oshima Island being over 12 feet (Fig. 13–35).

When the rocks are nearly at their breaking point, an earthquake may be triggered off by some extraneous agent such as a high tide, a heavy rainfall or flood, a rapid change of barometric pressure, the tremors from an independent earthquake originating far away, and now, it is suspected, the shock waves from an exploding hydrogen bomb. The principal shock, which generally lasts only a few seconds, or at most and rarely, a few minutes, may be preceded by fore-shocks and is invariably followed by a series of after-shocks. The fore-shocks represent the preliminary shattering of small obstructions along a fault plane or zone. When these have been overcome the main movement occurs. But complete stability is not restored immediately. The sudden jolt, or swift succession of jolts, often disturbs adjoining fault blocks. The after-shocks represent a long series of minor movements that accompany the gradual settling down of the region. Somewhere on earth, an earthquake of some kind takes place every few seconds, but many of these are so slight that without nearby instrumental records their occurrence would not be known. Really severe earthquakes, which would be

FIG. 13–34
Scarp produced by the sudden movement along the Neodani fault, 180 miles (290 km) west of Tokyo, Japan, which was responsible for the great earthquake of 28th October, 1891. The movement was oblique, the vertical component being 20 feet (6 m) and the horizontal 13 feet (4 m).

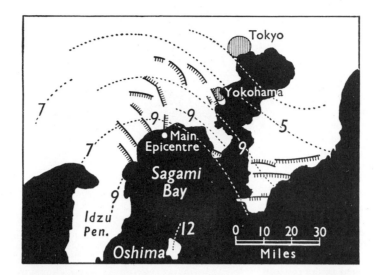

FIG. 13–35
Map of Sagami Bay, Japan, showing movements associated with the earthquake of 1st September, 1923. Vertical displacements ranging from a few inches to several feet are indicated by shading on the downthrow side of the fault lines. Horizontal rotation in a clockwise direction is indicated by dotted lines, with numbers representing the displacement at various localities in feet.

FIG. 13–36
Gaping fissures left in a country road near Yokohama; Sagami Bay earthquake of 1923.

disastrous in populated areas, take place every two or three weeks on average. Most of these originate beneath the continental slopes and cause little damage from the human point of view.

THE EFFECTS OF EARTHQUAKES

One of the most alarming features of a great earthquake experienced on land near the place of origin is the passage of ground or land waves which throw the surface into moving undulations. These may be 1 foot or so high and 20 or 30 feet from crest to crest. During the main shock of the earthquake swarm that ravaged Chile in May 1960, the motion of the ground was described by scientific observers as "slow and rolling like that of the sea during a heavy swell". Fissures gape open at the crests of land waves, only to close again as the crests turn into troughs. Sometimes a broken undulating surface is preserved as it was when the land waves suddenly ceased to move (Fig. 13–36). Railways are buckled and twisted, bridges collapse, and buildings crash to the ground. Land waves are a little under- stood local manifestation of the earthquake vibrations usually experienced, which are of a much smaller order. Frequent shaking through a fraction of an inch suffices to wreck most buildings not specially constructed to withstand earthquake shocks. A to-and-fro tre- mor of as little as 1/1,600 of an inch (0·002 cm),

241

can be distinctly felt if one is sitting or standing still. During a strong earthquake the effect of the up-and-down vibrations on the feet has been described as like "the powerful upward blows of a monstrous hammer".

In the regions of destruction, landslides are set moving on valley sides and avalanches are started in snowy mountains. Glaciers are shattered and where they terminate and break off in the sea icebergs become unusually abundant. Vast masses of loose sediments may be so disturbed by submarine shocks that they slump for miles down the continental slope. In Sagami Bay in 1923 landward parts of the floor were thus lowered by 1,000 to 1,500 feet (305 to 457 m), seaward parts being correspondingly built up. Ground water and its circulation may be greatly disturbed by earthquakes. Old lakes may be drained off through cracks, and new ones formed in depressions. In 1935, Lake Solar was engulfed by great fissures that opened across its floor in the Kenya rift valley. Not all fissures close up again as Figs. 13–36 and 13–37 clearly demonstrate.

Strong submarine earthquakes are followed by seismic sea waves, called *tsunami* by the Japanese (*tsu*, harbour; *nami*, waves). The celebrated Lisbon earthquake of 1755, one of the greatest on record, probably originated by sudden fault movements and fissuring of the sea floor to the west and south. At Lisbon the sea withdrew immediately after the principal shock, only to return as a gigantic tsunami up to 30 feet high, which swept across the lower parts of the city and completed the ruin and desolation. The ebb and flow of the sea continued for some time after the first wave, this being an inevitable characteristic of all tsunami. The Lisbon earthquake was of such exceptional severity that lakes were set oscillating as far away as Loch Lomond and Loch Ness, where the water continued to rise and fall through a range of two or three feet for about an hour.

The appalling loss of human life that accompanies great earthquakes in highly populated areas is mainly due to secondary causes such as collapse of buildings, fires, landslides, and tsunami. Gas mains are torn open and, once started, fires rapidly spread beyond control, since water mains are also wrenched apart. In San Francisco in 1906 far more damage was done by fire than by the earthquake itself. The Sagami Bay earthquake of 1923 occurred just as the housewives of Tokyo and Yokohama were cooking the midday meal. Fires broke out in all directions and completed the toll of death and destruc-

tion. At least two hundred and fifty thousand lives were lost and over half a million houses destroyed. In the loess country of Kansu in China, 200,000 people were killed in 1920,

FIG. 13–37
One of many permanent fissures opened during the Orleanville earthquake, Algeria, of 1954. (*Paris Match*)

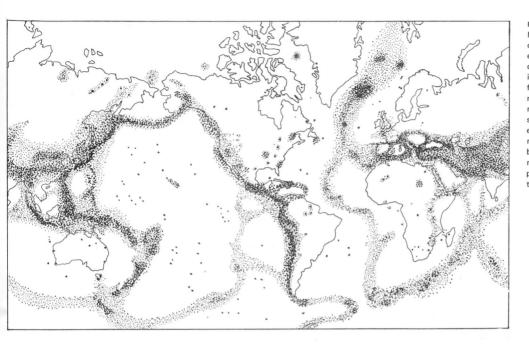

FIG. 13–38
Map showing the distribution of the epicentres of earthquakes during the present century. Heavy shading indicates the occurrence of frequent earthquakes, including most of those of great magnitude. The density of shading is relatively exaggerated along the mid-oceanic and rift-valley belts in order to bring out more clearly the significant pattern of distribution in these regions.

and another 100,000 in 1927 by catastrophic landslips of loess which overwhelmed cave dwellings, buried villages and towns, and blocked river courses, so causing calamitous floods.

DISTRIBUTION OF EARTHQUAKE BELTS

Earthquakes may be recorded anywhere, but they originate only in regions where earth movements or volcanoes are active. Fig. 13–38 shows the distribution of known epicentres during the present century. The distribution turns out to be essentially the same when all known epicentres are plotted and, moreover, the distribution of the most severe shocks corresponds closely with that of the most frequent. It will be noticed that most earthquakes originate in two well-defined belts: a *Circum-Pacific belt* and a *Mediterranean and Trans-Asiatic belt*. Most of the remaining shocks occur in the rift valley region of East and Central Africa, and along the rifted mid-Atlantic rise and similar structures traversing the other ocean floors. The Circum-Pacific belt, with its extensions into the neighbouring oceans, accounts for nearly all the deep shocks and about 80 per cent of the earth's more important shallow earthquakes, 90 per cent of the latter originating at depths between 60 and 300 km. Until recently the Mediterranean and Trans-Asiatic belt was thought to be free from deep shocks, but in 1954 a powerful earthquake originated at a depth of 630 km under the southern slopes of the Sierra Nevada in Spain. In a general way the two main earthquake zones follow the belts of Tertiary and Recent mountain-building movements, so indicating the many places where these movements are still actively in progress (compare Figs. 13–11 and 13–18).

The two main belts of tectonic earthquakes (Fig. 13–38), like the Tertiary mountain belts (Figs. 13–12 and 13–13), tend to form two rings surrounding *Laurasia* (North America, Europe, and most of Asia) and *Gondwanaland* (South America, Africa, Arabia, Peninsula India, Australia and Antarctica). From Portugal to Burma the two rings coalesce. The continental regions, more or less bordered in this way, contain the more stable regions of the earth's crust, the old Precambrian shields. But even these, as the African rift valleys bear witness, may be reawakening to activity; and this applies also to the north and central Pacific, which has its apparently stable floor rudely interrupted in and around the Hawaiian Islands both by active volcanoes and by tectonic earthquakes. The other ocean floors, as already mentioned have belts of epicentres along their ridges and rifts, and these tend to surround some of the individual continents, notably Africa and Antarctica (Fig. 13–38).

Even in the more stable regions of the continents and ocean floors, sporadic shocks occasionally occur. No place can be regarded

243

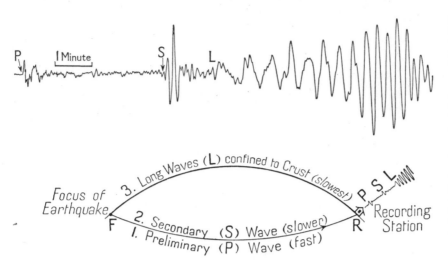

FIG. 13–39
Seismogram recorded at Pulkovo Observatory, Russia, of an earthquake originating is Asia Minor on 9th February, 1909. The time interval S–P is 3 minutes 43 seconds corresponding to a distance of 1,400 miles (2,253 km) from the epicentre. (*After B. Galitzin*)

FIG. 13–40
Section through a segment of the earth, showing the paths followed by the P, S, and L waves of an earthquake originating at the focus F and recorded at a station R.

as permanently immune from shocks. Earthquakes are rare in Britain and most of those that do occur can be traced to belated movements along ancient faults such as the Great Glen Fault in Scotland (Fig. 4–27).

EARTHQUAKE WAVES AND THE EARTH'S INTERNAL STRUCTURE

From the focus of an earthquake, waves are propagated through the earth in all directions, and when they arrive at a seismological station they are recorded by seismographs on seismograms. The record of a distant earthquake on a simple seismogram has the appearance illustrated in Fig. 13–39. A first or primary pulse P is followed by rapid oscillations; then comes a second pulse S, followed by more oscillations; and finally a third pulse L initiates the long vibrations. The P or "push-and-pull" waves are compression-dilation waves, like those of sound, in which each particle vibrates to and fro in the direction of propagation. The S or "shake" waves are *shear* waves in which the motion of each particle is at right angles to the direction of propagation, like the waves in a taut rope that is shaken at one end. Shear waves cannot pass through fluids: only through solids. Through rocks of the same kind P waves travel faster than S waves and are therefore the first to be recorded on seismograms (Fig. 13–40). Surface waves, known collectively as L waves, because they have long periods, travel through the crust only, being reflected up and down at its lower and upper surfaces. Because of their zig-zag path, L waves arrive later than P or S waves (Fig. 13–40).

The times of arrival of P and S waves are used to determine the position of the epicentre. When the *times* taken by P and S waves to travel to seismological stations in various parts of the world are plotted on a graph against the respective *distances* from the epicentre, they fall on smooth curves. Fig. 13–41 shows that the time interval between the P and S waves steadily increases with distance. Thus when an earthquake is recorded at a distant station, the time interval between the arrival of P and S waves serves to determine both the distance of the epicentre and the time of origin of the shock.

The idea of X-raying the earth, as it were, with its own earthquake waves was introduced on page 4. The zig-zag path of the L waves, for example, shows that there *is* a crust overlying a substratum with different properties. The P and S waves of distant earthquakes reach great depths and their travel times and velocities increase with depth, P waves always travelling faster than S waves. The P and S waves that just reach the base of the mantle emerge at the surface at places about 11,500 km (125°) from the epicentre of the earthquake concerned. At stations beyond this distance from the epicentre the seismographs record no P and S waves for the next 4,500 km, although L waves are recorded as usual. At distances greater than 16,000 km (143°) from the epicentre P waves reappear, and continue to do so right up to the antipodes of the epicentre (the *anticentre* as it is called). Corresponding to each earthquake of sufficient magnitude to be recorded so far from its source there is thus a ring-like shadow free from P and S waves as illustrated in Figs. 13–42 and 13–43. This shadow was first noticed by Oldham in 1906. He at once inferred that the earth has a core which acts like a spherical lens by reflecting the deeper waves inwards, so concentrating them in the antipodal region at the expense of a surrounding zone of shadow. In accordance with this strong refraction, the velocity of the P waves is greatly reduced when they pass from the mantle into the core. The S waves, however, are not transmitted through the core at all, so indicating that the discontinuity between mantle and core is also a boundary between states of matter that behave towards seismic waves as if they were solid and fluid respectively, and it is inferred that the earth's core is essentially fluid.

SEISMIC EXPLORATION OF THE CRUST

Records of P and S waves from near earthquakes have been extensively used for estimating the nature and thickness of the dominant layers that make up the earth's crust and upper mantle. The waves travel with velocities that depend on the densities and elastic constants of the rocks through which they pass. For P waves these range from speeds as low as 2 km/sec (6,562 ft/sec) for loose or poorly consolidated sediment, through a range of higher values for indurated sediment, to 5·2 – 6·2 km/sec for sialic crystalline rocks, including granite, and 6·2 – 7·2 km/sec for

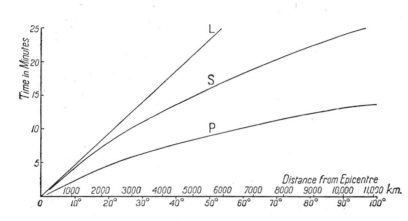

FIG. 13–41
Time-distance curves for P, S, and L waves. The curve for L waves refers only to those that have traversed the continental type of crust.

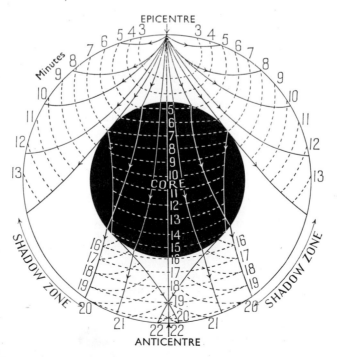

FIG. 13–42
Section through the centre of the earth showing the wave paths (firm lines with arrows), wave fronts (dashed lines), and arrival times (in minutes reckoned from the zero time of the shock). Since there is a shadow zone free from P and S waves for each such earthquake, it is inferred that the earth has a core which refracts the deeper waves as shown in the diagram.

245

FIG. 13–43
The shadow zone cast by the earth's core in the case of an earthquake originating in Japan.

basic rocks such as gabbro and its common metamorphic equivalents. In addition, the velocities for the various kinds of rocks are found experimentally to increase with rising pressure.

The principles involved in seismic exploration of the crust can be most easily illustrated by considering the simplest type of case that arises in seismic prospecting. Here the vibrations are produced by artificial explosions which have the great advantage over natural earthquake shocks in that they can be completely controlled and used wherever and whenever it is convenient. On land a charge of dynamite is lowered into a shot hole, previously drilled to a depth of a few feet, and at sea the charge is floated behind a ship at a depth of a few feet. The charge is detonated electrically at an exactly recorded time. The place of origin is exactly known and the depth of focus is negligible. The problem is to determine the thickness h of an upper layer of rock (through which P waves travel with a velocity v_1) resting on a lower layer in which the velocity v_2 is considerably greater than v_1.

The waves from the explosion spread out in all directions from the shot point (Fig. 13–44). Some (a) reach the surface directly through the upper layer. Of those that reach the boundary between the two layers some (b) are reflected back to the surface; some (c) are refracted along the boundary, where they travel with the higher velocity v_2 and are bit by bit returned to the surface from each point along the boundary; and some (d) are refracted into the lower layer until they in turn are reflected or refracted at the next boundary. At the surface the time of arrival of the P wave can be recorded wherever a suitable instrument is placed for its reception. In practice geophones G_1, G_2 ... up to, say G_{20} are placed in line with the shot point at known distances and all are linked with a recording station. The geophones can be spaced to pick up the reflected waves (b) to best advantage, as in echo-sounding at sea (p. 206). This method known as "reflection shooting" is in common use in the exploration for structures that may contain oil or gas (p. 41). A different spacing of the geophones is adopted for "refraction shooting" designed to pick up waves (c), and also waves (d) which penetrate more deeply before returning to the surface.

Figure 13–44 refers to the refraction method in its simplest form. The waves (a) are the first to reach the geophones ($G_1 - G_3$) situated near the shot point. Beyond a certain distance, l, the refracted waves from the top of the lower layer arrive first because of their greater speed while travelling along the lower side of the boundary. l is the distance at which both direct and refracted waves arrive at the same time t. As indicated in the lower part

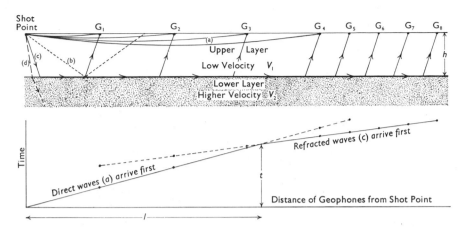

FIG. 13—44

Wave paths from a shot point to a series of geophones, G, with (below) the corresponding time-distance graphs for the first arrivals of direct and refracted waves. For details see text.

of Fig. 13–44, *l* is determined by the intersection of the graphs obtained by plotting the times of the first arrivals against the respective distances. In each case, the slope of the graph gives the corresponding velocity, for example, $v_1 = l/t$. Knowing the two velocities the thickness *h* of the upper layer can be calculated.

Much of the work on crustal and upper mantle exploration is carried out by utilizing the effects of artificial explosions just below the surface, as in ordinary geophysical prospecting, but on a larger scale. Fig. 13–45 includes some of the regions where sedimentary, sialic, and basaltic crustal layers have been separately recognized. Over vast areas, however, only the total thickness of the crust, down to the Moho, has been approximately determined, and for this purpose the surface waves have been increasingly used in recent years.

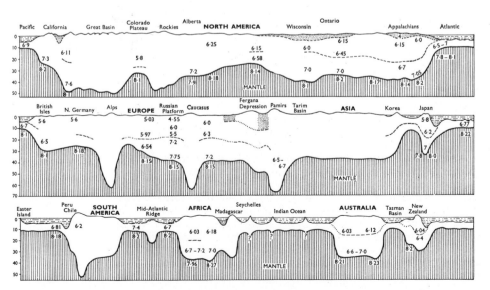

FIG. 13—45

Composite seismic section showing the thickness of characteristic parts of the continental and oceanic crusts. The figures represent the velocities of P waves in km/sec. The levels of discontinuities are indicated where they have been recorded. Certain thick layers of sediments are shown by fine dots. Compiled from the data available to the end of 1962.

247

14
Volcanoes and Volcanic Edifices

GENERAL ASPECTS

Volcanic activity includes all the phenomena associated with the surface discharge of magmatic materials, solid, molten, and gaseous, from pipes or fissures communicating with the heated depths (p. 21). In addition to the eruption of hot gases and molten lavas from volcanoes, vast quantities of fragmental materials (pyroclasts) are produced by gas erosion and explosion. The great clouds of ash-charged gases and vapours which are the most conspicuous features of explosive eruptions may be luminous or dark, according as the fragmental material is incandescent or not. These "fiery" and "smoky" appearances, together with the glare reflected from the glowing lavas beneath, were responsible for the formerly popular idea that volcanoes are "burning mountains". Actual burning, however, is confined to the almost imperceptible flames of certain gases such as hydrogen.

A few volcanoes remain continuously in eruption, but in most cases activity is intermittent, and sometimes there are long intervals of repose, during which all signs of activity either cease or are restricted to exhalations of steam and other vapours from vents called *fumaroles*, which at a later stage may pass into geysers or hot springs. As a volcano becomes extinct it passes through similar waning stages. Some volcanoes have even been thought to have become extinct, until a disastrous recrudescence of activity proved otherwise. A striking example is provided by the first recorded eruption of Vesuvius. At the beginning of the Christian era the volcano had slumbered so long that no tradition of its prehistoric eruptions survived. For centuries woods and vineyards had clothed the fertile slopes of the cone and the rugged walls surrounding the grassy floor of the summit crater were festooned with wild vines. In the year 79 A.D., however, after a period of premonitory earthquakes, the catastrophic eruption occurred which overwhelmed Pompeii—a cultured city of 30,000 inhabitants—in an appalling blast of white-hot ashes, and obliterated Herculaneum in torrents of hot mud.

Those who live far from volcanic districts sometimes express surprise that men and women should settle where their crops may be destroyed by vapours and ashes and their fields and vineyards blotted out by streams of lava. But volcanoes are not altogether unfriendly, nor are they uniquely so. Tornadoes, earthquakes, and floods may be equally devastating. Calamities like the horrible doom that overtook Pompeii in 79 and St. Pierre in 1902 are fortunately infrequent. All the volcanoes of the world fail to compete with motor transport as a menace to life—to say nothing of war. And compensating for the risk, there is the irresistible attraction of the fertile soils for which volcanic districts are renowned. The decomposition products of the lavas, rich in plant foods, are carried down the rain-washed slopes to the plains beyond, and intermittent showers of ash, if not too heavy, rejuvenate the soil and add to its bulk.

PYROCLASTS

Pyroclasts may consist of molten or consolidating lava, ranging from the finest comminuted particles to masses of scoriae and volcanic bombs of considerable size (Fig. 14–1), or they may be fragments of older rocks (including the lavas and pyroclasts of earlier eruptions), ranging from dust to large ejected blocks, torn from the walls of the feeding channel or from obstructions in the vent. When blown into the air, these fragmental materials shower down at various distances from the focus of eruption according to their sizes and the heights to which they are hurled. The coarser fragments, including bombs, blocks of scoria and pumice, and blocks of older rocks, fall back near the crater rim and roll down the inner or outer slopes, forming deposits of *agglomerate* (mainly rounded fragments or bombs) or *volcanic breccia* (mainly angular fragments). The latter term implies that the blocks consist largely of older consolidated lava or of country rocks from the foundations of the volcano. Volcanic *bombs* represent clots of lava which solidified, at least externally, before reaching the ground. Some of them have globular, spheroidal, or spindle-shaped

FIG. 14—1
Volcanic bombs. (a) Basalt, Puy de la Vache, Auvergne (0·13 natural size); (b) Bread-crust bomb of dacite, Mt Pelée, 1902 (0·13); (c) Basalt, Patagonia (0·38). (A. Lacroix)

forms due to rapid rotation during flight; others, of less regular shape because they were stiff from the start, have gaping cracks and are described as *bread-crust bombs* (Fig. 14—1).

Smaller fragments, about the size of peas or walnuts, are called *scoria* (or pumice) or *lapilli* (little stones) according to their structure. Still finer materials are referred to as ash or *tuff*. Sometimes showers of crystals that were already present in the lava (before its comminution) fall from the volcanic clouds and contribute to the tuffs. The finest particles, down to dust size, and including shards and splinters of glass, often travel far beyond the cone before they descend. When such material is hurled to great heights and caught up by the wind it may be carried for immense distances. Microscopic volcanic dust from the catastrophic eruption of Krakatao in 1883 encircled the world, and its dispersion through

FIG. 14—2
Collecting gases on the edge of the lava lake of Halemaumau, Kilauea, 28th May, 1912. The pipe line enters a crack through which gas was escaping from the spatter cone. (A. L. Day, *Geophysical Laboratory, Carnegie Institution of Washington*)

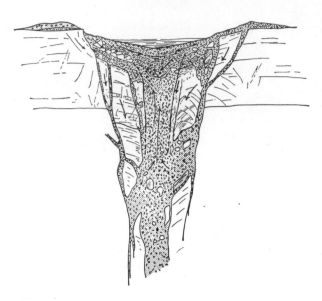

FIG. 14–3
Section through a Swabian tuff pipe. *White*: blocks of Jurassic strata, detached from the wall rocks, that have sunk within the tuff. *Grey*: tuff consisting mainly of small fragments of the Jurassic rocks and some micro-lapilli of melilite-basalt. (*Hans Cloos, 1941*)

the atmosphere was responsible for the vividly coloured sunsets that were seen during the following months.

VOLCANIC GASES

Steam is by far the commonest of the volcanic gases. Locally the steam may be partly or wholly derived from ground waters and crater lakes, but when full allowance is made for these superficial sources there is still ample evidence that the steam liberated in most eruptions is largely of magmatic origin. Gases have been collected from cracks in small blisters of lava formed over gas fountains on the edge of the lava-lake of Kilauea (Fig. 14–2). By this technique contamination by air is avoided as completely as is humanly possible. Besides steam (60 to 90 per cent) the gases are found to consist, in order of abundance, of carbon dioxide, carbon monoxide, sulphur, and chlorine. Similar assemblages of gases are liberated elsewhere from active lavas and fumeroles, together with various related compounds, such as hydrogen sulphide, hydrochloric and other acids, and volatile chlorides of iron, potassium, and other metals. Incrustations of sulphur and chlorides, as well as of rarer compounds, often in great variety, are deposited on cool surfaces. Furthermore, chemical reaction sometimes occurs between escaping gases and rocks adjoining vents. For example, after the 1902 eruption of Mt Pelée in Martinique, Lacroix discovered that an altered andesite from the orifice of a fumerole had been enriched in silica and potash, and had lost

various amounts of lime, magnesia, iron-oxide, soda, and alumina.

The gases play an important part in boring conduits through the crust. Volcanic vents are commonly formed by outward explosion, but they may also be drilled by escaping gas armed with rock powder, which erodes the walls of fractures as if by sand blast. Where outward explosion has been the process responsible for boring volcanic chimneys, blocks of country rocks fall back into the chimney with a haphazard arrangement, in addition to being deposited around the vent. Where gas erosion has been the main process concerned, only fine-grained material is swept out of the vent and deposited around it, and the blocks of country rock within the vent have an orderly arrangement (Fig. 14–3). In a detailed study of the Tertiary tuff pipes of Swabia, east of the Black Forest, Hans Cloos discovered what happens within volcanic pipes that have been formed mainly by gas erosion. He found that large blocks of Jurassic limestone within these pipes retain their original orientation with respect both to the limestone walls of the vents, with which their stratigraphic level can be matched, and to one another (Fig. 14–3). The blocks have merely subsided a little, but are surrounded and separated from one another by fragmented rock, which Cloos called *tuffisite*, the major part of which has been formed by comminution of the marginal parts of the blocks themselves. Moreover, this tuffisite penetrates the blocks as veins. Cloos envisaged the tuffisite as being gently agitated by through-flowing gas at the time when the blocks sank within it. For many years, however, the processes concerned remainded an enigma; for example, it was not understood how the tuffisite remained within the pipes instead of being carried out by the gas.

Since the time of Cloos' discovery, much has been learnt from industrial processes about the behaviour of fine particles within streams of through-flowing gas. If gas is passed through a bed of fine solid particles, there is always a particular rate of gas flow, relative to the size of the particles, at which the bed expands, that is its surface rises to a higher level but remains flat, and the particles being buoyed up by the gas become separated and free to move. With a slight increase in the rate of gas flow, gas bubbles form and rise upwards through the expanded bed within which the particles become turbulent, and the bed is said to be *fluidized*. If precautions are not taken at this stage, the fluidized particles abraid one another and erode the walls of the containing vessel. In industry a heated fluidized bed provides a means of obtaining maximum chemical reaction between gas and solid particles, and perfect mixing of the particles. When the process of *fluidization* is completed, the rate of gas flow can be increased until the solids become transported by the gas, and thus carried out of the vessel and collected in another. A further point of interest about an expanded bed is that it has

a measurable density and viscosity; objects of relatively low density will float on it whereas those with a higher density will sink.

The industrial process serves to clarify the volcanic process that was operative within the Swabian tuff pipes. Gas charged with some rock powder would erode the walls of fractures along which it escaped to the surface, and as the amount of rock powder increased the passage ways would be enlarged. When the velocity of the gas was insufficient to sweep the bulk of the rock powder up to the surface, it would remain and form an expanded bed.

As the process continued the volume of fluidized rock powder, filling and widening fractures, would eventually become so great, relative to the residual Jurassic limestone, that blocks of the latter would become isolated within it. Within the Swabian tuff pipes the blocks of limestone sank within the expanded and fluidized rock powder, and it can therefore be inferred that their density was greater than that of the expanded bed; had it been lower, then they would have risen. All the fragments, whether of large, medium, or small size, were constantly worn down by abrasion, and at the surface the materials transported by the escaping gases would at first be exclusively fine-grained, unless of course explosions occurred not far beneath the surface. As can be seen around some of

FIG. 14–4
A sheet of ignimbrite showing columnar jointing, near Waipapa dam, Waikato River, North Island, New Zealand. (*R. H. Clark*)

251

the Swabian tuff pipes, and even better around those near Ruwenzori in Central Africa, the earliest tuffs consist of exceedingly fine materials. At the surface the vents are shallow ring craters, rimmed by low mounds of tuff.

LAVAS AND IGNIMBRITES

The temperature of freshly erupting lava usually ranges between 900° and 1,200°C. Basic lavas such as basalt are generally the hottest; they are also the most mobile and tend to flow freely for long distances, even down gentle slopes, before coming to rest. In contrast silica-rich lavas, such as rhyolite, are so stiff from the start that they congeal as thick tongues close to the volcanic vent. There are, however, widespread flat-lying, sheet-like formations which, for many years, presented a puzzle because they were thought to be lava flows of rhyolite and therefore to contradict the observation that silica-rich lavas are highly viscous. In 1932, P. Marshall found that widespread sheets of this kind, covering about 10,000 square miles (25,900 km²) of the Rotorua volcanic region of New Zealand, are really deposits of silica-rich pyroclasts. They are composed of minute shards of glass which were sufficiently hot to adhere together as they accumulated, and to flatten out under the weight of later addi-

tions, so that they formed a compact welded assemblage of drawn-out glass shreds, some of which moulded themselves around crystal and other fragments. Similar rocks in Yellowstone Park, Wyoming, and elsewhere have been called *welded tuffs*, but the term *ignimbrite* (L. *ignis*, fire; *imber*, rain) meaning "fiery shower", proposed by Marshall, is coming into wider use as more and more rocks, previously thought to be flows of rhyolite are being recognized to be pyroclasts of this special kind (Fig. 14–4). In Britain, ignimbrites of Ordovician age occur in Wales and the English Lake District. Ignimbrites are erupted, not as coherent lava flows but as vast, swiftly moving clouds of incandescent spray that sweep down the slopes of the volcanic dome, as in the Peléan type of eruption described on p. 262. From these clouds the glass shards fall like rain.

The most common variety of lava is basalt, and newly consolidated basaltic lavas assume either of two contrasted forms described in English as *block* lavas (Fig. 14–5) and *ropy* lavas (Fig. 14–6). Technically these varieties are known by their Hawaiian names, *aa* (pronounced ah-ah; meaning rough or spiny) and *pahoehoe* (meaning satiny). Block lava tends to form over partly crystalline flows from which the gases escape in sudden bursts. As the lava flow advances the congealed crust

FIG. 14–5
Block lava, Etna, near Nicolosi; eruption of 1886. (*Tempest Anderson*).

FIG. 14—6
Ropy lava, erupted from a new
vent (1948) on the southern
flanks of Nyamuragira, N. of
Lake Kivu, in the Western Rift
Valley of Africa. (*H. Tazieff*)

breaks into a wild assemblage of rough, jagged, scoriaceous blocks. Through openings in the piled-up front the glowing pasty lava pushes forward between the clinkers, which come sliding down at intervals, to be rolled over and buried beneath the sluggishly advancing flow with its load of grinding blocks. Ropy lava cools more slowly and remains mobile for a longer period than the block variety. Minute bubbles of gas escape tranquilly and the flow congeals with a smooth skin which wrinkles into ropy and corded forms like those assumed by flowing pitch (Fig. 14–6). It sometimes happens that after the upper surface and edges of a flow of this kind have solidified, the last of the molten lava drains away, leaving an empty tunnel. Some of the lava caves of Iceland are famous for the shining black icicles of glass which adorn their roofs.

When lava of the ropy type flows over the sea floor, or otherwise beneath a chilling cover of water, it consolidates with a structure like that of a jumbled heap of pillows and is then appropriately described as *pillow lava*. By the time each emerging tongue of lava has swollen to about the size of a pillow the rapidly congealed skin prevents further growth. New tongues which then exude through cracks in the glassy crust similarly swell into pillows, and so the process continues. The structure is a common one in the submarine lavas associated with the geosynclinal sediments of former periods, and has been seen actively developing in modern flows that reached the sea floor.

Columnar structure (Fig. 11–14) develops within the interior of thick masses of lava which have come to rest and have consolidated under stagnant conditions. It is especially characteristic of very fine-grained plateau basalts which are relatively free from vesicles. It is equally characteristic of ignimbrites (Fig. 14–4).

VOLCANIC EDIFICES

Volcanoes can be classified into two varieties dependent on whether eruption occurs through a vertical chimney or orifice, or through fissures. In the former and most common variety, the vertical chimney is widened into a crater with flaring sides, partly by outward explosion and partly by inward slumping. By accumulation of volcanic products around the vent a conical or dome-shaped mountain or hill is gradually built. Nearly all the present-day volcanoes have this familiar structure (Fig. 14–7) and are said to be of *central type*, because the activity is centralized about a pipe-like conduit. In the second variety of volcano magma reaches the surface through long fissures from which lava flows spread over the surrounding countryside, filling up the valleys and forming wide-spread volcanic plains or plateaux (Fig. 14–15). This lava is generally basaltic, like that of the Antrim plateau in Northern Ireland (Figs. 1–3 and 14–14). Ignimbrites, however, also build up plateaux.

CONES AND DOMES

The forms of volcanic cones or domes of

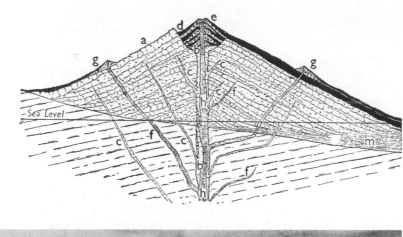

FIG. 14–7
Diagrammatic section through
a composite volcanic cone. The
main cone (*a*) is built of layers
of tuff and tongue-like flows of
lava fed from the conduit (*b*)
and is cut by dykes (*c*). If (*d*),
an explosion crater, is formed
at some stage, a new cone (*e*),
fed from the conduit (*h*)
may grow within it. Some of
the dykes (*f*) serve as feeders
of lateral parasitic cones (*g*).
Marine deposits interstratified
with tuffs and lavas are
indicated by (*m*). (*James
Geikie and Messrs Oliver and
Boyd*)

FIG. 14–8
Dome of Sarcoui, Auvergne: a
craterless dome of trachyte
lava. (*L. Hawkes*)

central type depend on the physical characters of the materials of which they are built. Some are built wholly or mainly of lava flows, others are built essentially of pyroclasts, but the majority are composite, being built of alternations of lavas and pyroclasts.

(*a*) *Lava domes.* The forms of volcanic structures built wholly or dominantly of lava flows depend on the fluidity of the lava concerned. The more silica-rich lavas, such as dacite (rhyolite) and trachyte, are commonly so viscous that they cannot flow far from the vent. Steep-sided and even bulbous domes are then constructed immediately over the pipe. Because of the obstruction, further growth takes place mainly by additions from within, the outer layers being upheaved, extended, and cracked. Sarcoui, one of the Puys of Auvergne is a notable example (Fig. 14–8). It has a sort of onion structure in which the inner layers of lava were erupted after the outer layers, and there is no sign of a crater or orifice.

Highly fluid basaltic lavas, from which gases escape so easily that explosive activity is subordinate, spread out as thin sheets for great distances. By the accumulation of suc-

cessive flows a wide-spreading dome with gentle slopes, rarely exceeding 6° or 8° is constructed. Volcanoes with this form are known as *shield volcanoes*, and those of the Hawaiian Islands are the classic examples (Fig. 14–9). Hawaii (Fig. 14–10) the largest of the island chain to which it belongs, has been built up from the sea floor by the coalescence of several shield volcanoes. Mauna Loa is the highest, rising 30,000 feet (9,144 m), that is, nearly 14,000 feet (4,267 m) above sea level, from a broad base 70 miles (113 km) in diameter (Fig. 14–9). Kilauea lies on its flanks, 20 miles (32 km) from the summit and 4,000 feet (1,219 m) above the sea (Fig. 14–10).

(*b*) *Ash and Cinder cones.* When the volcanic cone is built essentially of pyroclasts, the profile is determined by the angle of rest of the loose material that showers down around the vent. Fine ash comes to rest at angles of 25° to 35°, while nearer the summit the coarser fragments rise to slopes of 40° or more. In 1538, an eruption suddenly broke out in the country west of Naples, and in a single outburst, lasting only a few days, Monte Nuovo, 430 feet (131 m) high, was constructed. The first materials to be thrown out were angular

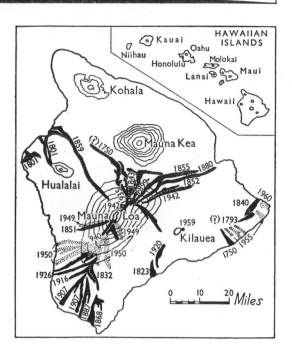

FIG. 14–9
Profile of Mauna Loa, the type
example of a shield volcano.
Length of section 21 miles
(34 km). Horizontal and
vertical scales are equal.

FIG. 14–10
Map of Hawaii showing its
lava flows from 1801 to 1960

fragments of the country rocks, but these were soon followed by ash and bits of pumice having the composition of trachyte.

Ring craters, otherwise known as ash or tuff rings, are low rings composed of pyroclasts which surround craters. Some of them have small craters with flaring sides and the pyroclasts of the ring include a high proportion of coarse angular material. These are obviously explosion vents. Others, have wide shallow craters with nearly flat floors and low rims, sloping outwards to thin deposits of ash spread widely over the surrounding countryside (Fig. 14–3). Most of the pyroclastic material is exceedingly fine, and the larger fragments are so well rounded that they have often been mistaken for "bombs". Such craters and their encircling rings of tuff were probably formed by the action of gas streams and the attendant phenomena of fluidization. Examples are the ring craters near Ruwenzori in the western rift valley of Africa, the smaller craters of Swabia, and the *maar* of the Eifel volcanic district (Fig. 14–11).

Where the floor of a ring crater is deep enough to fall below the local water table, it becomes the site of a shallow lake, for example, the Laacher See in the Eifel district (Fig. 14–11), and Lake Nyamununka, southeast of Ruwenzori.

(*c*) *Composite cones* (Fig. 14–7) are accumulations of successive layers of well-stratified tuffs, alternating irregularly with tongue-like lava flows. The lavas may escape through breaches in the crater wall, or through radial cracks which feed parasitic craters (often arranged in linear series) on the flanks. As magma solidifies in fissures, dykes are formed which help to strengthen the growing edifice. Etna, has hundreds of these secondary vents. All the larger cones around the Pacific and, apart from the great shield volcanoes, most of those elsewhere are of strato-volcanic structure.

CALDERAS

Some central volcanoes have gigantic depressions within the rims of their truncated summits which, at first sight, give the impression that the volcano has blown off its head, and sometimes its body as well. Such a depression, the diameter of which may be ten miles or more, is many times greater than an eruptive vent. Calderas result from foundering and engulfment of part of the volcanic cone as a result of a loss of support and provision of space into which the superstructure could subside. There are two varieties of

FIG. 14–11
The Laacher See, a lake within
a typical ring-crater or *maar*
in the Eifel district, west of
the Rhine.

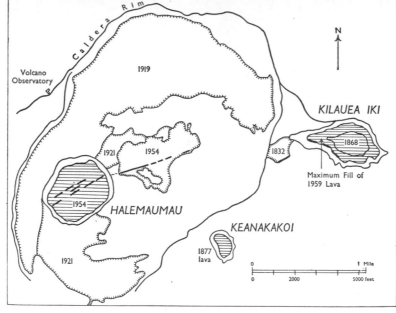

FIG. 14–12
Map of Kilauea caldera and
associated pit-craters, showing
the extent of the lava flows.
The heavy lines indicate the
1954 eruption fissures on the
caldera floor and those of 1959
on the side of Kilauea Iki.

calderas: one results from the underground draining away of lava, and the other from ejection of pyroclasts derived from the magmatic foundations.

The shield volcano Kilauea, provides an example of a caldera resulting from the subterranean draining away of lava (Fig. 14–12). Here, the caldera, bounded by lava cliffs, is about two and a half miles long by two miles wide (4 × 3 km), and its floor lies about 500 feet (152 m) below the highest point on the rim. Since scientific observations began, in 1823, the floor of the caldera has shown changes of level including bodily uplifts as well as subsidences. Within the floor is a pit crater, Halemaumau, within which the level of the lava varies from time to time (Fig. 14–12). In 1919, for example, it overflowed the caldera floor, but in 1924 the lava withdrew within the conduit, evidently draining away through subterranean fissures and probably finding exist on the sea floor. The walls of Halemaumau, no longer sustained by lava, avalanched into the pit, but ground water seeping into the debris, on passing into high-pressure steam, expelled the successive obstructions by a series of explosions. It was then found that the avalanches and explosions had increased the surface dimensions of Halemaumau from 800 × 500 feet (244 × 152 m) to 3,400 × 3,000 feet (1,036 × 914 m).

The other variety of caldera is associated with central volcanoes built of basaltic and andesitic flows and subsidiary pyroclasts. Preceding caldera-formation, however, both the composition and type of the ejected material changes. Vast quantities (measurable in many cubic kilometres) of either ash, or ignimbrite and pumice, with the composition of rhyolite or dacite, are ejected and deposited over extensive areas. This event is followed by caldera formation. Since pyroclasts matching the vanished part of the cone cannot be found at the surface, it can be concluded that the cone has not been blown away, and must therefore have foundered. This sequence of events, culminating in caldera formation is well established for many volcanoes, and Hakone, Japan; Krakatau, Indonesia; Crater Lake, Oregon; and Lake Toba, Sumatra, provide examples or relics. As two of these names suggest, ancient calderas may become filled with water and so form lakes. Crater Lake, Oregon (Fig. 14–13), occupies a caldera about six miles (10 km) in diameter, formed by the collapse of what was once a lofty composite cone; Lake Toba occupies a caldera at the crest of the Barisan Highlands in NW. Sumatra.

VOLCANIC PLATEAUX

As mentioned earlier, magma may reach the surface through long fissures from which basaltic lavas spread over the surrounding country and form wide-spread volcanic plains and plateaux. Similarly plateaux are sometimes built of layers of ignimbrite. There is no certain knowledge, however, that ignimbrite may be erupted from fissures rather than from central volcanoes.

The largest area of plateau basalts in the British Isles is that of Antrim (Fig. 14–14), but this is only a small part of the far greater Brito-Arctic region, extensive areas of which were flooded with basalts during early Tertiary times. Although considerable tracts have foundered and are now beneath the sea, 60,000 square miles still remain in Antrim, the Inner Hebrides, the Faroes, Iceland, and Greenland. Shield and other types of volcanoes arose later at certain localities, including Iceland, where activity still persists. In our own islands, especially in Slieve Gullion Mull, Ardnamurchan, and Skye (Figs. 4–36, 4–43, and 9–15) we see only the basal wrecks of the ancient volcanoes, worn down to their roots by millions of years of denudation.

Plateau basalts covering areas of 200,000 square miles or more occur in the Columbia and Snake River region of the north-western United States (Miocene to Recent), the Deccan

FIG. 14–13
Crater Lake, Oregon. A prehistoric caldera, with the cone of Wizard Island rising above the lake. (*American Museum of Natural History, New York*)

FIG. 14–14
Map of North-East Ireland showing the Tertiary plateau basalts (black), the Tertiary volcanic and intrusive centres of Slieve Gullion, Carlingford, and Mourne (dotted), and the Caledonian granite (broken vertical lines).

of India (early Tertiary), and the Paraná region of South America (Jurassic). Other vast areas which were flooded with basalts in Jurassic or Tertiary times occur in Mongolia and Siberia, in Arabia and Syria, in many parts of Africa (*e.g.* Abyssinia, around the Victoria Falls, and along the Drakensberg behind Natal), and in parts of Australia. Where the flows thinned out and denudation has since removed them, the underlying rocks are seen to be penetrated by swarms of dykes, some of which may represent feeding channels of the vanished flows. In many other regions such feeding channels failed to reach the surface and build up lava plateaux, but riddled the stratified rocks just below with innumerable sills. Altogether, more than a million cubic miles of basalt have been transferred from the depths during the last 180 million years or so.

During historical times Iceland has been one of the few regions in which fissure eruptions have been witnessed. The greatest basalt flood of modern times broke out at Laki during the summer of 1783 (Fig. 14–15). From a fissure 20 miles (32 km) long torrents of gleaming lava, amounting in all to three cubic miles, overwhelmed 218 square miles (565 km²) of

country, and sent long fiery arms down the valleys beyond. As the activity diminished in intensity, obstructions choked the long vent, and gases accumulated below the surface until they raised sufficient pressure to overcome the resistance. At the hundreds of points along the fissure where the pent-up gases eventually broke through, miniature cones, ranging in height from a few feet to a hundred or more, were built up and great quantities of pyroclasts were erupted (Fig. 14–16).

The vast plateau of the central part of North Island, New Zealand, is built of ignimbrite, as is the plateau of central Yellowstone Park, Wyoming, and that of the Lake Toba region, Sumatra. In all these, and many other areas, thick layers of ignimbrite have levelled off the pre-existing topography and are themselves characterized by essentially horizontal or gently dipping surfaces. Individual ignimbrite sheets are of the order of 400 feet (122 m) or more thick and characteristically they show vertical jointing (Fig. 14–4). In North Island, New Zealand, the ignimbrite plateau is block faulted in much the same way as the Columbia basalt plateau which forms part of the "Basin and Range" province of western North America.

FIG. 14–15
Eastern part of the Laki basalt floods of 1783, Iceland, as seen in 1957; looking towards the ice-covered Öraefajökull (2,119 m), an active volcano and the highest mountain in Iceland. (*Sigurdur Thorarinsson*)

FIG. 14–16
Pictorial representation of a ten-mile stretch of the Laki fissure, Iceland, showing conelets formed towards the end of the 1783 eruption. (*After Helland*)

TYPES OF CENTRAL ERUPTIONS

Eruptions vary widely in character according to the pressure and quantity of gas, and the nature of the lava from and through which it is released. Several well-defined phases have been recognized, of which the following are the chief (Fig. 14–17):

(*a*) *Hawaiian type*. Effusion of mobile lava is dominant and gas is liberated more or less quietly. From the surface of a lava lake jets and fountains of incandescent spray may be thrown up by the rapid emission of spurting gases. When caught by a strong wind the blebs of molten lava are drawn out into long glassy threads known as *Pele's hair*, Pele being the Hawaiian goddess of fire.

(*b*) *Strombolian type*. When less mobile lava is exposed to the air in a crater, the pent-up gases escape more spasmodically, with moderate explosions which may be rhythmic or nearly continuous. Clots of lava, often incandescent, are blown out, to form bombs or lumps of scoria. Stromboli, one of the Lipari Islands north of Sicily, normally behaves in this way, its minor eruptions recurring at short intervals ranging from a few minutes to an hour or so. In phases of more intense activity there may be outflows of coherent lava, while violently expanding gases ascending from a deeper source tear their way through the lava of the conduit and give rise to luminous fountains playing above the crater.

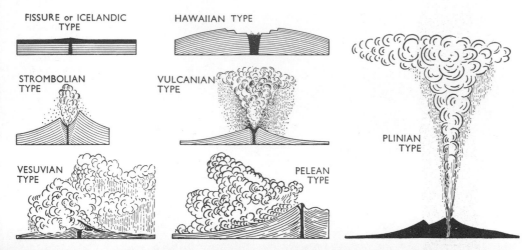

FISSURE or ICELANDIC TYPE

HAWAIIAN TYPE

STROMBOLIAN TYPE

VULCANIAN TYPE

PLINIAN TYPE

VESUVIAN TYPE

PELEAN TYPE

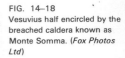

FIG. 14–17
Diagrams to illustrate the chief types of volcanic eruptions.

FIG. 14–18
Vesuvius half encircled by the breached caldera known as Monte Somma. (*Fox Photos Ltd*)

(*c*) *Vulcanian type* (named after Vulcano, also in the Lipari group). The lava is more viscous and pasty, and quickly crusts over between eruptions. Gases accumulate and gather strength beneath the congealed cover and blow off at longer intervals, with correspondingly greater violence. The viscous lava and its crust are shattered to angular fragments of all sizes down to the finest dust. The resulting ash-laden volcanic clouds are dark and often black, incandescent bombs rarely being seen, even at night. The clouds assume a convoluted or "cauliflower" shape as they ascend and expand. The major eruptions of many volcanoes begin with a vulcanian phase wherever an obstructed vent has first to be cleared out. They may end in the same way, with outbursts continuing intermittently until the waning gas activity no longer has the power to eject the debris that avalanches into the vent from the unstable crater walls.

(*d*) *Vesuvian type*. This is a paroxysmal extension of the Vulcanian and Strombolian types, the new and specific feature being the extremely violent expulsion of magma which,

FIG. 14–19
Diagrammatic representation
of the conelet within the
crater of Vesuvius, and of its
stages of growth since 1913.

FIG. 14–20
Ruins of St Pierre after the
1902 disaster. Mont Pelée and
its spine in the background.
(*A. Lacroix*)

during long intervals of quiescence, becomes highly charged with gas beneath a congealed cover. The magma then bursts into an explosive spray and expels itself as vast clouds of "cauliflower" form which ascend to great heights. During such violent eruptions Vesuvius has twice, within historic times, destroyed parts of its cone. Monte Somma, for example, which partly encircles the present cone of Vesuvius (Fig. 14–18), represents the base of the volcano prior to a violent eruption in 79 A.D. during which Pompeii was buried beneath pumice. Only minor quantities of pyroclasts, derived from the vanished part of the cone, were associated with the pumice. This suggests that Monte Somma is the rim of a caldera within which a major part of the volcanic cone probably foundered. A violent eruption in 1906 is well documented, for Frank Perret courageously remained at the observatory on the western slopes. On the fourth day, the Vesuvian phase culminated with a mighty uprush of gases which eroded and widened the volcanic chimney so that the crater walls, left unsupported, fell in. The volcano then remained dormant until 1913 when the building of a new cone began within the widened crater (Fig. 14–19).

(e) *Peléan type.* Here the limit of high viscosity and explosiveness is reached. Upward escape is prevented because the vent becomes sealed by an obstructive dome formed from highly viscous lava. Eruption of cloud-like masses of incoherent self-explosive lava, lubricated by constantly expanding gases and vapours, takes place through lateral cracks, as though from a cannon, and sweeps down the slopes as an intensely hot avalanche. This mysterious type of volcanic eruption takes its name from Monte Pelée in Martinique, one of the islands of the Lesser Antilles, a volcanic arc across the entrance to the Caribbean sea. In 1902, a "glowing avalanche" of this kind, known as a *nuée ardente*, wiped out St Pierre, the capital of Martinique, and killed about 30,000 inhabitants within the space of a few minutes. Perret, who has observed *nuées ardentes* at close quarters describes them as an "avalanche of an exceedingly dense mass of hot, highly gas-charged and constantly gas-emitting fragmental lava, much of it finely divided, extraordinarily mobile, and practically frictionless, because each particle is separated from its neighbour by a cushion of compressed gas". The devastation of St Pierre resulted from the fact that the *nuées ardentes* emerged through a gap situated at the head of the Riviere Blanche, and the *nuées* swept downwards and were confined within this valley as they rolled westward, with hurricane speed, towards the sea where St Pierre was situated. About five months later, a plug of almost consolidated lava within the conduit was forced bodily upwards, and a gigantic column of gas was projected high above it. Presently, part of the protruding plug broke away, and the remaining part assumed the form of a spine which reached a height of 900 feet above the dome in the course of seven months (Fig. 14–20).

THE DISTRIBUTION OF VOLCANOES

Nearly 800 volcanoes are known to be active or to have been active during historic times. Besides these, many thousands of extinct cones and craters are still so perfectly preserved that they must equally be taken into account in considering the distribution of recent vulcanism. A high proportion of late Tertiary to still active volcanoes is situated in or near the Circum-Pacific and Alpine-Indonesian belts of the latest orogenic cycle (Fig. 13–11). Two-thirds of the active volcanoes, and an immense number not long extinct, are distributed around the borderlands and island festoons of the Pacific, where they have an arcuate or linear arrangement along the orogenic belts.

Another noteworthy association of volcanoes with profound crustal dislocations is illustrated by the past and present vulcanism within and adjoining the African rift valleys and the oceanic ridges (Fig. 12–9).

Further Reading

BATES, D. R., 1957
The Planet Earth, pp. 312.
Pergamon Press, London, New York, Paris, Los Angeles.

BULLARD, FRED M., 1962
Volcanoes. In History, in Theory, in Eruption, pp. 441.
University of Texas Press. Thomas Nelson and Sons Ltd, London.

COTTON, C. A., 1944
Volcanoes as Landscape Forms, pp. 415.
Whitcombe and Tombs Ltd, Christchurch, New Zealand.

——————, 1948
Landscape as developed by the Processes of Normal Erosion (2nd edition), pp. 509.
Cambridge University Press, London.

DURY, G., 1966
The Face of the Earth, (revised edition), pp. 232.
Penguin Books, London.

FLINT, R. F., 1957
Glacial and Pleistocene Geology, pp. 553.
John Wiley and Sons, Inc., New York. Chapman and Hall Ltd, London.

GASKELL, T. F., 1960
Under the Deep Oceans. Twentieth century voyages of discovery, pp. 240.
Eyre and Spottiswoode, London.

HEWITT, R., 1957
From Earthquake, Fire, and Flood, pp. 215.
George Allen and Unwin Ltd, London.

HILLS, E. S., 1963
Elements of Structural Geology, pp. 483.
Methuen and Co. Ltd, London.

HOLMES, ARTHUR, 1965
Principles of Physical Geology, pp. 1288.
Thomas Nelson and Sons Ltd, London.

INGLE, JAMES C., 1966
The Movement of Beach Sand. An Analysis using Fluorescent Grains, pp. 221.
Elsevier Publishing Company, Amsterdam, London, and New York.

KING, C. A. M., 1959
Beaches and Coasts, pp. 403.
Edward Arnold Ltd, London.

KING, LESTER C., 1962
Morphology of the Earth. A Study and Synthesis of World Scenery, pp. 699.
Oliver and Boyd, Edinburgh.

SHEPARD, FRANCIS P., 1959
The Earth Beneath the Sea, pp. 275.
Oxford University Press, London.

STEERS, J. A., 1953
The Sea Coast, pp. 276.
Collins, Edinburgh.

WOOLDRIDGE, S. W., AND D. L. LINTON, 1955
Structure, Surface and Drainage in South-east England, pp. 176.
George Philip and Son Ltd, London.

H.M. GEOLOGICAL SURVEY
Geological Map of the British Isles (4th edition, 1957). Scale twenty-five miles to one inch.

Index